KU-287-589

FIRST EDITION

THE READER'S DIGEST ASSOCIATION LIMITED
25 Berkeley Square, London W1X 6AB

E READER'S DIGEST ASSOCIATION SOUTH AFRICA (PTY) LTD
Nedbank Centre, Strand Street, Cape Town

Printed in Great Britain by Petty & Sons Ltd., Leeds

Original cover design by Jeffery Matthews A.R.C.A.

For information as to ownership
of copyright in the material in this book see last page

ISBN 0 340 21949 1

READER'S DIGEST

CONDENSED BOOKS

THE

READER'S DIGEST
CONDENSED BOOKS

THE GLORY BOYS
Gerald Seymour

MAJESTY
Elizabeth II and the House of Windsor
Robert Lacey

ORDINARY PEOPLE
Judith Guest

A BAG OF MARBLES
Joseph Joffo

COLLECTOR'S LIBRARY
EDITION

In this volume

THE GLORY BOYS
by Gerald Seymour (p.9)

An Arab guerilla and an IRA gun-man: two vicious, faceless killers bent on glory. Their target: an Israeli scientist visiting London. Between them and him stands the British Secret Service, almost powerless, looking for anonymous assassins . . . A best-selling author at his most ingenious: tough, fast-paced, utterly compelling.

MAJESTY: Elizabeth II and the House of Windsor
by Robert Lacey (p.159)

Jubilee Year. A time to celebrate both the majesty and the humanity of our royal family. This book is about people—isolated by their position perhaps, but *people* all the same. The Queen's grandfather, as indulgent as only a grandfather may be; her parents, shy, utterly devoted; her raffish uncle, Edward; her sister, the rebellious one. And later, her witty, strong-minded husband and her children. . . . And, most significant of all, of course, the humanity of Elizabeth herself.

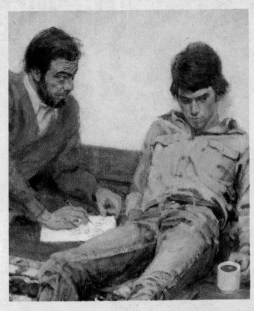

ORDINARY PEOPLE
by Judith Guest (p.279)

Perhaps the Jarrets weren't really so ordinary after all. Ordinary, successful middle-class people like them didn't have sons who tried to kill themselves. Nice ordinary boys like Cal just didn't do that sort of thing. . . .

But at least all that was over now. Cal was better, back at school, idling about the place the way boys did. Life could get back to normal. Except that his parents still didn't know just what craziness had got into him—or was it into them?

A remarkable first novel.

A BAG OF MARBLES
by Joseph Joffo (p.399)

"What is a Jew?" In Nazi-occupied France it was a question that only a child would ask—and one whose painful answer little Joseph Joffo and his brother were soon to discover for themselves. A Jew was a fugitive, a hunted animal.

This is the true story of two small boys whose wits alone held the Gestapo at bay for three long years, children who managed to escape the greatest murder machine the world has known. It is a story of innocence and courage, and indomitable high spirits.

THE

GLORY BOYS

A CONDENSATION OF THE BOOK BY GERALD SEYMOUR

ILLUSTRATED BY JIM SHARPE
PUBLISHED BY COLLINS, LONDON

It is in the early hours of the morning, just before dawn. Three Arab killers are making their way across northern France, to the ferry port of Boulogne. Their mission is to assassinate a senior Israeli nuclear scientist, due to arrive in London in three days time. . . .

Gerald Seymour's first and bestselling novel, *Harry's Game*, was the direct result of his experiences as a television reporter in Belfast. In this his latest novel he turns his attention to another subject of which he has first-hand knowledge: the "glory boy" world of guerilla fighters. Theirs is a grey world of amateurs and professionals, fanatics and opportunists where personal motives are fuelled by the cold and calculating decisions of distant government. In this thrilling account of a typically daring guerilla operation, Gerald Seymour has given us a unique insight into the lives of the gunmen among us.

CHAPTER ONE

There was quiet in the car now, all attention riveted on the twin headlights far behind in the darkness. The man in the back seat had swivelled around and wiped the condensation from the back window, and was peering out into the void of the retreating road. The passenger in the front was also twisting to watch the lights, while the driver scanned the front mirror. On sharp curves they would lose the lights, then find them again as the road levelled out.

For the three men the tension had begun almost fifteen kilometres back.

The driver had been the first to speak, but his companions had already noted his hurried glances at the mirror.

He'd spoken in the dialect of the pure Palestinian Arab. "It's been with us a long time now, the car behind. Three times I've pushed the speed up seven or eight k's an hour. Then by the big farm near the wood, you remember, I slowed right down. He didn't close up, just kept the same distance."

That was when they'd all started to pick up the two powerful beams away in the distance, begun to sweat a little. It had been a long drive, three days, across Italy and France. And now, with so little distance left to the ferry port, the first crisis, the initial moment of the unexpected.

The front passenger pulled the glove compartment open and rummaged for the maps, felt in his pocket for his cigarette lighter, and, with the small flame, he bent himself over the paper that showed in detail the intricate road system of northern France. "The last town was Béthune," he said. "Another two or three kilometres there's a little road off to the left. Runs through some villages, Auchy . . . Estrée. Look for the signs. We can get through that way and still be in good time for the boat."

"Yes, there's time enough," the man in the back agreed. He continued to search the road behind. "I'd lost him a moment, but he's there still."

The road was straight now. Clear and fast, high trees on either side, an occasional lighted farmhouse, but no other sign of the living. Three in the morning, with the soulless cold of the early hours settled deep on the countryside. The men in the car shivered, fear accentuating the chill.

The man beside the driver cried, "There! Auchy and Estrée."

They came too fast to the junction and the driver had to brake hard to avoid overshooting. The car protested fiercely as he swung left. The watcher in the back steadied himself against the heavy grip-bag that slid across the seat. When he looked again, the twin lights had disappeared.

It was a winding, delaying road, uneven, pocked by heavy farm machines. The speed came down. The driver kept his eye on the mirror, but there was only darkness. "The curves are too quick for us to see him," he said.

The minutes went by as the driver threaded his way along the road. The man in the back allowed his eyes to wander, the compulsion of his vigil at the rear window waning. "Can we have the window closed? It's all right for you up there, but here I'll die of cold."

"I can't have mist on the windows. You shouldn't mind. You said you spent your winters in the Jordan mountains."

"Not the Jordan mountains, the mountains of Palestine."

Laughter spread through the car. The driver smiled. "Accepted. There was no snow, no mountains for it to fall upon in Haifa. Palestine Haifa. No cold there."

"What can you know of Haifa? You were too young when you left to have memories of it."

The driver said, "No. There is memory though it is faint. I was

10

four. But one doesn't know how much is memory, and how much is the image of what one has been told of the former life—"

"I have been to Haifa," the front passenger interrupted, "to work on a building project. Before I went to Beirut to study."

They drove downhill into a tight-knit village. Church, market, a ribbon of houses. A grey, hostile, hedgehog community, battened down for the night, offering no refuge to strangers. Road running straight through, no reason to stop, nor even to slow. A bridge, then they were climbing, and the driver looked again in the mirror. Two bright circles of light, perfectly and symmetrically framed in the chrome fitting. He said nothing, but the man in the back saw his head flick from mirror to road and swung heavily around on his seat.

"It's still with us," he said. "Go faster."

The car surged forward. No consideration now for ruts and holes. The chassis jolted and bounced on the uneven road. "Get me a route mapped out," the driver snapped to the man beside him. "So we don't get boxed in some miserable farmyard. And give me good notice of all turns."

The front passenger had the maps spread out and was struggling with the lighter. Tortuously he traced out a path. Every movement of the car jolted his finger from the network of country lanes he was trying to trace on the map. He was aware of the frustration building inside the car as his colleagues waited. Let them wait. Just one mistake would be disastrous. When he was satisfied, he drew an envelope from an inner pocket and began to write. At last he flicked the lighter closed.

"We are well, I think. We pass through Estrée to Fauquembergues, where three roads divide just past the village. We take the most northerly. After that, on to Samer, where there must be signs for Boulogne."

"How far to Estrée?" said the driver.

"Two, three kilometres, perhaps. To Fauquem . . ." His voice tailed away as he sought to read his scribblings in the half-light of the dashboard.

"You're sure, now. No doubts about the route?"

"None at all," the passenger snapped back. We hardly know

11

each other, he thought. Had never met before the planning of the mission. That was as intended. From involvement follows collapse under interrogation. Each one was dependent on the others, needing to trust totally in the skill and resolution of his colleagues, but without the deep-rooted certainty that comes from long-standing knowledge and companionship.

The driver stamped his foot on the brake. The speedometer needle sagged from over a hundred kilometres an hour to below forty. Straddled across the road was a herd of cows.

"Murdering hell, what do we do with this?"

"Blast the horn. Get the old peasant in front to move them."

"The car behind, it's closing quickly."

"Get off the road onto the grass. We have to go round them."

The driver wrenched the car onto the grass. The wheels spun, then bit into the soft ground. Huge dark figures of cows were snorting and scraping against the vehicle. Their smell crept in.

"He's right on us. Not sixty metres away—" The shout from the back seat was cut off as the glare of the pursuing headlights illuminated the interior of the car. The passengers ducked down.

"All right. All right. He has to come through this crowd, too."

The three men heard the first wail of the siren as the vehicle behind them attempted to untangle itself from the shuffling barricade. Then flashing among the confusion of cows was the blue rotating police lamp.

The man in the back pulled the bag towards him, slid the zipper open, and pulled out a Luger pistol. "Now we know who we have running with us," he said quietly. He cocked the gun.

FROM HIS office in police headquarters in St. Omer, twenty-five kilometres to the north, the man who had been issuing orders for the last hour could plot with exactitude the position of the fleeing car. On the wall map an aide continually moved coloured pins. The position of the car, kept up to date by the constant radio calls from the pursuing police vehicle, was shown by a yellow one; his own men by red. Stretched out ahead of the path of the three Arabs was a near-continuous line of blue pins, straddling all roads that led to the port of Boulogne.

12

He had not expected their turn off the main coast road, across which his major force was concentrated, but as a precaution he had placed single police cars, each manned by two officers, on all parallel B routes. It had been his intention that the fleeing car be unaware of surveillance until it was stopped by one of the sixteen roadblocks now in place. The pursuer's siren and lamp had changed that.

It had been a brutal day's work since the message from Paris had ordered him to set up a major operation. By the time he would normally have been thinking of home and supper, the fleet of black Citroëns had started to arrive at his headquarters. Men from the security services. And one who spoke French with a Central European accent and around whose neck a silver six-pointed Star of David dangled.

The local man had been earning congratulations from the Paris big shots, until the intervention of the cows. But little, he reflected, was lost. The quarry was still being shepherded into his net.

"When will they reach the blocking point?" he asked his aide.

"Four to five minutes, sir. At the Fauquembergues crossroads. Where the petrol station and the café are."

"Two men?"

"Roben and Miniux, sir. They have only to hold the *fedayeen* a few minutes. The larger force is on its way."

"Tell them to go carefully." He was now consumed with concern. "It was not intended only two should make the interception."

THE DRIVER spotted the red light waving slowly up and down, the international sign to halt. He shouted to the others. "There in front, a police check. He's waving us down."

It was the moment for one of the three to take control. The man in back reacted first, perhaps because it was he who clasped the only firearm. His voice was shrill but commanding.

"Burst right past him. Don't hesitate. Put on speed as we go by. He'll be armed, so keep your bodies low. When you get very close, put down the front lights . . . then on again."

The car hurtled towards the lone policeman. The driver could see the whiteness of his face, could see the fear fill his eyes.

"Kill the lights."

The command was barked from the back seat, and the driver instinctively obeyed. Fifty metres in front the policeman disappeared in the blackness.

"On again, the lights."

The driver shrieked with horror. Directly in their path was the policeman, his submachine gun pointed at the windscreen. He never fired. His body jack-knifed into the air. The car recoiled from the impact, then shuddered again as the policeman clipped its roof. The driver swerved to the right to avoid the patrol car that was parked at an angle and filling half the road. The man beside him choked with nausea. The third man had closed his eyes to shut out the vision of the gaping, incredulous mouth.

As the gendarme named Roben hit the road surface the other one, Miniux, opened fire.

The men in the car never saw the second policeman, crouching close to the ditch, the steel-framed butt of the squat MAT-49 at his shoulder. There were thirty-two 9-millimetre rounds in the magazine and he fired them all. The first to die was the front passenger. He went wordlessly. The driver, too, was struck, feeling the pain spread from his left arm into the wounds in his side. But the man behind, protected by the seats, survived.

The car veered to the left, then wove down the centre of the road as the driver fought the damaged steering system with his weakening strength. He managed another three hundred metres, then with great effort dragged his foot to the brake. Vermilion blood, his own blood, billowed and spilled across his knees and ran to a pool at his feet. That was death, he could recognize that. He heard the rear door open, saw the face at his window, then his own door was open. He felt himself sliding out. A hand held him upright.

The voice was close to his ear. "Dani, Dani, can you hear me, we have to run. Bouchi is dead. But I can help you. . . ."

The driver shook his head. "For me, over. Gone." He seemed to suck in air that his carved lungs could not accept. "For Palestine, for a free Palestine. Remember Palestine, and remember me, when you meet with him, with the Mushroom Man."

14

His eyes blinked, and he died.

The sirens came no closer. Stopped at the roadblock, the survivor thought as he pulled the bag from the car. The Luger was now in his pocket. He unscrewed the cap of the petrol tank and thrust his hand into his trousers for a pack of cigarettes which he crumpled to fit the petrol aperture. With a match he lit the paper mass and sprinted for the comfort of darkness.

He heard the explosion behind, but didn't turn.

AN OFFICIAL black car brought the Israeli secret service officer to the crossroads. Roben still lay in the road, a policeman's cape draped over his face. By the parked patrol car a knot of uniformed men were feeding Miniux brandy. A long way beyond was the smoking skeleton of the burned-out vehicle.

"How many have we found . . . of them?" the Israeli asked.

"Two. Unrecognizable. The car caught fire after it stopped. That could be expected, it took many bullets."

The Israeli looked hard at the detective who had spoken. "Strange. The information we gave to Paris was that there were three who were travelling. Perhaps we have lost one."

THE YOUNG Arab's sole preoccupation now was to put distance between himself and his pursuers. He'd sprinted until the sodden fields slowed him to a jog. He punched his way through thick hedges, tore his coat on a strand of wire, fell when he tried to jump a dried-out ditch. There was barking once, when he slipped past a darkened farmhouse, but he kept going.

He reasoned that the gendarmes would be satisfied with the debris of the car and would find little justification in launching a manhunt for him. But that was if he was lucky. If they were coming after him now, it meant that the pursuing car had spotted the three of them just before they ducked to avoid its lights. Or the one who had fired from the roadside had seen them in silhouette and counted three. In that case they would now be massing with their dogs and cordons and large-scale maps. The bag he was dragging with him would be his salvation, he believed. Here was the vital change of clothes, the travel documents for the

15

ferry port. But now he must keep going, however much the stomach pains caused by violent exertion without food slowed him down. It would be difficult to move once the sun rose. Till then he must continue to run, whatever the agony.

This was what his training had been for. This was why they had pummelled the recruits up the soft shale hills of Lebanon, kicked them to the point beyond exhaustion, toed them into activity when they collapsed, then left them to find their own slow path back to the tented camps. They had driven them till their stomach sinews were hard and their lungs cavernous. Then and only then, they had taught them the weapons drills and the sophisticated arts of disguise and concealment.

When he had first arrived at his camp, he had been a raw, attractive and intelligent young man, but they had spotted the bitterness and turned his hatred of Israel into overwhelming obsession. It had not taken them long. Seven weeks, and the product was ready for use. Determination sharpened, viciousness honed, Abdel-El-Famy came out of the course bearing the mark of the killer. That was the role they had fashioned for him. They were pleased with what they saw, confident of success when they gave him his orders.

THE MAN who now heaved his way over the fields of northern France was a very small pawn in the complex power game of the Middle East. He was insignificant, unexceptional; his name appeared in none of the files maintained by Israeli and European intelligence services.

Back in Nablus, the sprawling town on the Israeli-occupied West Bank of the Jordan River, he had flung stones at the Israeli soldiers who massed close to the school gates every afternoon. All the high-school children did that, and all of them were at some stage caught, thwacked by Jewish billy sticks, and taken off in lorries to the barbed-wire compound to cool their heels for a few hours.

The afternoon rock-throwing affected young people in different ways. Some learned to co-exist with the occupying force, but a few were left scarred by the experience. Abdel-El-Famy was one of those. At eighteen he left Nablus and took the bus that crawled for fourteen hours across Jordan and Syria before dropping down through the Lebanese hills into Beirut. There were always places in Beirut universities for Palestinians from the occupied West Bank. He enrolled in English studies, but throughout was brushing against the quite new science of revolutionary politics.

Through the long dryly hot afternoons after classes, the Palestinian students sat at the café on the Corniche, sipping their Pepsi-Colas with restraint, making the few bottles they could afford last for hours. And while they sat and watched the affluence and arrogance of this foreign country, they argued and bickered over the way to regain their own state. And they had listened on their transistor radios to news of the assault on the Olympic village in Munich. September 5, 1972—a heroic day. They had worshipped the *fedayeen* who died at the Munich airport, and rejoiced at the death of eleven Israeli sportsmen.

After Munich, the arguments at the café tables became more heated. Some said any Palestinian state, however small, was better than nothing. Others saw only the complete return of their former lands as sufficient. This was the view of Abdel-El-Famy. He began to understand that these arguments would only sap his resolve and desire for revenge. So he sought out the men who were prepared to fight on, regardless of any moves towards compromise by the Palestinian leadership.

He joined the General Command, a small but deadly offshoot of the Popular Front for the Liberation of Palestine. He became one of fifty-five young men, age seventeen to twenty-five, who had taken a solemn oath, who knew they would be sent on missions with little prospect of survival.

Just eight days ago he had been instructed to present himself to the leader of the General Command. In the tent of the man who directed operations were two young men he knew only as Bouchi and Dani. The three were told they would be travelling to London, that their mission was of the utmost importance to the whole Arab movement. With a code name, an operational plan, and a target to seek out, Abdel-El-Famy was no longer a penniless nothing from the hills above Nablus. Like a stoat hungry for rabbit's blood, he would not be easily deflected. His threat to the uneasy peace of the Middle East was enormous, and if he succeeded, the reverberations of his action would be felt throughout the Western world.

FAMY LAY high up among the bales in the roof of the barn. He had been resting there for more than twenty minutes, but the breath still came hard for him. He estimated he'd come twenty-five kilometres. Four hours' travelling. One more such effort and he would be in Boulogne and ready for the ferry. Better arrive a day late in England than risk all trying to find a bus or a lift on the roads. He would stay in the barn until nightfall. Desperately in need of rest, he slept, body splayed out on the packed straw.

It was dark when he set off again. By dawn, if he pushed himself, he should be near the boat, ready to dispose of the muddy clothes he had on and substitute the precious garments in his grip-bag. He could then assume his final identity, Saleh Mohammed, Algerian passport Number 478625, born August 22, 1953, at Oran.

THERE IS A restaurant, specializing in fish delicacies, that overlooks the sea at Sidon, halfway between Beirut and the nest of tents to the south where the PFLP, General Command, maintained its headquarters. This was a spot that tourists had delighted in. But holidaymakers are prepared to give the possible excitement of a war zone a very wide miss. So the restaurant is almost deserted, and the terrace, with its white-clad tables, makes a discreet place to discuss matters greatly confidential.

The leader of the General Command seldom went to Beirut. His presence in the Lebanese capital would make him vulnerable to the attentions of Israeli agents, on whose death list he was high. So it was here that he came for his secret rendezvous with a journalist from one of Beirut's biggest dailies, a journalist who sympathized with the politics of the General Command.

As the dark, intense-eyed man picked the flesh from a small mullet, the journalist passed to him a piece of news agency copy. He had ripped it from a teleprinter in his office that carried the reports of Agence France-Presse exclusively and had realized the significance of the eight-line story.

"They are reliable, this agency?" asked the General Command leader.

"There would be little room for error. Associated Press and UPI are carrying much the same. The facts are not in dispute."

"It speaks of roadblocks stopping them. Of the car being machine-gunned. Now, at that time in the morning why are there roadblocks, why have country police been issued submachine guns? I think you will agree there is only one explanation."

The journalist nodded. "It has to be that the Israeli secret service prodded the French into action. On their own, the French would let our people through. Did they have arms, our men?" It was a bold question; normally the journalist would not be privy to mission details.

The leader smiled. "Perhaps one pistol. The rest is to be collected later. But that is not for your paper. Possibly you could let it be known from a high source that they were not armed."

"Two unarmed Palestinians gunned down by the French police, that will make good reading. Maybe our paper's Paris office can work up the involvement of the Israeli secret service."

The two men attacked their meal. When they finished, the commando leaned forward. "The reports speak of two men found in the car. There could be no doubt of that fact?"

"No doubt at all. That is common to all the stories."

"And if they had captured a third man, would they say so?"

"Most likely. No reason not to."

A smile, mirthless, played around the leader's mouth. It would be ironical if the death of his two colleagues were in fact to enhance the safety of the man who lived. "I would be interested to hear if there are any further arrests or . . ." The leader let it tail away as he drew a paper from inside his khaki combat jacket, revealing for a moment the polished shoulder holster he always wore. "There is a message I want you to deliver to a man in Beirut." His pen moved with bold strokes across the paper. "It is to be handed, straightaway this afternoon, to the commercial secretary of the embassy that I have written on the folded paper. I'll tell you what it says, I know you pressmen, you'll open it if I don't. . . ." He laughed, and the journalist shuffled in embarrassment. "No, you are all the same. It merely says that we go on as before, but at reduced strength." And he was gone, striding from the terrace towards his waiting Fiat. One bodyguard fell in behind him as he left the restaurant; two more were sitting in the car.

"We have to be patient," he said as the driver engaged the gears. "Two of the men on the European operation are dead. No word of the third. If there were to be one who survived and could go on with the task, which one would we select?" He was speaking to the man beside him, an older man he trusted implicitly, who cradled a Kalashnikov automatic rifle across his lap.

"Of those three?" The older man paused. "The one we code-named Saleh Mohammed. The one that calls himself Famy."

"Pray to God it is that one. The youngest, but the best. If indeed he lives, it is a great problem that he faces."

The old man stroked the rifle barrel, his eyes watchful, alert, as the leader talked softly on. "These Irishmen are an unknown factor, and one man on his own must be more dependent on them than we had planned. More is required now than their providing weapons, explosives, transport and a safe house. They must become involved."

The other man said, "Will they do that?"

"They were anxious to cooperate with us because they want to buy weapons. We can only wait and see."

AFTER their swim in the pool the young man and the girl had spread their towels on the grass. It was hot that evening in London's southwest suburbs, and other couples shared the grass with them, but they were all out of earshot. Five and a quarter miles down the road were the runways of Heathrow airport, and about every two minutes their voices would fade out as Rolls-Royce and Pratt and Whitney engines roared overhead. But in between there was time for talk, nothing special, just young talk.

She was seventeen and a half, called Norah, and punched a cash register in a supermarket from eight thirty to five fifteen. She lived at home, and thought the boy she had met at the pool the previous evening quite the most interesting she had encountered in her limited experience. She wore last year's bikini,

20

which now felt tight on her, but he seemed to like it; his eyes were seldom off it. They lay on their backs, fingers touching. He'd kissed her last night after the cinema, quietly and gently, in the lane behind her house. There was none of the frantic endeavour she was used to from boys who took her to a film and then believed it their right to maul her. This one had just kissed her, no fumbling, told her he'd see her tomorrow, same place. And he'd been here and looked happy to see her again.

She had done most of the talking, both times, chattering about her friends, her mother and father, her work, the films she'd seen. He looked interested, but didn't reciprocate. Last night, when she was in her bed in the semi-detached house a mile and a half away, she'd blamed herself for that, hadn't given him a chance to get a word in.

The coolness of evening was beginning to embrace her bared shoulders. She shivered a little and reached out for the jersey she had brought in her bag with her. "I'll catch my death, dressed with nothing." She giggled, and turned towards the boy, expecting he'd be smiling back at her, laughing with her.

But he was sitting up, his head arched back, long fair hair pressed against the shoulder blades, eyes staring at the huge aircraft three thousand feet above them. "You're late, big bird," he said soundlessly against the roar overhead. "Don't be next week, for the plucking of the Mushroom Man."

"What did you say?" she shouted. "What plane is that?"

"That, my little girl, is a Boeing 747, valued in the millions. That one is Israel's El Al, and it's late again." He spoke softly, his delicate Irish brogue flavouring the words.

He got up and began to pull on his trousers over the dried-out swimsuit. She saw again the reddened disfigurement of the healed puncture wound, low on the left side of his chest. She'd asked about it, been told of a stumble while carrying a pitchfork.

"Are we doing anything tonight?" she asked hesitantly.

"I'm sorry," he said, seeing her face fall with disappointment, "but I can't tonight. I have to meet a man . . ."

"About a dog," she said.

"No, it's real. He's coming from abroad to see me. Really.

21

There's some business I have to do, take a few days. I'll see you then. Definitely. Come on, I'll walk you to the bus."

She was near to tears when he left her.

FOR TWO hours Ciaran McCoy stayed beside the train departure board at Waterloo Station, waiting for the man he was to meet. He had fulfilled all his instructions. Red tie, raincoat over his right arm, AVIS RENT A CAR sign in his hand. He'd been pushed and shoved, but not acknowledged. Close to midnight he went into a telephone booth and dialled a number he had been given.

His call was answered by a switchboard deep behind the ornate façade of an Edwardian building at Prince's Gate overlooking Hyde Park. The building housed a North African embassy. McCoy asked for an extension, was surprised that the phone was answered at this hour. Then couldn't remember the word he was supposed to give. Been waiting too long, too wrought up. Some bloody foreign word.

"It's McCoy here. Ciaran McCoy. Our friend hasn't shown."

The voice at the other end was calm, unconcerned by the lack of the code word. Perfect English. There had been a delay. The project might be called off. He should phone tomorrow, but not so late.

Five seconds after McCoy put the receiver down, the tape recorder stopped rolling. All calls to that number were automatically monitored; had been ever since the extension was obtained from a high-ranking member of that embassy in exchange for Foreign Office silence about his drinking habits.

The tape was one of scores recorded that night which would be replayed by shorthand typists in the basement of a building in Curzon Street, Mayfair, a bare mile away.

CHAPTER TWO

David Sokarev always carried the Mauser pistol in the glove compartment of his car. It was loaded, but was fired only twice a year, when he went on the shooting range east of Beersheba. Left to himself, he wouldn't have had the pistol. But he had been

22

ordered to possess a gun, and rather than making an issue, he obeyed and kept it in the car. If he was ever obliged to fire in anger he would probably miss. His chunky spectacles proclaimed his poor eyesight.

There had been a suggestion that his work made him too sensitive a man to be driving himself to the laboratory at Dimona and home again to Beersheba. He had railed at that as preposterous, had won his case. A careful and methodical man, he drove with circumspection, his mind concerned with problems of plutonium, subcritical masses, fission, isotope separation, neutrons —they were what enveloped him as the little car trudged back and forth across the Negev Desert. He would read, too, as he drove. Few of his colleagues lightly accepted the offer of a lift.

Sixteen years earlier, when Sokarev started to work at Dimona, the project had been at the apex of Israel's secret list. He had not been able to tell anyone where he went each day or what he did. But the Bedouins who used to pass, listlessly urging their camels between the dunes, had taken news of the cranes and bulldozers to the military governor of Egyptian Al-'Arish. The message had gone to Cairo of huge construction deep in the Negev, of armed troops patrolling. Cairo's concern was passed to the State Department in Washington, whence the foolproof method of international espionage was set in motion.

On an October day in 1960 a U-2 spy plane had taken off from a U.S. base in Iran with orders to overfly Dimona and photograph the new complex. When the U-2 landed in Turkey, the film was rushed to aircraft standing ready to fly to Washington. There, experts in interpreting altitude photography identified a medium-size nuclear reactor, the integral plant necessary in the manufacture of the plutonium that is at the heart of an atomic explosion.

In the halcyon days after the June victory in the Six Day War of 1967—when Israel's defences seemed secure and the Arabs had been pushed back across the great buffer zones of Sinai, the Jordan Valley, and the Golan Heights—the Israeli government issued statements about nuclear energy for peaceful uses. Sokarev directed his energies towards the "agro-nuclear complexes": the

23

reclaiming of desert land with sea water distilled through nuclear power. He was young for his job and regarded by his colleagues as brilliant. But the project did not last.

New tensions rose along the Egyptian and Syrian borders. And on Yom Kippur, October 1973, when Sokarev and his family were at prayer, the Arab enemies breached the great defensive lines along the Suez Canal and bestrode the Golan. The peace was hard-won this time; it was no Six Day War. Reports filtered through of new, far-reaching Soviet rockets, sited on the plains behind Damascus.

To the Israelis it was clear the time had come to consider what the world called the nuclear option. The days at Dimona started earlier, ended later, as Sokarev and the team that was built around him wrestled with the problem of speeding up construction of the bomb. And so from the reactor in the desert came tiny quantities of plutonium 239, barely eight kilograms a year, in bulk the size of an orange but with the capability to create a twenty-kiloton explosion. Israel's bombs, equivalent to those dropped on Hiroshima and Nagasaki, could not be tested, but at least the stockpile was starting.

It had been a brutal twenty months for Sokarev, months of fierce hours and interminable arguments over government money. He longed for the days when his working brain had been overwhelmed only by scientific equations. That he was tired and worried showed on him. His face was grey from lack of sunlight; his shirt bulged over the lower abdomen from denial of the tennis that he had played with joy twice a week.

But the armed guard who stopped him that Thursday morning at the first of the security gates noted that the worn face of David Sokarev was a little brighter. "You're looking well today, Professor," he said.

"So I should. My last day here, then away for a bit."

"Holidays?" the guard asked, before moving back to swing up the red-and-white-painted STOP barrier that blocked advance.

"Of a fashion. A few days in London, then New York. A few lectures, to meet old friends. Something of a holiday, yes."

Twice more the car was stopped by grey-brown-uniformed

guards with Uzi submachine guns. All three men who spoke to the professor as he arrived that morning noticed the fractional bounce that had lifted him.

"I'm late in," he said to his secretary in the outer office. It was one minute past eight o'clock. "What have we today?"

"Mostly meetings. There was a call a minute ago from the Foreign Ministry, the security division. They want to drive down from Jerusalem this afternoon to talk about your trip."

It was six o'clock before David Sokarev's desk was clear enough for him to feel able to abandon it for the three weeks he would be away. There were then no more excuses to prevent his inviting in the two men from the ministry's protection branch who waited in his outer office. Joseph Mackowicz and Gad Elkin were both young, fit and good-looking. Sokarev did not apologize for keeping them so long, and they did not seem to expect it.

Mackowicz said, "We are to be travelling with you, Professor. We will be very close to you at all times. It is best that we meet the people we are to accompany before we get to the airport. What we want now is a guarantee that you will cooperate and take most seriously our advice."

"I would never knowingly not cooperate."

"That, Professor, is excellent news. Not everybody in a position similar to yours is happy to have us in immediate proximity. Some talk of embarrassment from foreign colleagues. I assure you, if there is embarrassment, it is a necessary cross to bear."

"I had not given myself such importance," said Sokarev with a tinge of sadness. "Nor realized that I might be at risk."

Mackowicz said, "We had not considered our athletes at Munich to be at risk. We knew an Arab attack, from the Black September faction, would come at about that time somewhere in Europe. No one put the sum together, and our people died defenceless. It will not happen again. A single tennis player representing Israel is protected. Inevitably, so must be a scientist of your status. It was all laid down in the reorganization that followed Munich."

"Gentlemen," said Sokarev, "I can accept the possibility of a threat. But I would take it as a small risk only. So why do we need two men to look after me? Why in any case cannot this be done

25

by our own embassy people or the police forces of the countries I visit?"

It was Elkin who spoke now. "You are regarded by government as high-risk category. You have much specialized knowledge and head an important team here. Thus you are an important target."

"We have informants, people who listen for us," Mackowicz added, "and people who interpret what they hear. From what we learn we try to anticipate possibilities. The pattern is not yet whole in this instance, but it has a form, an outline."

"Specifically, there is a threat to me?" There was puzzlement from Sokarev, confidence about to drain.

"We know," Elkin said, "that a Palestinian terror squad has been moving north across Europe. They were intercepted, on our advice, by the French authorities. Two of them died. We believe there were three. If so, one is not accounted for. They were on the road to Boulogne, heading, we assume, for the ferry to Britain. We have no one going to Britain except yourself, Professor."

Sokarev was quiet. Subdued. Unhappy in the presence of these chilling young men, growing resentful of their message.

The silence, long and perceptible—to the point of shuffled feet —was broken by Mackowicz. "You will not have read about this, nor will you need to repeat it. Six nights ago a terrorist group mounted a border raid from their advance base in Lebanon. They were ambushed by an army patrol. There were five in all. Four were killed in the action. We captured one. He talked to us. Under interrogation. Information is not easy to come by, and when we get it, we listen."

Sokarev rose unsteadily from his chair and moved across the room. He felt more than his age, a great weariness. By the door he switched on the light, banishing the spreading shadows. Apart from a single photograph, the walls of his office were bare. Uncomplicated, as he liked it. The photograph showed his three children: two girls in army slacks and regulation V-neck navy-blue sweaters; between them his son, a head taller, in air force summer khaki with pilot's wings on his chest. They'd all be home together on leave tomorrow.

"What did this terrorist say under questioning?"

Mackowicz and Elkin stood up. Mackowicz said, "He told us the PFLP, General Command, had been planning an attack in Europe. He did not know the target. Under extreme interrogation he gave us the code word for this operation. *Kima*. It is an Arabic word, of the Palestinian dialect. It means 'mushroom'. Not the small button-shaped type, but the large, free-growing sort that magnifies and flourishes. That is why we consider a man from Dimona to be at risk. That is why we will be at your side."

AFTER they had gone, David Sokarev sat a long time in the room. Then he packed his papers into the old frayed leather briefcase and locked the door behind him. Surrounded by the brilliantly lighted wire fences, he walked to his car. He could see men high up on the watchtower platforms, and below them the dog handlers with the attack Alsatians. This was the oasis that he knew, safe, rewarding, isolated from the world outside.

When he reached for his keys he found that his hands were trembling. He rested in the seat for a few moments to mollify the breathiness that affected him, then drove off for home.

For the first time in his adult life he was experiencing fear. Fear of the unknown. He could not remember a similar sensation of such intensity. Like a child afraid of being left alone in an unfamiliar darkened room, he began to dread the visit to the strange city—a city of millions, where one man . . . or two . . . or three . . . or four had a solitary and inflexible purpose; the destruction of David Sokarev, of himself. His wife noticed the drawn look that spilled out from the side of his mouth, and the tension about his eyes. She brought him his meal, liver, watched him toy with it, eating to please her. He told her nothing of Mackowicz and Elkin.

Afterwards he sat slumped in his deep chair. There were often times when his work had seemed to force him down, literally bowed his shoulders with its pressures. On previous occasions they had been able to discuss his exhaustion and depression, thereby lessening the load. But not this time. She found little response to her gentle feelers for information. She was just shrugged off, left with a feeling of frustration. She hoped that the arrival of the children tomorrow would rouse him.

27

CHAPTER THREE

A city is vulnerable to an act of terrorism. Huge and preoccupied and indifferent. The ideal hunting ground, and never more so than if the stalkers are a small, motivated group of men whose numbers can be counted on the fingers of one hand. The Provisional IRA has proved conclusively how defenceless a great international capital is—bombs exploding in busy shops and on railway platforms, and the mighty carcass of London barely knew it was under attack.

Where eight million people are gathered together, everyone is a stranger, no one belongs. The terrorist can blend into whatever background he chooses. If he has funds, he can take a smart flat in Mayfair or Belgravia, where a porter will salute him as he comes and goes but will ask no questions. Without money he can turn to the myriad of small hotels of north London, pay when he registers, and bide his time in total anonymity. In the big city a man who is skilled in the art of guerrilla warfare can blame only himself if he fails.

In London the forces ranged against him are meagre, the principal one being the metropolitan police, the civilian police force headquartered at Scotland Yard in the new building close to Victoria Station. Confronted with the increasing problems of conventional crime, the metropolitan police have also been forced into a crash course in combating international violence. The whole concept was far from officials' minds when they built New Scotland Yard and moved people, files and laboratories into a towering, glass-faced structure so vulnerable to car-bomb attack that patrolling police now prevent any vehicle from parking within fifty feet of it. And of the hundreds of detectives who scurry in and out of its main swinging doors, relatively few are engaged in anti-terrorist operations. Those who are belong to Special Branch, the wing formed close to a hundred years ago to counter the Irish Fenian threat.

Though the Irish problem still dominates their work, the Branch men also have to concern themselves with the potential of subversion, fringe anarchist groups, the most militant of the background trade union officials, Iron Curtain bloc diplomats. They have the responsibility of personal protection for important Britons, from the Prime Minister down, and also for foreign persons of rank arriving in the country.

They had been informed of the planned visit of David Sokarev to Britain only four days before his arrival at Heathrow airport. They were unaware either of his crucial importance to Israel or of the extent of the threat against him.

But, for the survival of David Sokarev on his journey through London, there was another group of men far more important than the officers of Special Branch. They worked from little-known premises in one of the most fashionable districts of the capital. Close to the Playboy Club and the London Hilton is a gaunt five-story building much in need of repair. Its windows are shielded from outside view by lace curtains and are protected by half-inch-thick concertina steel meshes. Side entrances have been bricked up. Above the doorway, never cleaned and all but unreadable, are the words LECONFIELD HOUSE. The building carries no other identification that might give a clue to the occupation of those who work there.

It is the nerve centre of Britain's most secretive organization, responsible for deeply undercover counter-espionage and counter-terrorist operations: the British Security Service.

Eleven hours after the tape recording of Ciaran McCoy's conversation with the Arab diplomat had been completed, the spools and a transcript of them were on the desk of a man on the second floor of Leconfield House. The room occupied by Philip Whilloughby-Jones was bare to the point of starkness. Against one wall was a steel filing cabinet. Grouped in a semicircle in front of the desk were four chairs, framed in metal, not designed for comfort.

Jones—he detested the hyphenated name his father had taken to using—was sparely built. A sharp gull nose jutted out above the brush moustache that was a legacy of Royal Air Force service. His cheeks were thin, his hair wispy and greying. The brightness lay in his eyes; deep set, alert and alive. It was his lower jaw that separated him from other men, the way the skin, lacking wrinkles and hair, had been transplanted from his buttock to cover the incinerated layers he had lost so many years before.

Jones was responsible for the general surveillance of Middle East embassies in London. Duggan, of Irish Affairs, would be down in fifteen minutes to talk with him; and also Fairclough, of Arab Affairs (Palestinian). Before they came, there was time to look again at the file on the embassy in Prince's Gate. He unlocked the centre of the three drawers of the cabinet and pulled out a thin folder. At this particular embassy several telephone lines were listened to, each extension warranting a separate folder. This extension was only recently known, and little traffic came through it. Jones read the few sheets quickly and expertly. There was time for a pipe before the others came, and he lit up, sucking deep.

WAIT till a big party goes through, then move, they'd told him. So Abdel-El-Famy had merged with the student group that was swamping the French immigration officials. But the precautions Famy took were unnecessary; the checks at Boulogne were casual, guided only by the report that they should be vigilant for a man, mud spattered and probably unshaved. Famy, in laundered jeans, orange shirt, and hip-length navy jacket from his grip-bag, fitted no such description. The pistol and the soiled clothes were buried in a wood to the east of Boulogne.

As the ferry ploughed its way across the Channel, Famy made acquaintance with some of the young people. His French was good enough and spirits were high. The lecturer in charge of this eight-day trip to London was vaguely aware as the ferry approached the jetty that the tall, swarthy man, a little older than the others and now among them, had not been at the station in Paris. But perhaps this was someone's friend from home.

Famy saw the white ribbon of cliff as the boat swung to port and began its run to the long jetty. Not as formidable a barrier as he had expected. The castle caught his eye, powerful in its toad squatness, but antiquated. He smiled to himself, savouring it; that was his enemy, tired now, outdated. Unable to compete in the new and modern world that he sought for, unable to comprehend the hitting power of the Palestinian movement, unable to defend itself against the new philosophy of revolution and attack.

The two girls from Orléans and the boy from St. Étienne were a long time getting their baggage together after the complicated process of docking and tying up. There were cries for them to hurry from the others. The delay suited Famy well. Out of it would come anxiety about the train connection for London, and that would mean a concentrated, excited rush at customs. Which was how it was. As customs quizzed the first four of the party, the lecturer began to shout and wave the folder with the rail tickets. The officials were good-humoured enough, and the party went through. Famy was talking with the two girls as they swept past the Special Branch men on port-watch duty. He didn't rate a glance from them. His passport was still in his pocket, unrequired, unexamined.

He now faced a moment of indecision. The orders for the three of them when they left Beirut had been specific about the next stage. Under no circumstances were they to travel via the direct Dover-to-London rail connection. If for any reason you are suspected, his people had said, the authorities have two and a half hours to decide to intercept at Victoria Station. So they had provided a bus timetable that would enable the squad to move down the coast and then link up with a train not connected with cross-channel services. Famy had felt safe with the French group, but his orders made no allowance for personal initiative at this stage. When the girls looked again for him, he had disappeared.

There were endless waits at bus stops. Dover to Folkestone, seven miles. Folkestone to Ashford, seventeen. Ashford to Maidstone, eighteen. In Maidstone he walked to the railway station through streets busy with late Friday afternoon shoppers and took a slow train to London. He was now, he reflected, within an hour of the streets on which it had been determined that David Sokarev would die.

IT WAS a difficult meeting in Leconfield House. Jones, Duggan, Fairclough close around the desk, with copies of the recorded transcript, attempting to read more into the words than they could find.

"Let's establish what we have from our own material first," Jones said. "The extension McCoy telephoned is rarely used, but was considered of some importance by that little sod that gave it to us. So, it's sensitive. And the other calls on that line have all been in some code, not yet broken." He took a paper out of his file. "Stuff like this. 'Accommodation one-seven-three, six-four, one-six-two.' That was three days ago. Next night. 'Rendezvous as arranged seven-seven-one-six.' The message last night indicated a failure of rendezvous. But where the pattern breaks down is that though the voice is the same as the first two calls, this time he introduces himself by name. Doesn't use a code word, busts straight in."

Fairclough spoke. "Try the simplest way through. The name McCoy is perhaps genuine. He's hanging about, waiting for someone. Gets fed up. Wants to know what's happening. So he calls—in that Irish voice, the magic accent that gives us all bad dreams."

"And what," Jones said, "is McCoy doing phoning a confidential embassy number when his blind date doesn't show?"

Duggan's turn. The other two men were working on hypotheses, dealing with the possible. His concern was the exact and known threat that went under the initials PIRA—Provisional Irish Republican Army. He had already checked all his own lists for any mention of Ciaran McCoy. None existed. He had telephoned Military Intelligence in Northern Ireland. They would feed his request into the computer, reply on the telex by midafternoon.

"If the boy is a Provo, it's difficult to explain," Duggan said. "They've had contacts with Arab governments, bought arms from them. The Kalashnikovs were intercepted. They've had meetings, discussions, with them. But their politics are the width of the Sahara apart. If a liaison exists, it's to do one thing, then forget it. They couldn't hold together for anything sustained."

"The boy's the only place we have to start," Fairclough chipped in. "It's from McCoy we start pulling the pieces together. But if they're talking about linking up, then we're not far off the spectacular. After rendezvous the Arabs don't hang about knitting, they move onto target. They come in late and they hit and they shift; it's all planned with thoroughness. Munich's the best example. The crowd that went into the Olympic village arrived

32

two and three days before the attack. But they set it up seven months earlier."

"Perhaps this time they'll not arrive at all," Jones murmured, the smile playing around his lips. "You saw the paper. Two men believed to be Arabs stopped at a roadblock near Boulogne."

"Nice thought," agreed Fairclough.

There was a knock on the door. The girl who came in was tall, a little plump, fair hair over her shoulders, her sweater an inch too tight. Helen Anderson had been secretary to Jones for eight years. "Sorry to interrupt, sir," she said quietly, "but there's a message for Mr. Fairclough from Foreign Office. The Israelis have made a contact with our people in Cyprus. When they've put the report through the mincer, found the right code book, it'll be sent over. They said you should wait for it."

"That's the evening gone, for the lot of us," said Fairclough. They bitched and moaned every Friday night when work saturated their desks, but they always stayed.

THE Israeli who had flown to the Akrotiri Royal Air Force base in southwest Cyprus was travelling anonymously and under the direct instructions of the director of intelligence in Tel Aviv. Much of the exchange of information between Israeli and British security people was conducted in this immense, sprawling RAF camp. London always took seriously any warning flashed from Cyprus; on at least half the occasions that troops had been drafted into Heathrow, it followed close on information from Akrotiri.

That evening the Israeli wasted little time. To the member of the British team who had driven there to meet him, he had made five points in crisp succession. A Palestinian assassination squad had been intercepted in northern France. Israeli security in Paris was uncertain that all members of the gang were accounted for. The operation was code-named Mushroom. Israel's foremost but largely unknown nuclear scientist was due in Britain on Monday to fulfil a long-standing speaking engagement. And the Israeli government would react extremely unfavourably if any incident should mar the professor's visit. Understatement was the man's style, but he repeated the last point three times.

The Englishman said, "If he's so important and the threat exists, why not call the visit off?"

"If we did that every time there was a threat, we would become immured, be sterilized. We do not bend the knee to terrorists, and we expect the support of your agencies."

"Anything else that could help us?" asked the Englishman, thinking, he enjoys it when they can wrap the rest of us up in their interminable problems.

"Nothing more. Just keep it tight round our professor."

THE INFORMATION that Duggan had requested from Northern Ireland was brought from Leconfield House's basement bank of teletype machines at four that Friday afternoon. The frown deepened on his forehead, anxiety growing as he read.

Subject: McCoy, Ciaran Patrick Aloysius
Address: Ballynafeigh fm, nr Crossmaglen, S Armagh, NI
Age/Date of Birth: 22 years, 14/3/54
Security File: For three years member PIRA. After one year reported I/C Active Service Unit, Cullyhanna area. Expert rifle shot. Natural leader. Arrested Sec Forces 8/12/74. Held HM Maze Prison where became PIRA cage commandant. Freed on Sec of State's instruction 3/7/75. Since then active political work, could return to violence. Last is Mil Intelligence and SB assessment. Believed responsible for shootings in S Armagh, specifically patrol car 17/8/74 and sniping of paratroop killed 10/10/74. Pix and prints follow.
Background: Undermentioned is person-to-person confidential from Mil Intelligence, to your department only. "We are astonished at the release of McCoy and protested via appropriate political offices. Reply was that McCoy, as the only detainee from his area, was freed in response to his local PIRA requirement in existing cease-fire situation."

Regarded as exceptional calibre, good educational standards, could pass well in all company, considerable disguise capabilities. Last seen in area approx 10/12 days ago. No known visits to London, but sister once worked St Mary's Hosp, London W2.

Last interrogated by Maj Ian Stewart, Intelligence Corps, retired.
Summary: Hard boy. Best of luck.

Duggan photocopied the paper for Jones, for Fairclough, and for his departmental head. He reread the information. To his trained mind the implications of the message were fearsome. A top man, in a top-grade Provisional setup. Responsible for at least two deaths. So what was he doing now, running around London, calling up embassies, missing his links? Duggan hurried down to the floor below where Jones had his office.

AT VICTORIA STATION the Arab pushed his way past the surging crowds of homeward-bound commuters and into a telephone kiosk. He read the instructions, found a two-pence coin, and dialled the number he had memorized. There was the noise of the beeps instructing him to feed his coin into the appropriate slot, a pause, then the answering voice. He spoke the number of the extension they had given him. Another voice confirmed the number for him.

Famy said, "Mushroom, one has arrived."

From the other end, curt, "Same rendezvous as if you had been here last night." Then the line was dead.

Three hours to kill. Famy walked out into the late evening sunshine. In front of him was a tourists' stall. Union Jacks, guardsmen dolls, postcards of Buckingham Palace.

"Excuse me," he said to the elderly man sitting by his stall. "Do you have the book *London AZ*? A map called the AZ?"

The man handed the blue, white and red book to Famy. "A *to* Z," he said patronizingly.

Famy moved away with the book. Across the busy road he could see a sign. SANDWICHES AND SNACKS, it proclaimed. He felt hungry, tired. He joined a group of pedestrians as they scurried across the street. In the café, an Italian brought a coffee to his small table, and he ordered some bread and salad. He flicked at the *A to* Z, taking in the labyrinthine network of lines and words that made up the Greater London area. Then he reached inside his jacket for the slim diary he carried, and among a jumble of figures in the section for accounts, selected the top line. It read 77.1.6. He shouldn't have written down those numbers. The order had been to memorize them. But Famy had been nervous of forgetfulness. He was aware that he had broken an

35

instruction of the mission and guilt caught him as he started to work the code system.

He went carefully through the book to the map on page 77. There were letters across the top and bottom of the map, squares, and numerals down the sides. He counted through his alphabet, searching for a letter that corresponded to the number 6. On his fingers he came to the letter F. In the square below the letter F and across from the figure 1, there was a shaded-in area marked Waterloo. They had said the rendezvous would be at a station, so he would go straight to Waterloo Station.

Next he checked the figures to see where his accommodations would be: 173.64.162. This time he turned to page 173 and began to work his way down the back index of street names. The sixty-fourth read Englefield Road, N.1. 4C 46. The accommodation address was therefore 162 Englefield Road, on the fringes of Islington and Dalston in north London.

A TRANSCRIPT of Famy's call to the embassy was hurried up to Jones. "There's no chance of a trace," said the man who brought it. "The call lasted about fourteen seconds. Originated, probably, in a public place, and not inside a building. No way at all we can pick up a call like that."

"And the voice?" queried Jones.

"Foreign. I'd put in a bid for eastern Mediterranean."

So, he had arrived, their little friend. Missed his first appointment, but was here with the right code word, and ready to meet up with his sodding little Provo.

Jones reached for his telephone and dialled his home number. "I'll be late, dear. May not be back at all tonight. Boys all right? Good. I'm sorry . . . I always say that. Mean it, though. Love you, darling."

There were two files now. One for the embassy calls, one for McCoy. He took them both with him to the basement and pulled up a chair beside the man who monitored the number he was concerned with. The man passed him a pair of earphones. And they waited, concentration building up, for the next call.

Jones reflected that there was no complacency among his small

team. All appreciated that they were catching up in a few hours on what it had taken the enemy months to prepare. There was never enough time in this business. Always running from behind.

THE RETIRED major from the Intelligence Corps told Duggan little of McCoy that he did not already know. On the phone from Wiltshire, the major's mind was more fully attuned to his rose garden than to the young Irishman he had interrogated months earlier. "He was a cut above the usual cement-between-the-ears boyos. We didn't budge him at all. Clamps were well down on what we could do to them by that stage. I didn't see that he had any great political leanings. Funny, few of them have. He reacts to orders, but he's tougher than most. Has a lot of hate."

The major paused, seeking for anything that could be of use to the man in London. "He plans his operations well. Lots of patience. Oh, and one thing. If you're looking for him in London —he has a sister, a bit older. Worked in a hospital. Girl went a bit haywire. Got mixed up with a load of hippies. Packed her nursing in and went to live with them. McCoy didn't approve. They're a very puritan crowd, the hard-core Provos. I tried to talk about it to him. Didn't work."

"That could be very helpful," said Duggan.

A COURIER came by car with the report, decoded, from the meeting at Cyprus. Fairclough had to come down to the lobby of the building to sign personally for the plain buff envelope. Back in his office, he read the typed sheets with attention for detail. It was very thorough.

He buzzed through to Jones's office. Helen answered. "He's down below. Eavesdropping. He asked me to stay behind. Said there might be some reports to type."

Annoyance surged through him. His secretary had gone home hours ago. Jones's girl was always there, never went home when they worked late. "Get a message to him. Mr. Duggan and I need to see him. Whatever time he's through, we'll be waiting."

Fairclough phoned his home to warn of a late night. Duggan did the same.

Down in the basement, a man was hunched intently over the monitoring machinery. "Here it goes, sir," he said. Jones winced at the noise of the amplified beeps searing through his earphones.

The man reacted to it. "Have to have 'em up full blast. They can whisper, and you've lost the lot while you're fiddling with the volume." He had switched on the tape recorder.

"It's McCoy," muttered Jones as the Irish voice came through. He heard the switch made to the extension inside the embassy, heard the code word given, and the single sentence in reply.

"Two hours waiting for that!" Jones spat the words out. "Used the code word though. Mushroom—confirmed."

Helen was waiting when he emerged. She said, "Mr. Duggan and Mr. Fairclough want to see you. They—"

"Get them to my office, and quick." And he was past her, attacking the broad central staircase, three steps at a time.

FROM AMONG the crowd by the tea wagon in Waterloo Station, Famy watched McCoy as the Irishman stood in front of the train information board. Wearing the right clothes. Shirt correct, draped coat correct, sign correct. Not furtive, just anxious. Passengers swayed around the fair-haired Irishman as his glance swept the concourse, searching for the contact. Famy, watching, reflected that this was completely new for him, beyond the range of his experience. He had had no contact with foreign groups. If it had happened as planned, Bouchi would have been the one to make the approach. But Bouchi was in a morgue, cold on a slab in northern France. Famy drank his tea, his eyes searching for any other man who might be lingering overlong. He took many minutes to be satisfied, then began to thread his way forward.

McCoy saw him coming and stiffened, breathing faster. Contact just a few seconds away. Slightly built, dark skin, short well-groomed hair, brightly dressed. A stranger, something separate, and then he was close, speaking.

"The mushrooms are—" Famy broke off. The words they had told him to say—how idiotic they sounded, spoken to a fellow human in the chaos of a railway station. "I think you are here to meet me?"

McCoy just said, "Come on. No need to hang about." Already on the move, "Where are the others?" he asked over his shoulder.

"It is just me," said Famy.

There was a hint of suspicion in the way McCoy tilted his head, swerving around to focus on the other man. "They told me I'd meet three men," he hissed. "What's happened to change it?"

"Read today's papers. Of events in northern France." McCoy shook his head, his lack of comprehension overwhelming. They were standing now at the bus stop. Famy went on. "There was a shooting, at a roadblock. Early yesterday. My friends did not survive."

Shorter than the Arab, McCoy looked up into his face. "Dead? Is it called off, is it over? The plan?"

"It is not over. There is no possibility of our abandoning the plan. We have been launched. Setbacks are not infrequent. But it is not a thing to talk of here."

The Irishman wanted to say more. But it was difficult against the unfamiliar logic spelled out in the curiously precise voice. The bloody team shot to pieces, and this one carrying on as if nothing had happened. Daft, mad. He saw the face of the other man, masked, unemotional, staring down the road. Out of their minds, this one and the ones who set it all up. What can one man, what can two, achieve compared with four? Four was the minimum number, all had agreed. And now it's halved, and this idiot says it goes on. He silently rolled his tongue around a string of oaths, savouring the words that slashed at the anger he felt. When the bus came, he led the Arab up to the top deck. They took front seats, Famy pushing the bag underneath his knees.

"We can talk up here," he said.

"There is no problem, my friend." Famy spoke with calm certainty. "We two are sufficient. I was told you had a plan. That is correct?" McCoy nodded his head, numbness setting in with the knowledge that he was no longer in control, that the tall stranger had taken command. "If there is a plan, we can execute it," said Famy. "He is only one man. He will be guarded, but not thoroughly. If we are determined, there is no difficulty."

Nothing more was said as the bus jolted its way to Islington.

McCoy looked sideways occasionally, and realized that the Arab's eyes never shifted from their relaxed, unseeing gaze to the front. He's like a bloody train, thought McCoy, on course, all signals green. New city, contact man he's never met before, half the back-up dead behind him, and he doesn't even turn his stupid head.

The time he had shot the paratrooper was very clear to McCoy. He could recall the clammy nausea in his throat as the gangling soldier had come in sight. He'd waited so long for him, he'd hardly been able to focus his eye down the smooth, crisp barrel of the Armalite. Cold sweat running under his shirt. He'd fired, watched the soldier heave and clutch at himself, seen the disbelief that comes before the pain and before death. He'd sprinted then, with the adrenalin pumping through his veins, and for hours afterwards, even in the womblike safety of the barn where he lay up after missions, he had panted with the excitement, close to exhilaration, of the moment he had fired. A near-orgasmic movement of release as the butt of the rifle thudded into his shoulder—he could relive it hour after hour.

But this bloody Arab . . . It's animal, when you don't care, thought McCoy, unnatural when you don't feel the tension. Subhuman. McCoy had read of these people when they went into Israel. Suicide squads, like *kamikaze*, there to kill and be killed. He'd seen pictures of them training with explosives strapped on their waists. This man beside him, with the vacant, contented eyes, would be one of those hard, mean bastards.

"We get off here, next stop," said McCoy.

Down on the pavement, they began to walk. Famy fractionally behind McCoy. The street was made up of four-storey Victorian terraced houses. Up to fifty years ago, expensive homes. They had disintegrated into flatlets. McCoy stopped outside one of them.

"A word of explanation," he said. "We've tried to find new territory. None of the haunts our people use. It's what we call a commune here. Young people who drop out of the rat race, as they say. This place is up for sale. The kids have moved in, taken over, till they get chucked out. But it's safe for us. People come and go at all hours. Nobody asks questions. Just don't get involved. Keep to yourself and no one will bother you. I got them to clear a room for us. Remember, nobody gives a damn who you are here."

McCoy pushed the door open. They were met with a flood of hard-rock, shrieking pain-bearing music.

INSIDE the diplomatic bag sent out of the embassy that Friday night was a high-security sealed envelope. It would be flown from London the next morning to a North African capital; from there, again inside the web of diplomatic immunity, to Beirut. A telephone call, person-to-person, would be made to a writer on Lebanon's biggest daily. The message that the man code-named Saleh Mohammed was in London would then be just a hard drive away from the camouflaged tent of the leader of the PFLP, General Command. By Sunday evening he would be aware that his plan was still in motion.

UNDER THE harsh fluorescent light the files in front of the three men had begun to thicken. Every half hour or so Helen would bring in the mugs of coffee on which the department seemed to exist. They were all tired now, weary from the strain that had begun more than twelve hours earlier, but aware that no sleep could be taken until the next day's plan was prepared. Jones knew the danger of exhaustion, had seen it sap men, make them vulnerable. But no way around it. No point in mobilizing the forces at their disposal—police, detectives, army—until they had a plan. The problem was to find the shape of the threat. Then, and only then, could the big battalions be drawn in.

Past midnight Jones dialled the Director General of the Security Service. It was rare for him to be called at home, let alone at that hour. Jones spoke to the DG with deference, described taped conversations, the background of McCoy, the rendezvous with the unknown man, the Israeli warning.

The DG listened without interruption as he sat, pyjama-clad, on the side of his bed. "Suggestions?" he said at the end.

"Perhaps you could come in tomorrow morning, sir. Have a conference with us. Then I think we should bring Scotland Yard in, ask them to get Special Branch to hunt out the Irishman. The Israeli security attaché will have to be brought in. We'll have to

42

do a card check on airports and ferries, though that will probably narrow down to the Channel ports. This Israeli professor comes on Monday. There's not a lot of time."

"Right. Thank you, Jones. I'll see the three of you at eight thirty. Get some sleep."

Jones repeated the instruction to Duggan and Fairclough. As they were leaving, Helen came in. "What time in the morning?" She said it casually.

"Eight thirty, my love. We're seeing the DG then. Far to go tonight? Or Jimmy's, is it?"

A light laugh. "Jimmy said he'd sit up, make me some cocoa."

"Tell lover boy not to burn the candle too hard. Might be needing him. All fit and fighting fresh. Tell Jimmy that."

CHAPTER FOUR

The music went on through the night, deafening, raucous. It blasted its way through the floorboards, concentrating around Famy as he tossed in his sleeping-bag. They were on the top storey of the house, but still the noise sought him out, wresting him from the sleep he craved. A few feet away McCoy lay still, impervious to the cacophony. There were no curtains at the window and the moon threw light enough into the room for him to make out its bareness. Rough, uncovered boards, peeling wallpaper, a naked bulb hanging from the low ceiling.

They'd offered him food when he'd arrived. Talked of beans and bread. He'd declined, and watched the Irishman eat from a scarcely-washed plate. It had revolted him. Later he'd allowed himself a cup of milk.

Famy had waited out in the hall when they first came to the house, while McCoy entered a downstairs room. A group had come to the door to look him over. Long dark hair, boys distinguished from girls by beards and moustaches, but in the mutual uniform of tight jeans, sweat shirts and jerseys, beads and badges. Some wore sandals; others were barefoot.

There was no life like this in Nablus, he thought. Some might live unwashed and dress in rags, but not from choice. In camps away up the hill on the Jerusalem Road, where drains were open, roofs were corrugated iron, and walls were fashioned from packing cases, there was no satisfaction in the awfulness—there was no option. Those who lived in the camps had come in 1948, bred their children, built their shanties, and when the Israeli advance had rushed farther forward nineteen years later, had been stuck there. No one sought such degradation purposefully.

But the Irishman had said it was safe to stay here. That was sufficient while the operation went ahead. Famy fell into a half sleep, imagining the couplings of those boys and girls below him, almost nauseated that anything so precious could be consummated in all that dirt. He had never slept with a girl, never known the reality of his imagination.

The thin grey light of dawn had begun to penetrate the room when, still wakeful, he was alerted by the turning of the door handle. It was done quietly and with care. He lay very still, tensed, controlling his breathing, and watched the dark shape glide across the floor. For just a moment there was a silhouette against the window, and he could make out long hair and the shape of a coat thrown shawl-like over shoulders. He was fearful of moving his head, vulnerable on his back. A flashlight at the edge of his vision, hands probing in his bag. Then darkness again, and the sound of feet hesitating at the door, where his clothes were hanging. They were smoothly rifled through. The sound of the door closing, but no movement of footsteps away in the hall. Waiting to see if I'm awake, he told himself. Fifteen seconds, perhaps more, then the shuffling of bare feet on the landing.

For a long time Famy lay frozen in his sleeping-bag. Anything, anything he would have given for the company of Dani and Bouchi, someone to confide in other than the stranger who slept and ground his teeth in the other sleeping-bag across the boards.

The fool had said it was a safe place he was taking him to. But in only half a night his possessions and clothes had been searched precisely and systematically.

At first light he slid out and examined his bag. He heard McCoy stir, and turned quickly.

"Someone has been in here searching my things."

McCoy stared hard at Famy. "In here, giving us a look-over?"

"I couldn't sleep," said Famy. "And someone came in, went through our things. It was about two hours ago."

McCoy sat up. "Probably on the scrounge for a few pence—"

Famy cut across him, excited. "Nothing was taken. I tell you, it's the wrong place for us here, not what I was expecting."

"You'll stay where I say and that's here!" McCoy was close to shouting. "This is a no-questions place. If some sod frightens you, I can't help it."

"And if you're wrong?" Famy said.

McCoy quieted suddenly, recognizing the anxiety as genuine. "I'll put a bit of heat on downstairs, but gently. There's all sorts drifting round these places, looking for something to pinch. Nothing extraordinary about it. Remember, you are in London, and it's Saturday, and the man you want will be here Monday, whatever it is you call him . . ."

"Al Kima. The Mushroom Man. My friends would like to see me meet him. To avenge them."

Crisis over, chance of more sleep. McCoy turned away. "It's sleep we want now. Later today we walk round the university. Tomorrow it gets interesting."

The Irishman could not see the gleam in the other's eyes, the brightness that comes from erotic and compulsive anticipation: the dream of gunfire; international headlines, adulation in the tents far away in the desert.

When Famy looked again, McCoy was asleep with his left arm high around his head to shut out the light; his bullet wound below was exposed. The sight of it bruised the Arab. He who was assuming leadership had never known the reality of conflict. He could not know how it would affect him, the moment, when it came. Deep in the sleeping-bag Famy's legs trembled.

THE ALARM bell, furious, demanding attention, woke Helen.

She strained across Jimmy towards the bedside table and the offending clock till she found and silenced it. He hadn't moved all night. Still on his back, with his eyes hermetically sealed, mouth open, he slept on.

45

"You're hopeless," she told him. "Come on, wake up." Arms came up and around her, eyes opened for a brief flicker.

He spoke, as if it were the ultimate struggle. "It's Saturday, you're not going in today, and what time did you get here last night? I'm sitting here half the evening waiting."

"I am going in. Jones's special request. There's a big flap, all hands to action stations." She slid out of his grasp.

Jimmy had begun to take an interest. "What's the big panic?"

"Don't worry, lover boy, you're included in the cast. Some hit-and-runners after a nice plum Israeli target have the whole place running round like it's declaration-of-war day."

Jimmy was trying to focus. "What way am I in?"

"Jones said he might be needing you. 'All fit and fighting fresh.' That was all."

"Ruddy fine message for crack of dawn Saturday. What am I supposed to do? Sit here all weekend, hanging on the phone?"

"That's what you do every weekend." She eased her skirt into position and grimaced as she looked at herself in the mirror.

"He didn't say anything else?"

"Patience, lover boy, patience. Be a good lad and go back to sleep, so you sound all sweet and sober when he calls."

"Give us a kiss and tell me what it's all about. Come on."

She leaned over. He was considerate enough not to spoil her makeup. "I don't know, really. There's an Israeli, a nuclear scientist arriving, and a couple of boys are after him. One's IRA, the other probably Middle East. Their code word's Mushroom. But don't tell Jones I told you that. I'll try not to be late again tonight, and we'll cook something."

Helen gave the prone figure a wave, and was out of the flat. Two years she'd been coming now. First time after a department party, and Jimmy too drunk to notice she'd driven him home. A sort of habit had set in. The department governed both their lives; restrictions about social contact with people who did not share an existence governed by the Official Secrets Act ensured a curtailed horizon of friends. It was not a bad arrangement. They satisfied each other's immediate needs, but never at the expense of the department. There was no talk of marriage.

46

Be a hell of a day, Jimmy thought, waiting for Jones to call. Always the same when there was something rumbling. Wouldn't go out, not even to the off-licence, though the whisky supply was thin and there was a nerve-breaking ache in his head. He lay back, trying to shut out the pain. He hadn't had anything from Jones for four months. Life had been hard since then. The department's retainer fees didn't go far.

For Jimmy, existence on the fringe of the Security Service had started on a moonlit night in 1944. The twenty-fourth of August. He was aged nineteen, flight sergeant (rear gunner) in a Lancaster bomber. The whole eight-man crew had bitched about flying that night. Sitting ducks, the navigator had called them.

They had been more than a hundred and fifty miles short of the target when the night-fighter was guided onto them. Jimmy had time to shout a warning and bring his machine guns to bear before the cannon began to rake the airframe of the Lancaster. Fire was quick to follow, and the order to abandon the aircraft. Jimmy crawled sixty feet down the belly of the plane to the forward escape hatch. Six men had already jumped into the night that stretched more than three miles beneath. As Jimmy was about to commit himself to the slipstream, he saw the pilot edging towards him, his face contorted from the effort of movement and pain from the fire that had caught at his flying tunic. They had jumped virtually together. The officer had landed less than a hundred yards away, the fire on his body extinguished by the rush of air during his fall.

They had barely disentangled themselves when the German soldier reached them. Jimmy had gestured into the distance behind the soldier, and as the man had turned, Jimmy's heavy boot thrashed into his crotch. As he jackknifed, the outside edge of a hard right hand chopped down on the exposed inch between his helmet and the collar of his greatcoat. The German had died there instantly, giving Jimmy and the officer time to fade into the sanctuary of the trees. When light came, Jimmy had seen the pilot's face, seen the mashed raw damage, legacy of the clinging cockpit oil.

The pilot's name was Philip Whilloughby-Jones. He was two

years older than the rear gunner. He would never forget the speed and ruthlessness involved in the death of the German; nor the fresh pleasure that played in Jimmy's eyes, reflected by the moonlight, before they reached the trees—and the French Resistance. After the war, when Jones was a full-time deskman with the department, he had let it be known that there existed a man who could kill without scruple.

THE NEAREST police station to Englefield Road in Islington is some six streets away and to the north. Police Constable Henry Davies, Alsatian dog handler, nine years in the force, was going off duty. As he passed the main desk in the front hall, the dog Zero on its leash, the sergeant spoke to him.

"Off home, then, Henry? Not been much for you tonight."

"Not a damn thing, Sarge."

"Seeing Doris this weekend?" He'd need that for his dossier, knew everything about everyone, the old boy.

Davies paused near the door. "No way. She's staying in through today and tomorrow. Won't be coming out till Monday."

"I don't know how she does it," said the sergeant. "Nice clean girl, living with all that muck."

The constable smiled. "She doesn't seem to mind. Gets a bit deep about it all, says it's what police work is all about. Laughs at me for lugging this piece of dog flesh about."

"I couldn't do it. Living amongst them, weekends and all."

"She says the weekend's when all the action is, on the hippy scene. You have to be there, part of the furniture."

But he'd told Doris himself that he wasn't that keen on her living in the communes. She'd said it was a lot more interesting than driving around with a dog. He'd see her on Monday when she came in to file her twice-weekly report.

SINCE the Security Service began back in the sixteenth century, the department had successfully remained shrouded in total secrecy. For years its operators congratulated themselves that they had found a near-divine formula for the working of the department. But politicians, looking for economies in the 1960s and 1970s, instituted many cutbacks in Leconfield House. The department staff shrivelled with the funds. Worse followed when the politicians decided that the autonomy of the service should be curtailed, and appointed a conventional career civil servant to take charge. Only recently, after a series of publicly castigated mishaps, had the Prime Minister reverted to tradition and put a senior man from the Security Service itself into the Director General's office. His name was unknown to the mass of the population, and the media kept it confidential. But inside the department the new man had revitalized morale and effectiveness. The Irish problem had played its part in lifting the tempo at Leconfield House, and more recently came the wave of Arab terrorism. The DG could note with satisfaction that the building no longer operated on a five-day week. Many key men would be at their desks through the weekends, even in high summer.

He was a short, heavily built man, the DG. Papers spread across his desk, he sought the relevant facts from the files that had been left for him to digest. He gave it monumental concentration, head quite still, eating into the typescript, seeking for flaws in any argument, high spots in the information.

Promptly at eight thirty on that Saturday morning came the knock at his door, and Jones, Fairclough and Duggan came into the bright first-floor office and sat down. The DG closed the file on Ciaran McCoy that he'd been reading, and looked up at the men sitting around his desk. He could see their tiredness in their hastily shaved faces. A short meeting was required, nothing rambling that would escape the main issue.

"There's not much time, gentlemen." Voice calm, easy. "Our guest arrives Monday, his public appearance Tuesday, the flight out Wednesday or Thursday. We can probably ensure that he goes on Wednesday. The threat seems real enough. If this was simply an IRA affair, I would say that saturation protection would see us through—they tend to like to make it home all in one piece. But if the other half of the team is Palestinian, we must accept that he is prepared to die along with his target. It makes the protection of our scientist friend infinitely more complicated. The suicide killer always has things stacked in his favour. It means that we have to

49

widen the number of people involved. Thoughts, gentlemen?"

Duggan spoke. "This McCoy is a hard operator, but he's on strange ground here. He'll need a safe house where he can hole up with the other man. He can go in with the usual Provo crowd, or he might go right outside the norm. The only line we have on that could be his sister. She went through a spell in a commune in north London. McCoy was reported as disapproving, but he might use the contact."

"Good suggestion," said the DG, "but it'll take time to check out, and that's one for the police."

"Presuming that the Palestinian has joined up with McCoy, and we have to believe that from the rendezvous call," said Fairclough, "then we can just about guarantee that he's dependent on McCoy. It makes sense that the Arabs would provide the attack team, and the Provisionals the local knowledge."

"It's strange they should have chosen McCoy, with no experience in London." The DG was thinking aloud. "But what we have to consider is this. If the original team is decimated and one man wants to go on alone, how far does McCoy involve himself?"

"He's a killer," said Duggan. "It's clear from the file. He'll try and make sure he walks out of it, but he won't step back, not unless the odds are right against him."

"And our unknown friend will need him?"

"He's essential. The Arab needs him, and badly. But the two make a formidable threat. Make quite a handful."

"What brings these two together? No common ideology . . ."

"Necessity only," said Duggan. "The Palestinians must have the accommodations, transport and cover. With local providers, then can travel clean of firearms. Same for the Provisionals. They'll have become involved because it's to their own advantage. They've tried hard to get their hands on Iron Curtain weapons. . . . Europe's difficult as a supply source, and the American market is not adequate. The Middle East is their best chance. If they pull this off in successful harmony, it'll guarantee top-grade hardware for the Provos in the near future—Kalashnikovs, rocket launcher RPG-7s, perhaps even a missile."

"And the man Sokarev . . . ?"

"Important to the Palestinians; big coup if they drop him. Irrelevant to the Provos. Chances are they'd claim no part of it."

"And this bomb that the Israelis keep under the table, that our Mr. Sokarev is credited with—what state is that in?"

"The Americans call it the screwdriver state. Well off the design bench. Probably just needs putting together."

The DG straightened in his chair. "We'd better get the following done this morning. Details on McCoy to all police stations in London, particular reference to communes. Run a check on all yesterday's immigration forms coming in from Boulogne—that's for Special Branch. Fix a meeting with the Israeli security attaché at Home Office, only don't let him think he's running the show. Jones, I'd like you to coordinate. Final point. I'd like a man right beside this professor night and day, not just Special Branch, one of our own. So we know what's going on."

Jones spoke for the first time. "There's Jimmy. He's the best we have." No one in the room was prepared to debate the choice. Jones's loyalty to his men and the special bond between Jimmy and him were familiar to his colleagues. To make an issue of the decision would be futile.

The DG nodded. He liked Jimmy's results, stayed ignorant of his methods. He said, "That's it, gentlemen, and remember, there's very little time."

FROM THE outer office Helen called the home number of the commander in charge of Scotland Yard's Special Branch and connected him through to Jones. Copies of McCoy's file and the folder that had arrived from Northern Ireland would be sent by motorcycle to Scotland Yard.

Helen then called the Israeli embassy and left Jones's number for the security attaché to call back, with a view to an urgent meeting in midafternoon.

Next she traced Scotland Yard's assistant commissioner for crime to a golf club in Hertfordshire. The conversation Jones had with him caused him to scratch from the game he had arranged and head for home.

And lastly she raised Jimmy. Would he come in at four thirty?

51

THE CABINET MINISTER who rejoiced in the title of Secretary of State for Home Affairs liked to keep in touch with his constituents. On Saturday mornings he set aside time when the electors who had returned him to Westminster for the past eighteen years could meet him with their problems. He had dealt with fifteen constituents when the Director General of the Security Service asked to see him. The DG had direct access to the Prime Minister, but he preferred not to go too high up the ladder too fast, thus leaving no one senior to fall back on if the initial contacts went sour.

When the DG arrived in midmorning, he sensed that the Home Secretary was wary. Security only surfaced when political gales were blowing.

"I think we're running into something you ought to hear about." The Director General could see the Home Secretary's nervousness, and so in a subdued voice he explained the situation.

The Home Secretary felt trapped. "How important is this Israeli?" The question was barked, staccato.

"Not well known, but critical to their nuclear programme. Not on the civilian programmes; he's on the side they don't talk about. Sensitive work."

"Is it an important meeting he's coming to address?"

"There's nothing so far to suggest it's world shattering. . . ."

"But it would be if those boys get to him." This blighter, the Home Secretary thought, wants me to tell him he's doing a grand job, let him run off and take charge on his own, and when the fiasco comes he can say the Home Secretary was fully aware of the situation right from the start. No way you get me that easily. "The Prime Minister must be told of this. I'll do that. If it's not an important meeting, the Israelis should call off the visit. What's the point in risking him?"

"Foreign Office have tried that one, sir" said the DG. "Got a straight shutout. But I agree it would be the easiest solution."

The Home Secretary shook the DG's hand. The DG departed.

AS THE sun rose high that Saturday morning, warmth streamed through the window of the room that housed Famy and McCoy. The Arab pulled on his clothes with a shyness that came from

52

never before having been separated from his people. McCoy, still in his sleeping-bag, called across to him. Not to worry about shaving. Don't want to look too pretty here, doesn't fit with the surroundings, then a quiet laugh.

When he had dressed, Famy, waiting for some movement from McCoy, went to the window and peered down onto the street. It fascinated him, but he was loath to go beyond the door of this room on his own. In his mind was the image of the dark, cloaked figure he had seen moving dreamlike in the room. He felt frustrated, affronted at the casualness with which the Irishman had greeted his revelation.

"You can go downstairs if you want to," McCoy said. "They won't eat you, you know. They're just ordinary kids."

"I'll wait."

"Please yourself," McCoy said. He lighted a cigarette, smoked with deliberation while Famy watched, finally climbed out of the sleeping-bag. Standing in his underpants, he stared directly at Famy. "Have you done this sort of thing before?" he said. Not much more than a whisper, but demanding an answer.

Famy wavered. "No. No. It was planned that I should have moved into Israel to fight there. Then they had the information about Sokarev, and all was changed for me."

"Have you been in action before? I mean fired a gun?"

"Only in training. I have never fought." Famy struggled to control what he felt to be the inadequacies of his answers.

"It'll be difficult to get near the target, you know that?"

"With preparation, there is always a way."

"You don't mount a thing like this on wishful thinking," McCoy snapped. "You have to know what you're about."

"It is unnecessary to talk to me as a child." Famy's tone was very clear, soft, almost singsong.

McCoy retreated. "Don't get me wrong. I wasn't suggesting—"

"Then don't speak to me as if I were a fool. If you want no part in the rest, say so now. We can separate. Your role forgotten."

"There is no question of that. I'm under orders. From the Army Council. They've made a decision, and they'll stick to it. They won't go back on it. Our chief of staff has given his word." McCoy

53

smiled, feeling the cold on his skin, waiting for the response.

The relief flooded through Famy. "What do we do today?" he asked. There was excitement in his voice.

"Take a look at the university, I thought. Can't do that on a Sunday, all the students would be back in their digs, lodgings. A few of them will be about this afternoon. Would have been better yesterday, if you'd showed up on time. No. I'm not blaming you. You were a bloody genius to make it at all. Tomorrow we go down to the country. Where the guns and grenades are. We'll try and hit at the meeting."

"In Lebanon they thought there might be two opportunities— the meeting and at the airport when he leaves."

"The airport will be sealed, it's difficult there. The best chance has to be the meeting. How close do you need to get to him?"

"As near as is necessary."

"There has to be a way out."

"We have not come here to escape but to kill Sokarev."

McCoy fumbled with his socks. He felt the chill of the moment. Remembered newspaper pictures of Palestinians who had gone as near as was necessary. "There has to be a way that leaves us a chance of escape," he said.

"Perhaps," said Famy, and the Irishman left it there. He was some kind of madman, this Arab, a suicide merchant. When the time came, he'd need holding back. McCoy'd make his presence felt then, and his skill.

But they were not a team, and both men longed for the companionship of their own people.

McCoy led the way down to the front hall and opened the door into the main room. Eyes, heads, bodies swung to look at them. Like a zoo, thought McCoy. He stared back, waiting for someone to speak. They had little resolution against his gaze, and one by one the youths and girls returned their attention to their own groups. All except one girl. Rather plain, McCoy thought. A black shapeless dress, witch clothes, empty of anything feminine.

The girl, Doris Lang, was trained to observe and make deductions from what she saw. The two new arrivals were out of place in the commune. The Irishman was too countrified, too healthy,

54

and there was too much command in his face. And she sensed the nervousness of the dark man. He had cold, cruel, intent eyes that roamed without settling, always coming back to her. Strictly transit travellers, she decided, using the house for their own purposes. It surprised her that she had found nothing in their possessions last night to give her a hint of what their business was.

She felt the two men's eyes stripping her now and turned away, unwilling to appear curious. Marijuana smoke drifted through the room, cool and heady. Smoking had started early.

CHAPTER FIVE

The car of the Israeli ambassador came to the back door of the Foreign Office.

It was a Mercedes, low on its wheels because of the armour plating that was standard for the senior members of that country's diplomatic corps. There was a large radio aerial, which maintained communications with the fortified embassy building set back from the private Kensington Palace Road. Most ambassadors accredited to the Court of St. James's travelled with just a chauffeur, but in this car there were two other young men, both of whom had special licences to carry Uzi submachine guns. As it had made its way through London traffic, the Mercedes was shadowed by a powerful Rover, painted an anonymous blue, in which sat two men from the protection division of Special Branch.

When the car pulled up, the bodyguard in the front seat stayed where he was, his hand on a hidden Uzi. The other, who had ridden with the ambassador in the back, unlocked the door, climbed out, scanned the pavement and nodded. The ambassador was out and through the narrow door in seconds. Both he and his bodyguard ignored the Special Branch man who had also stepped onto the pavement. Assigned to the Israeli embassy, the London detective was used to this treatment.

During the work-week a liveried official would have been there to escort the ambassador to the second-floor office where the Under Secretary specializing in Middle East affairs now waited. But at the weekend there was simply a man in a dark suit.

"Thank you for coming, your Excellency," said the Under Secretary. "The Minister would have liked to see you personally. It is regrettable that he was unable to return to London in the time we felt was available." Liar, thought the ambassador. Likely up to his thighs in a trout stream. The smooth voice continued. "The Minister has asked me to request of your Excellency that further thought be given to Professor Sokarev's visit to Britain."

The Israeli ambassador said, "Further thought? To what end?"

Spell it out, thought the Under Secretary. "With a view, Excellency, to deciding whether the visit should take place at all, in the face of the serious threat reported to us by your own security services and confirmed by ours."

"Only if I were to believe that the police and other agencies of Britain were incapable of providing protection for the professor, would I suggest to Jerusalem that the visit be cancelled."

Cunning fox, the Under Secretary said to himself. "There is no question of that. We will provide protection—"

"Then there is nothing to discuss." The ambassador's voice was cold. "When you report to the Minister, I would be grateful if you could relay a sentiment of my government. Professor Sokarev has been offered the hospitality of a learned and illustrious body in your capital. We intend to make sure that he honours the engagement. The rest, my dear fellow, is in your hands."

The Under Secretary bridled. "You must understand that I was passing on a request from my Minister."

The Israeli ambassador smiled without friendship. "And I will pass on to my Minister what you have said. Perhaps you should know, since it seems you have not been informed, that while we have been discussing the suitability of the visit, the security attaché at my embassy has been talking with the relevant people here on the very question of Professor Sokarev's safety. At times like this, it is liaison that is needed."

He turned on his heel and made his own way out of the room.

IN THE early afternoon McCoy took Famy to a car parked fifty yards up the road. "I didn't bring it to the station last night," he said. "It's nicked—stolen—and that's too public a place."

It was a two-door Ford Escort, green, unscratched. Famy waited for the passenger door to be unlocked for him, and they headed for the university. As he drove, McCoy was realizing the extent to which he was now involved. It had begun simply: he was merely to provide backup. The shooting in France had changed that, ensured that if he carried on, it would be as equal partner.

There's no help from this fool, he thought to himself. Doesn't give a damn whether we come out of it or not. A different war from the hedgerow actions he had perfected in South Armagh. This was a totally new concept to him: a killing on such a grand scale that the shockwaves would fill world headlines for a week. One thing to blow a Woolworth's, one thing to take out a policeman, but this . . . And he was being drawn into it; the point of no return had already passed. He was experienced, had known the tension of guerrilla combat, given orders, had men follow him. Yet this man, who had known none of this, was directing him, controlling him, had outstretched him in commitment.

Perhaps it was the hate. He'd heard it, the simple hatred the Palestinian hard men felt for Israelis, and he knew he couldn't match it. Even in the British prison he could not hate to the exclusion of all else. When these people blasted their hostages, threw their grenades without remorse into cinemas, they put themselves beyond the reach of McCoy's understanding. There had to be a purpose to killing; every victim ought to know why he would die at McCoy's hand. Just for the gesture . . . that was not enough.

Finally he asked the question.

"Why this man? Why Sokarev?"

There was no urgency in the reply. Famy said, "Three times the Arabs fought the Israelis and were shamed. At their Yom Kippur we surprised them with our technique and our bravery, but we did not win. The next time, we will take them so close to defeat that they will threaten to use their bomb. Sokarev is an architect of that bomb. If we kill him, we demonstrate that we fear nothing from them. If we eliminate a man so much at the centre of their national survival, we have achieved a great victory."

"There'll be others who know as much as this one man."

"It is not to deny them Sokarev's knowledge that we attack. It

57

is the symbol that matters. That we prove we can strike where, when we please."

McCoy was still silently repeating, Bloody maniacs, when he pulled up outside the massive mausoleum structure that marked the centre of London University.

"Look as though you belong," he said as they walked up the steps. "If anyone asks, you've left some notes behind."

"Do we know which entrance he will use?"

"No, there are a stack of them. This is the main one."

The Arab was relaxed, unhurried, as he peered around the echoing, high-roofed hallway. "We know which room he will use?"

McCoy smiled as he took an embossed white card out of his wallet. "It's the real thing," he said.

The name of David Sokarev in ornate, copperplate writing was followed by a string of academic initials. Also the words LECTURE ROOM D, GROUND FLOOR, FOURTH ENTRANCE TO THE RIGHT AFTER ENTERING THE MAIN HALLWAY. "Where did you get it?" Famy asked.

"Acquired it. Long story. I'll tell you sometime."

"What time does he arrive? When does he speak?"

"There's a reception, sherry and sandwiches, before the speech; he'll probably take in the end of that. He's to talk at eight."

But Famy was not listening. His eyes were taking in the pillars, the various shadowy entrances that led to other rooms. Assessing cover, the space he would need, the speed at which a small man could travel across the floor, the angle required to see him if he were surrounded by people. He decided there would be no possibility of gaining direct admission to the lecture room, particularly with the bulky firearms that would be needed for the killing.

"It has to be from outside." Famy walked out of the building, then moved along its side, his attention locked on the windows just above his head. High above him the building towered, intimidating in its grey strength. But since time started, there has been a way into every citadel, a gap in the defences.

The base of the building was in the form of a giant cross, the main doors at the north end, the lecture room at the end of the western arm. Famy hurried around to look at it, and in his step there was a lightness and excitement. They had taught him the art of what they called using dead ground, moving in terrain which was denied to the vision of the enemy. Those who stood at the main door would have no sight of the windows he wanted, the butting corner would deny them. He went around the corner, McCoy following blindly. Beneath the windows on this side, cars were closely parked, near the wall. He scrabbled onto the roof of one of them. It gave him the necessary elevation to see inside the lecture room, across rows of benches, to the lectern which on Tuesday night would hold the typed notes of David Sokarev.

"Would you go inside," he said to McCoy "and if there are curtains, draw them across the window?" McCoy stood his ground, confused. The Arab's voice rose. "Just do it."

Famy waited a full two minutes before the curtains swished across the broad window. He noted that when they closed they were completely, tightly, together. He picked up a bit of gravel and marked the wall at the place where they met. While he waited for McCoy, he deepened his scratch, drawing a six-pointed star about four inches across from tip to tip. He was smiling about it when McCoy joined him.

"We must get some gloves," he said. "Thick ones that will withstand broken glass, cover the hand and the wrist." In the mind of Abdel-El-Famy the assassination plan was complete.

THE DRUG scene in London, as in any major capital, is a brutal one. Detectives like Doris Lang, who attempt to infiltrate the market, go through extensive training. They learn the medical side of the menace, and they learn the arts of survival. Doris was a capable young woman. The detective inspector to whom she reported had few fears about her safety. And she had the patience to get the detail he wanted.

She saw McCoy and Famy leave the house, and spent twenty-five minutes gossiping casually with her new friends before she excused herself. On the way upstairs she took every precaution to make sure she would be alone. In daylight her search of the room could be slower, more observant than at four a.m.

For a concentrated twelve minutes she worked through the Arab's bag and McCoy's old suitcase carefully, so they would

not detect her hand among the socks and shirts. She found no papers—no passports, no driving licences, no hint of their identity. It was the contents of the Arab's bag that fascinated her. The clothes were unremarkable, except that every maker's tag, all washing and cleaning instructions, had been conscientiously unstitched and removed. She wrote that down on her memo pad, following the times of arrival and departure, and descriptions of the two men. She felt deep frustration from her inability to clarify their business in the commune. Perhaps, she thought, they would return from their trip today with papers or something.

AT SCOTLAND YARD, Jones saw the Assistant Commissioner (Crime) in his office. Two wide-scale programmes were to be set into operation. First, a dragnet for McCoy and his unknown partner. Second, the gathering together of security to protect Sokarev. It was the first plan that took the most time. Jones suggested a possible connection between the Irishman and the north London communes.

"You have a difficulty there," said the Assistant Commissioner. "We have a good many communes under surveillance, several from the outside. On those I can call in information at any time. But there are seventeen where we have operatives living inside. They come out on Monday mornings. To justify breaking all those covers to get the people out this afternoon, I would need rather more positive information than you have provided."

The Security Service is a force without powers. It can only request. Jones looked pained, face set with disappointment.

"I'm sorry, Mr. Jones. Tell me it's essential, give me an address, something clear, and we can act." Like so many who rarely came into touch with the Security Service, the Assistant Commissioner distrusted them, remained unconvinced of their effectiveness.

"Nothing is clear," said Jones, "except the danger." He felt anger growing at a man who could not see the difference in scale between marijuana problems and political assassination.

"I'll ask around," said the Assistant Commissioner. That was the concession. Trifling, thought Jones. Half another day gone.

Then the Israeli security attaché was late at the Home Office.

Jones's disposition, deteriorating fast, was not helped by the lack of any apology. But he recognized this was not a time to make a scene. The Israeli did bring information. Sokarev's timetables, his hotel and room number, the invitation list to the speech. "And he will have two men from our own security division of the Foreign Ministry with him. Joseph Mackowicz and Gad Elkin. Charged with his safety."

That was the best news of the day, thought Jones. If the apple-cart goes, then those two will be picking up the load with me.

He related the known history of McCoy. The Israeli said, "With respect I would suggest that if the other is a Palestinian, he is the creature to be on guard against, not the Irishman."

Too right, Jones said to himself as the meeting ended. And we've no name, no description, no fingerprints, no file. This was a new form of warfare, where his enemy was insignificant in stature and strength, had none of the force and intellect his side possessed, and yet dominated the initiative. For the first time in close on three decades in the department, he felt fear and helplessness. He had no idea what to do next.

JUST BEFORE the light faded in the Beersheba flat, the boy suggested it was time for him to be on his way. David Sokarev was not surprised. The drive to the IAF fighter base would take three hours, and he knew his son had to be on duty in the ready room at five thirty on the Sunday morning, on three-minute warning.

"There is a matter I want to talk to you about before you go," Sokarev said quietly. "Can you come to my study? It will not take long."

And when they were together there, Sokarev spoke to his son shyly, without confidence. "Don't interrupt me. Not till I have finished. And I have not told your mother this. There is a threat against me when I go to London. Two men from the Foreign Ministry came to see me two days ago. They told me they are to guard me. I've been looking forward to the chance to meet old friends and talk. But the world would not topple if the trip, the speech, were cancelled. If there is a risk, I'd presume the ministry would cancel the visit. But they have not done that. All they've done is send me men to tell me I will be guarded. What should I do?"

His son answered him, predictably, in the language of a service-man. "If they didn't think it was safe, they wouldn't let you go. So have no fear, Father. You are too precious for them to risk you."

Sokarev kissed the boy on both cheeks, dismissing the idea of telephoning the director of Dimona.

JIMMY had shaved, put on a suit and the old squadron tie, and cleaned his shoes. He had now sat in the outer office beyond Jones's door for half an hour, exchanging small talk with Helen.

He was past fifty, tall, not overweight, not much flesh on his face. Grey hair, slicked down with water. There were dark, blotched patches, fierce and red, on his cheeks, not as bad as before he went to the clinic, but still evident. A blood vessel had fractured in his left eye, leaving a small oasis of crimson in the corner closest to his nose. Helen could see that he was ill-at-ease. He loathed the time that elapsed before he was briefed, back inside the team, part of the new operation. Leaves you like a bloody vegetable, in limbo, he thought.

Jones came in. Nodded to Jimmy, but spoke first to Helen. "Any messages, anything new in?"

"The DG would like to see you before six. Nothing else."

Jones masked his disappointment, motioned Jimmy into his office. Expertly he set out the skeleton of the problem. "You can pick the rest out of the paperwork when we've finished. Normally we'd concentrate on lifting them before they hit, but as you'll see, we're cold on that score." Just as Jimmy would want it, thought Jones. Proper job for him, one to test him. "We have to be prepared for an actual attack. I want our Israeli brother never out of your sight, Jimmy, except when he's safely locked in the loo. He'll have two of his own men with him, plus a cattle herd from Special Branch, all falling over each other. I want you tighter on him than any of them. Adhesive close. Normally we wouldn't be in a thing like this, it would be straight police, but the ramifications are too big if it goes wrong. So have no doubts about your position, Jimmy. If you see anything that bothers you, you act. If you see a gun close to him, you shoot. Don't concern yourself with the rule book."

Jones looked thoughtful. Needed to leave him in no doubt. Owed it to the man at the sharp end. "And if you hit some poor devil out for a walk in the park with his dog, we'll cover for you."

"You always say that," Jimmy said. Would he cover—would he, hell. If the balloon filled up, Jimmy'd be in the courts like anyone else, only double fast.

"I need," Jones went on, "to know every move Sokarev makes. Not via the Israelis or Scotland Yard. From you."

"If everyone is twisting their knickers at this rate, why isn't the visit called off?"

"If anyone knows, I haven't been told."

Jimmy left it at that. He could see Jones was close to the end of his patience.

Jones said, "I'll circulate your name to the Israelis and to the Special Branch, and have it backed by the Home Office. The Israelis'll want to run the show. The DG is mildly anxious it doesn't happen that way. You'll need some weapon practice. Fix that for the morning. Get along now and pick up some clothes. Fairclough and Duggan and I are sleeping in. You'd better join us."

Jimmy stopped beside Helen's table on his way out. "Unlucky again tonight, sweetheart. We're all kipping on the job."

"I told you they were in a flat bloody panic."

CHAPTER SIX

When they left the university, McCoy found a small Indian restaurant where they could talk while they toyed with the rice.

McCoy talked of Ireland—of the sharp rising hills, the farms that barely supported life, the large families, the economic hardship. He told of the fierce independence of the people. He related the story of his friend, Mick McVerry, killed in the attack on Keady police station. He'd been in Long Kesh then, he said; otherwise he would have been on hand with his Armalite, made in Japan, paid for in Boston, Massachusetts. Famy had raised his eyes inquiringly at the mention of Long Kesh, and the Irishman launched into stories of the prison where he had been held. How they, the prisoners, ran the premises. How they held court, organized escape committees. How they held their weapons and explosives classes. How they rioted and went on hunger strikes.

Famy had looked amazed, disbelieving, at almost everything McCoy said. But what astonished him most was that McCoy was here at all. "Why when they had caught you did they release you?"

And McCoy had just laughed, and known that it was not possible to explain this to a man whose knowledge of guerrilla warfare was based on fighting an enemy as hard and intransigent as the Israelis.

McCoy wanted to talk, and Famy had no choice but to listen. He was at once lost in the intricacies of Irish politics. He reflected that about his own cause there was nothing so complicated, nothing that could not be taught to a toddling child. Because we know what we want, he thought, we are prepared to strive with sacrifice for our victory. Not in a pathetic cowboy world of minimal heroics, shooting down one soldier or one middle-aged police-man and claiming the acts as political victories. Perhaps because the Irish do not know what they struggle for, they cannot steel themselves to acts that will shock on the grand scale. He will learn, this Irish boy, what it is to kill when every major capital in the world reacts. He will find out what it is to earn the hatred of one-half of the world, the gratitude and adulation of the other.

But Famy enjoyed the meal, felt the security of the restaurant. It was not till they were in the car that he thought again of the figure that had searched in the night, and of the girl in the living room who had stared at them. He spoke of that.

"We will sleep in different places tonight. You go to the far wall, and I will be close to the door. If someone comes, they will have to move deep into the room, and I will be behind them."

SHE HAD seen them through the open door of the living room when they came in from outside. Then she had heard their footsteps on the stairs. She had stayed with her book, waiting till the time was right, as the young people drifted up towards their mattresses and sleeping-bags.

She wriggled inside her wool jersey, fighting off the nighttime chill of the old unheated house. It was around four o'clock when the last of her fellow squatters staggered, as if sleep-walking, towards

65

the stairs. She was used to lack of sleep and was able within moments to drag together her concentration. It was papers she wanted, indications of why these two unlikely figures had come to the commune, indications of identity.

Her tennis shoes were noiseless as she went slowly up to the attic. Outside the door, she paused, listening. Silence. She eased her hand onto the doorknob, listened again, and went in.

The movement of the doorknob, the tiniest of sounds, alerted Famy. His eyes focused instantly on the white handkerchief he had tied to the inside handle. He could see the door move fractionally at first, then open as the faintly silhouetted figure came in. He felt sweat trickle down his belly. They are in no hurry, he thought. Then there was the soft scuffing of a long skirt on the floor that told him his intruder was a girl. He pictured the one he had noticed downstairs. He saw her bend down and open McCoy's case, heard her hands among the clothes.

That she had found nothing she sought he could understand by the way, unhurried, unexcited, she put down the top of the case. Then he saw confusion. She looks for me where I was last night, but she'll need the flashlight to find me over here. He closed his eyelids tight, unwilling to risk the involuntary blink if a light should come on. The footsteps were very near when he felt on his face the thin beam of light, and then her breath as she bent low over him, painstakingly sliding back the zipper of his grip-bag, which lay close to his head. Then her hands were inside the bag. As she straightened to move away, Famy grabbed her ankle, pulling her off balance. Before she realized what had happened, she was face down on the boards, her right arm twisted high behind her back, gripped by Famy, whose knee was indented into the pit of her back. The shock had been too great for her to scream.

"McCoy. Come here." He hissed the command, and the other man stirred. "I have her."

There was a flurry of movement as McCoy groped through the darkness. His hand reached out for the light still shining on the floor where she fell, and beamed it into the pale, fear-stricken face. She tried to turn her head away, but he grasped at her hair and, as she cried out, pulled her back.

She started to struggle, with McCoy clinging to her hair and Famy still twisting her arm behind her. Her free hand found McCoy's face, and with extended fingernails she gouged for his eyes, raked across his cheeks. She heard him cry out in a mixture of pain and astonishment. His hand let go of the hair, but his foot lashed into her head. Accurate and vicious, again and again.

She convulsed, then lay inert.

"Roll her over." McCoy was panting, and they pushed so that she lay on her back. The Arab had his weight high on her thighs and pinned her arms to the floor above her head. She closed her eyes and felt McCoy's hands begin to search, expertly, down her body, over her breasts, but rough and uncaring till they fastened on the memo pad in her skirt pocket. He pulled it out and she could hear him flicking its pages.

"She's a bloody tout," said McCoy. "An informer. Names of people living in the house, times and dates of arrival. Including us. Clever, she is. You've no tags in your clothes, right?"

"We took them out before we came."

"Well, it's written down here." McCoy's eyes were delving into the young face beneath him. His voice was frozen, without pity. "Who are you, you cow?" He hit her with the edge of his hand, finding the tip of her chin bone, jerking her head back, banging it on the boards. Still she said nothing, and he struck her with his fist clenched hard, into the softness below her rib cage. She gasped for air, tried to speak, but there were no sounds. Her chest heaved and writhed before the words came.

"Get off me, you pigs. I'm a police officer."

The thought through Famy's mind was immediate. In France the police had been waiting; here in the safe house, police again. "How did they know we would be here?" he shouted.

McCoy saw her reaction to what Famy had said. Saw her flick her head forward to stare at the shadowy face above her. It was that movement that sealed his resolution. His hands came down, settled on her throat, and tightened. She tried to speak of drugs and hippies, but the air was already denied her.

When McCoy had finished, he realized that Famy was heaving his stomach in the far corner. It had come easily to McCoy. In the world in which he fought, the penalty for touts was clear-cut.

"Pull yourself together, stupid," he said. "We're moving."

All was quiet as they went downstairs and out to the car. While McCoy drove, fast and with concentration, south towards the river, Famy sat rock-still beside him. It was the first time he had encountered violent death. The speed, the simplicity, with which life had been crushed from the girl amazed him. His doubts of McCoy had vanished. The Irishman, too, was prepared to kill. They were now a team. In the darkness of the attic the link between them had been joined. His mission would succeed.

"Where are we going now?" he asked.

"The Surrey hills, south of London, where the guns are. We'll sleep rough tonight and tomorrow. We have to ditch this car, get another. Come back to London on Tuesday, probably late."

"How long do you think before they find her?"

"A while. And when they do they won't make much headway with the commune."

"How far do we have to go?"

"An hour and a half. Get some sleep." It was an instruction.

But for Famy there was no sleep. As the car jolted along, the image of the girl and her big pleading eyes endlessly repeated itself. And the hard, calloused fingers on her neck.

But the killing of Doris Lang had not gone unnoticed.

A young woman nursing her baby a floor below had heard sounds—bumps on the boards above, a half-stifled scream, the noise of a struggle, muffled shouts. Footsteps hurrying down to the main door, then the sound of a car starting and driving away.

It was light before she summoned the courage to go and see whatever had been left in the room. When she did, her screams, hysterical and piercing, woke the building.

CONSTABLE HENRY DAVIES was drinking tea in the police station canteen when the sergeant came in.

"Henry, the DI wants you down Englefield Road. Number 162."

"What for?" Davies asked.

"I don't know," the sergeant lied. "He just asked for you."

The detective inspector was waiting on the steps of the house

68

for him. There were three police cars and a small knot of half-dressed onlookers. The inspector, unshaved, roused from his Sunday-morning bed, walked towards Davies. "I've bad news, Henry. I'm very sorry. . . . It's Doris. Some bastard's killed her."

He stopped. Let the words sink in, saw the mask of overt self-control slide across the police constable's features.

"When did it happen?" Davies said, remote, something to say.

"Early this morning. We had a call about forty minutes ago. I've identified her. Do you want to see her, Henry?"

"Not with them working round her. But I'd like to go to her mum's. Has she been told?"

"No, not yet. I'll get someone to drive you round. Fred can come down and pick up your motor, and take your dog home."

"Do you know who did it?"

"Two men. But they're long gone. They're telling us more in that commune than they usually do."

THE COMMUNE'S inhabitants were herded into the living room while the coffin was carried to the unmarked hearse. When it had gone, the detective inspector walked back into the room. He had spotted the spokesman for the group, older than most, a fragile and defiant figure. The DI called him out.

"You've been helpful. I want it to go on that way. The woman who found the body tells me two men left after she heard the noises. About half past four. Who are they?"

The man pushed his fingers through his long hair. "We knew one of them. An Irishman." He hesitated.

"Go on. I haven't got all day. This is a murder inquiry."

"There was a girl who used to live here. Eilish McCoy. He was her brother, Ciaran. He turned up here about a week ago, said he had some people coming. Said they needed . . ."

The inspector said, "Somewhere quiet, somewhere to lie up?"

"Something like that."

"And the second one. Was he Irish, too?"

"I'd say he was an Arab."

"No name? Didn't McCoy call him anything?"

"The second one only came the night before last."

69

"You say McCoy said he had 'some people coming'."

"He told me there were three others; only the one showed up."

A detective came in holding, gingerly, a memo pad. "It's Doris Lang's log for the week. Seems she searched these guys' room on Friday night, again yesterday. There's a bit about what she found and a description of the two men. Proper detailed one."

The inspector motioned the detective into the corridor. "Get onto Special Branch and have them shove over all the stuff on McCoy."

Back at the police station, he was told by the desk sergeant, "There's been a man called Jones on the phone, from Security Service. Wants to come and see you as soon as you've a minute."

"Coming up in the world, aren't we?" said the DI.

LIKE an incoming ocean tide, the name Ciaran McCoy swept through the many departments of Scotland Yard. Photographic section, fingerprint section; Special Branch and its Irish section; murder squad. The photograph of McCoy was dispatched to all police stations, and the photokit team began work on a compilation of the unknown Arab's features, using principally Doris Lang's written description. The picture of McCoy was released for the Independent Television current affairs programme at lunchtime and for a BBC newsflash. That was where Norah saw it.

Her father always insisted that the television be on during the formal eating of the Sunday roast because he liked the farmers' programmes. As the programme ended, the screen went black and then on came the newsflash symbol. The three around the table, Norah, her mother and father, all stopped eating and turned their attention to the set. A policewoman had died, strangled, in a commune. Police were anxious to trace a young Irishman. Name— Ciaran McCoy. The picture came up then, stayed on the screen for twenty seconds. Ten had elapsed before she recognized the boy she had kissed, the boy who had left her so abruptly last Thursday night.

"Swine," her father said. "We should string them up."

Norah said nothing. She put her head close to her plate lest her parents should see the tears. She bolted her food, made an

70

excuse, and ran through the front door. That afternoon she walked
endlessly, conscious of an overwhelming feeling of shame, of
having been dirtied in some way.

WHEN JONES came back from the police station, he brought with
him photostats and transcripts of the memo pad. Duggan and
Fairclough were waiting in his office.

Duggan said, "He's blown it, hasn't he, our little boyo? His
picture will be plastered everywhere by tonight. His concentration
now is how to stay free. He'll pack it in."

"That's one viewpoint." Jones looked sceptical.

"If we look at the Palestinian, or Arab, or whatever he is,"
Fairclough joined in, "we can come out with a different answer.
He's been through a crisis in France on Thursday and is still on
the move. If he doesn't go on, what does he go back to? They
won't welcome him with open arms back in his camp. He'd be a
miserable failure. This is when the suicide mentality breaks through.
The harder the going gets, the more he will be prepared to risk."

"And the conclusion from that?" asked Jones.

"The Arab is now extremely dangerous. A killer still."

"A picture of one, description of the other, available to every
man round Sokarev. That stacks the odds a bit." Jones smiled.
"But if the Arab wants to go on, what about McCoy?"

Again it was Fairclough, hunched forward in his seat. "The
critical factor is how much of a bond they have made. McCoy'll
stay in, providing he thinks there's a chance of living through it."

Jones envied the younger man his certainty. But it was not the
moment to discuss what the older ones in the department knew,
that there were no simplicities in this business. Problem was, as
Jones could see, that men like himself hadn't much to contribute
to short-term affairs. When there wasn't time to build up the overall picture, it would come down to Jimmy's level. Who shoots
best? That's why he'd brought Jimmy in. Liked the man, but to be
dependent on him, to recognize he had more to offer now than
Jones himself—that left a sour taste in the mouth.

And now, as usual, Jimmy was taking considerable care over his
firearms.

For close protection work he favoured the Walther PPK. And this was the gun he drew from the armoury in the basement of Leconfield House. It's length was little more than six inches, its weight just over a pound. It was not new, manufactured in 1938, but the department's armourer maintained it with studied attention, knowing it to be the weapon of Jimmy's choice.

With the PPK signed for, and two dozen rounds with it, Jimmy drove to the police firing range in an old building the far side of Euston Station. There were policemen there, firing at targets. Jimmy showed his identification to the instructor, and the policemen were called back from the shooting line. They watched as Jimmy fired all twenty-four rounds. Some in near darkness, some with a bright light shining at his face, some on the move, some stationary. All hit the human-shaped target, all in the torso area.

"Bit of a show-off, isn't he," said one of the watching policemen, but his whisper was overheard by the instructor.

"Look, boy," his voice boomed. "There's a fractional possibility he might miss. And there's a fractional possibility you might hit. That's the difference between you and him."

Jimmy was well pleased with the session, and he could fit in a drink before he was due back at the department.

THE TWO of them were asleep in the car. McCoy across the front seat, Famy curled up in the back. They were parked deep in a grassy clearing invisible from the road. There were many such places here in the Surrey hills, southwest of London. Later they would become a haven for Sunday walkers, but in the early morning the two men had the clearing to themselves.

"We must sleep any time we can," McCoy had said.

They missed the rising of the sun. It was the noise of children that aroused them. Two boys, about ten years old, faces pressed against the car windows, and running, giggling, away as McCoy started up from his sleep. He shook Famy. "Come on, lover boy. On our way."

"Where are we?" Famy, too, had awakened confused.

"Out in the country, taking in the sunshine. Remember?"

Neither man saw the two boys who lay in the thick green

bracken watching them rub their eyes and stretch and then walk down the path among the pines and the birches. Neither wore country shoes, and both slipped and stumbled where the rain had made the surface glistening mud.

They walked in silence for more than twenty minutes; then Famy noticed that McCoy was slowing down, searching for something. When he came to an old perambulator he stopped. "That's our first marker. From here we go fifty paces down the path."

Famy followed McCoy as he paced the distance. "At home," said McCoy, "we have to hide our guns out in the countryside, somewhere you can get them night or day, so you need markers you can find in the dark. Now look, what's the most prominent tree close to us? Has to be the one with the ivy up it. That's our main marker. Now we have to look for something else that's off the path but equally clear. Walk round the tree, try to find what stands out. Right? If you draw a line between this tree and that big one, the one the lightning hit, you go on and into the bank. There are rabbits' holes all along the bank. Well, what we're looking for is the hole in the straight line of the two trees."

McCoy walked forward and sunk his hands into a rabbit hole. Famy watched fascinated as they emerged clutching a white plastic bag. "I had to dig the hole out a bit," McCoy said. "But who's going to notice fresh earth at a rabbit burrow."

He scanned the path in both directions, then, satisfied that they were alone, took from the bag three rifles, each about two feet long with the steel skeleton of the shoulder rest bent back alongside the barrel. He placed them on the plastic and with them two bulky cloth bags.

"What are they?" asked Famy.

"A version of the M1 carbine. World War Two American. These are the paratroopers' ones, with the folding stock. They wouldn't give me Armalites, said three was too many. These were test-fired ten days ago in Armagh, stripped down and cleaned—"

Famy anxious, interrupted. "There were no Kalashnikovs?"

"We haven't any. Our stuff is American. One reason our big men got involved in this operation of yours was to guarantee a supply of Kalashnikovs."

"I've never trained with any other rifle," said Famy.

"These have packed enough coffins. And they're untraceable."

"Why only three? There were to be three of us, and you."

McCoy looked into Famy's face. "The deal was you'd do the shooting. I'd look after accommodations and the car."

"And now?"

McCoy had taken loaded magazines from one of the cloth bags and was laying them out side by side, twelve of them. "Well, it can't be done by one alone, so we'll need two of them, and have one spare."

There was a huge smile across Famy's face as the strain of the last few hours fled from him. He has been suffering, disbelieving, thought McCoy.

"We've got the best grenades, though," McCoy said, and opened the second cloth bag. "These are Dutch, the V 40 Mini. Tiny, but hundred-per-cent casualties guaranteed at ten feet. What we want for close work, not a great bomb that'll demolish half the audience, but something that can land nice and near your man and take him out." He held one in his hand, nestled in the palm, where it fitted snugly, an inch and a half in diameter and deadly.

McCoy repacked the grenades, magazines and rifles, and led Famy back to where they had left the car. His mind was now tuned to the next steps. Where to ditch this car, where to get another. Where to lie up for the next two days. Famy could see he was thinking and did nothing to break the train of thought.

THE PRIME MINISTER had cut short his Scottish weekend, a move generally believed to have been precipitated by the country's economic plight. In his office overlooking the immaculate gardens of his Downing Street residence, he now listened to the Director General of the Security Service give a detailed exposition of the problem at hand. When the Director General had finished, the Prime Minister turned away to the window, searching for the words he wanted, then spoke.

"There is a chance, then, that a massive screen round the man will deter any attack. Total saturation. I gather, however, that you put no trust in such a deterrent. So we will move, Director

General. into the realm of what is called late-at-night thought, not to be attributed to this building. I would like to think that should the Arab be taken prisoner, arrested, he would violently resist such action. In his escape attempt I want him to be shot dead. We've had one package of hostages on a VC-10 sitting it out in the Jordan desert; we've had another VC-10 wrecked at Schiphol, another held at gunpoint in Tunis. I don't want to have to hand this man over at the point of a rifle with a fourth planeload of lives at stake, and that is what will happen if this man is held for trial. The Irishman in that context is unimportant."

The Prime Minister wished the Director General luck, smiled bleakly as they shook hands, and showed him to the door.

IN THEIR small bedroom the Sokarevs were both involved in packing for the trip. His wife folded the clothes, and Sokarev placed them with care into his old suitcase. He took two suits, the only two he possessed—one for best, for making his speech; one for wearing in the daytime. He would travel in a jacket and a pair of slacks. When they had finished packing, the case bulged, and both of them had to press down hard so the clasps would fasten. This suitcase had special importance in the life of David Sokarev, because thirty-nine years ago his father had bought it for him and carried it to the Frankfurt station and handed it into the train. His father had waved goodbye, full of assurances that he would wind up the family's affairs, and then follow his wife and son to Israel. David Sokarev never saw him again.

His wife fussed around him that evening in the bedroom. She could see that the anxiety that had oppressed him for several nights was now something of the past. They laughed with each other, and he put his arm around her shoulders and talked of the friends he would see in London, scientists he had met on previous visits or who had come to Israel. When she moved to the kitchen to cook dinner he went into his study to work on his speech.

He was still working when the telephone rang. He picked it up.

"Mackowicz here," said the voice.

"What do you want?" His voice showed the resentment he felt at the other man's intrusion into the private oasis of his study.

"Just to be clear about tomorrow. You need have no fears of London. The British are taking many steps to ensure your safety."

"I have no fears." Sokarev spoke sharply. What more do you want to say, he thought. Why burden me at my home?

"I will be picking you up myself—"

"But I have a taxi ordered." He was close to anger.

"It has been decided that I shall take you to the airport. Elkin will be with me. You can cancel the taxi."

"Who has decided it?"

"The ministry, the superiors in our department."

Sokarev sank back in his chair. Depression surged through him. He would be like a toy passed from hand to hand.

THE YOUNGER of the two boys that had played in the clearing in the early morning recognized the picture of McCoy on afternoon television. His father telephoned the police. From county head-quarters a tracker dog was sent and Special Branch officers drove down from London, and in the fading light the dog found the rabbit hole where McCoy had secreted the rifles and grenades. The policemen had moved with caution lest they disturb the footprints. They would return on Monday for a detailed examination. In the meantime the ten-yard square in front of the hole was covered with plastic sheeting, and a constable left on guard.

From Scotland Yard the report of all this was passed on to Jones. So Fairclough had been right. They were on course still, and visiting a cache. Well, they had their guns now, thought Jones.

Jimmy came into the office. Jones pushed the picture of McCoy and the photokit impression of the Arab across his desk. "Those," he said, "are our little boys. Get those faces stuck in your mind."

CHAPTER SEVEN

From behind the driving wheel Elkin could see that the scientist's face was taut, stretched with emotion. Mackowicz tried to get a conversation going, but gave up. Security men were not unused to being resented. If the little guy didn't want to talk, fine; he and Elkin had enough to concern themselves with.

Their selection for this task had not been accidental. Both were expert shots, thorough professionals. They travelled light, with just two canvas bags. Along with a few changes of clothes, one bag carried files containing all available intelligence on the threat, and a complete dossier on Sokarev, from his blood group to his family and financial arrangements. In the other bag, wrapped in shirts, were firearms, and two-way radios which would be modified in London to the wavelengths of the Israeli embassy.

They had left at seven and turned into the airport seventy-five minutes later, a good hour before takeoff. Sokarev was dominated by a feeling of isolation. Nothing to talk to his travel companions about, no point of sympathy. Killers. Cloaked in legality, but how different were they from the terrorists who might be awaiting him? They all killed from a sense of duty, acted without hesitation. He recognized that he was afraid of the men he had been given to keep him safe.

The baggage check took half an hour. Thirty minutes of shuffling the cases forward inch by inch before they were allowed to make their way to the ticket desk. From there the three of them walked towards the staircase that reached up to the departure lounge. Sokarev noticed now that Mackowicz was to his right, Elkin to his left. Not out of my own country, and already I'm like a prisoner under escort, he thought.

In the lounge, after the body search, the three men sat in total silence till the flight was called, the guards reading newspapers, the professor staring emptily through the windows. He wanted to discard the journey, go home to his wife and his laboratory, and shut out for ever the nightmare world of guns and terrorists. Then the flight was called, and they walked together down the steps and out into the blazing heat of an August morning in Israel. There is no going back now, thought the scientist, there is no escape. Whatever happens, he said to himself, it is out of my control.

HIGH in the building that housed Scotland Yard, they had taken over the main lecture theatre for the Monday briefing of all those detectives and senior uniformed officers involved in the protection of David Sokarev.

Jimmy sat at the back. He never felt totally at ease in the company of policemen, nor did they react well to the presence alongside them of a free-lance operator not conditioned to their rule books. The details that the big man in uniform read out concerning the timings and locations of the professor's visit failed to hold his attention. All that drawing on the blackboard, green lines and red circles and blue crosses. Can't fight terrorists with maps and diagrams, old soldier. There's only one place you'll get Master McCoy and his little friend, and that's close to Sokarev. Wasting your time in transit with the motorcades and escort riders. Stands to reason. They're not going to risk their all on a potshot at a cavalcade. Better get up to the university, Jimmy lad, and have a look. Should have done that reconnaissance yesterday.

He knew it. Comforted himself with the thought that he would be near Sokarev. True, he'd be a human wall, without pension rights. But perhaps he'd be safe for all that. Who ever heard of the bodyguard catching it? JFK, RFK, Faisal; all had the detail round them, who'd lived to go to the funeral.

That was where the careering of Jimmy's thoughts came to a stop. Below him, pinned to the side of the blackboard, were the pictures of McCoy and the man whose name they didn't know. Nasty, rough people, Jimmy said to himself, very hard, very serious. His gaze rolled around the briefing room at the officers listening intently, taking notes. If those two decide to come on in close, thought Jimmy, this lot'll wish they'd never got out of bed.

THE EFFECT on McCoy was less violent than on Famy. The Arab looked with ill-concealed horror at the pictures blazoned across the front pages of the papers. They were standing outside a small newsagent's shop in southwest London, waiting for a bus to take them to the suburbs. The pictures, reproduced hugely, covered half the front page of the tabloids, with banner headlines screaming, THE KILLERS . . . MOST WANTED MEN IN BRITAIN. . . . HAVE YOU SEEN THESE MEN?

"Don't gawp at them," McCoy hissed in Famy's ear.

"They took it from that girl's notebook. We left it behind," said Famy.

"They'll have talked in the commune. Got my name there. An artist drew you from the descriptions. It's not very good."

"Not for positive identification, but close enough. The height, weight, the general effect. And the clothes we still wear."

"Get away from the damn thing. Anyone could spot you if you're pressed tight up against it."

"They have no name on me," Famy said as he moved to the back of the bus queue. He felt again the uncertainty that had dogged his first hours in London. Orders had been clear that they should have been safe and secure in the house. There was to have been no question of their hanging about in crowded streets as they were now doing. Every time a man or woman or child turned to him he imagined the dawning of recognition. How, he wondered, do people relate a picture in a newspaper to the flesh and blood beside them on the street? It's a difficult step, Famy told himself.

McCoy was accustomed to having his picture in the pockets of British soldiers and was familiar with life on the run. But he realized a fundamental danger in their present position. The newspapers put the two men together, and that was how they were travelling. Moving as loners, how much safer they would be. But what to do with the bloody Arab? Couldn't have him wandering the streets solo, liable to panic.

The green bus pulled up and they made their way to back seats, where their faces would suffer least exposure. Famy had the grip-bag, which contained a selection of both their clothes, and the rifles, magazines and grenades. They sat in silence, McCoy working out his next move. They were past Hampton Court when he spoke, close to Famy's ear. "We have to separate. The danger's in being together."

There was startled surprise in Famy's eyes that suggested he felt betrayed. McCoy saw it. "Just for today, I mean. There are eight more hours till darkness. Then we should meet again."

"Where would I go?" Famy said through tightly clamped lips.

"I don't know yet. But together there's too much risk."

"We could have stayed with the car instead of leaving it there in the woods—"

McCoy cut in, anxious lest he sacrifice the initiative. "We could have. But we have to get another car in town. In the country they can check it too easily." Famy did not reply. "Look, I've told you I'm in this with you." McCoy was talking quickly, urgently. "Think about it. After the girl, after taking you to the guns, am I going to bunk out now?"

Famy nodded, too exhausted from four nights of broken sleep to argue. "Where do we get off?" he asked.

"Farther on—about fifteen minutes. We get to a town where there's tubes and trains, cinemas. Whatever you want."

"And you, where will you go?"

"I'll just lose myself," McCoy said, "till we can meet up and get a car."

Famy saw the hesitation, sensed a lie. Loneliness again welled up inside him. How far could he trust the Irishman? He was sure he was not being confided in. What could he do? He was powerless.

Five stops later McCoy rose and started down the aisle. Famy followed. On the pavement, they stood for a moment before McCoy saw the tea shop down the road and began to walk towards it. Famy looked at him as they went in through the door of the shop, quizzing with his eyes. He found no answer.

"Just round the corner and up the main drag, that's where the cinemas are," McCoy told him. "There's one there that shows three films, separate theatres, divided up. It's dark in there, you'll be O.K. We'll meet back here. Eight o'clock. Now don't just walk round. Get something to eat if you want, then get into the cinema and stay there."

When McCoy left, the grip-bag stayed with Famy. "Safer tucked under your legs in the cinema than with me lugging it round."

McCoy ducked out into the sunlight. Relief at being on his own again flowed through him. What a boring sod the man was. He was half running when he entered the supermarket.

The cash registers, he saw, were at the far end. He picked a single bar of chocolate off the shelf, something to stave off the hurting pain of hunger, and joined the queue at the checkout counter. He watched the girl as she deftly sorted the bags and packages and tins. Her face was set, dedicated to her task of extracting the right money, giving the right change. When he put the chocolate down, her slim hand was there in an instant, pulling it clear, showing the amount on her machine.

"Hello, Norah," he said. Very quiet, conscious of impatient people behind him. And she looked up at him. Startled recognition. Taut, strained, wide eyes pierced at him. The will to say something, but no voice.

"I have to see you." He gave it the stress of dependence.

"What are you doing here?" Bewilderment, but conspiracy, too.

"I have to be with you this afternoon, now," he said urgently. "Make an excuse. I'll be outside."

On the far side of the street he waited. Twenty minutes perhaps, then she was there. He took her hand, soft, small, fitting inside his fist, and kissed her on the cheek.

She pulled back from him. "Your picture. You're in the papers, on the telly. What have you come here for?"

"I wanted to be with you, girl. I wanted . . ." and he did not finish. He clenched her hand tight. How can you tell her that you have to get away from it? That you're not just a machine, a killing apparatus. That there's need for a break, away from the awfulness of the running. There had been a girl at Cullyhanna, and a place on Mullyash Mountain where she would go with him and let him love her and relax with her, till the sleep came. Then he could go back to his war. But how to tell Norah, the little shopgirl from southwest London, that the time comes when a man who fights must fall asleep in arms that hold no danger, must escape to exist again in the world which he has denied himself.

"I needed to talk to you where we could be alone," he said.

They walked together through Richmond, into the vast open expanse of the park, and deep into the bracken, along a path used only by red deer that scampered as they approached. He put his coat down, and they sat together, surrounded by a wall of green that hid them from all eyes. McCoy sank onto his back, reaching up with his arms and pulling the girl down onto his chest, so that her head rested under his chin. They lay there a long time, and his thoughts were of Armagh County and the other girl, who understood what overwhelmed him.

It was Norah who broke the spell. "Is it really you they are hunting?" Frightened, small voice, and his dreaming reply failed to take her fear away.

"It is. And they won't find me."

"But you killed a girl, strangled her, it said on the TV."

He rolled over and leaned on one bent elbow above her, his free hand in her hair, stroking, caressing it into shapes. "I won't tell you I didn't, and you wouldn't believe me if I did. But it has nothing to do with you. It is something separate."

His hand came down from her hair and a finger flicked carelessly at the buttons of her blouse. He saw the tears coming and kissed her. Sobbing, she put her arms around his neck, dragged his head down to her. She could not account for her actions, could not justify the tenderness of her own hands or her longing for the touch of his. And then there was pain and a power she had not known before, and she tried to escape. But could not.

Norah lay on the ground, unmoving, while the man beside her slept, his face with the quietness of a child's, its smoothness broken only by the tram lines worked by the nails of Doris Lang.

FROM THE tea shop where McCoy had left him, Famy went to a telephone box. He had no difficulty remembering the number, nor the extension to ask for.

"Mushroom here," he said, and heard a scuffling on the line. Clearing the room, he thought.

"What is it you wish to say?" a voice asked.

"Are there any new instructions?" His tone echoed the hollowness of his request. He knew there was no chance of further orders.

"Nothing has come through."

Famy paused. He could not speak of his isolation, of his fears. "Nothing? No word from home?"

Perhaps the man at the embassy recognized the helplessness. "Nothing was to be expected. You are allowed a free hand. Your arrival has been communicated." There was a sharp click on the line. "There are difficulties?"

"It is so confused. Because of the girl, we have lost our—"

The voice cut in sharply. "There was a clicking noise on this line. Be very brief, then ring off and move away. Is there more?"

82

"The Irishman. I do not know whether I can trust him. He said we must separate for today. We have the guns, but—"

"Ring off. And get away from the telephone box. Far away."

The voice was at shouting pitch, and the line went dead.

Famy picked up the bag and ran.

JONES was poring over the McCoy file when his phone rang.

"Monitoring here, Mr. Jones. Your embassy number is on."

Jones ran downstairs in a headlong race to get to the basement before the call terminated. The earphones were ready for him.

"They've just heard the intercept switch go, the embassy's trying to wind it up," he was told.

He was in time to hear the reference to guns, then shouts, and the line was cut. Almost at once intercept reported that the call was made from Richmond, in Surrey, on a public phone.

Jones dialled the special number in Scotland Yard assigned to this operation, reported briefly, and rang off. Best bloody break we've had, he thought. They played him back the tape, and he asked to hear it four times.

In Fairclough's office, Jones said, "The nerves are fraying a bit. The Arab onto the embassy, doubting McCoy, wanting word from home, sounded really miserable. But he says they've got the guns, which confirms what we had from Surrey."

"Did he say whether they were going on with it?"

"No. Only that McCoy had said they must separate for today."

"Not bad thinking. They're more vulnerable together. They'll resume harness tonight. I suggest they're still operational."

Jones walked slowly back to his own office. He knew he had to find a way to their thought process, to make the men who were just dossiers into human beings. That was the only way to anticipate their next decision. But he was so out of touch with their world that he evaluated his chances as minimal.

IN RICHMOND, on the outskirts of London, police radios had begun to chatter locations, descriptions. Men were hauled from other duties. The chief superintendent's first priority was to block all major roads leading out of the area. He had a vanload of police take over the station that served British Rail Southern Region, and London Transport District Line Underground. He put cruise cars in the centre of town. Revolvers were issued to all car crews. When he was satisfied that the town was sealed as well as possible, he came on the radio to issue clear instructions.

"The man we are searching for should not be approached by any unarmed officer. If you see him, call in. We'll send help."

That was the message that first excited the radio ham who sat whiling away the time till his night shift began at the Hawker Siddeley factory in nearby Kingston. He ignored the stringent law that forbids the public to listen to or make use of the police messages and left his set tuned in to the police frequency. When he heard the words of the chief superintendent he called the *Daily Express*, the paper known to be the best payer for news tips.

As the net was closing around Richmond, Famy was paying his money at the cinema. James Bond was in town—double feature.

"YOU'VE nothing to fear. The British have a big force out. Our own people will be close by. But do as Elkin and I say, with no questions." Those were the last words Mackowicz said to Sokarev when the plane taxied down the Heathrow runway.

The passengers were already in the aisle, waiting to leave the plane, when the chief steward and the man that Sokarev knew as El Al security cleared the route to the steps for Mackowicz, Sokarev and Elkin. Greeting them on the tarmac were the Special Branch men. Six of them, three on each side of Sokarev, faces turned outward towards the black Mercedes of the Israeli embassy that waited nearby. The security attaché spoke briefly to Mackowicz and then came alongside the professor.

"May we welcome you, sir. We will go to the lounge at the terminal building while your baggage is taken care of."

When the car started up, Sokarev could see two heavily laden unmarked vehicles take up positions behind. He sat in the back seat squashed between the attaché and Mackowicz. Elkin was in front with the driver and another man, tall and middle-aged. From the car windows Sokarev looked into the expressionless faces of uniformed policemen. There were dog handlers in the background, and men in civilian clothes who stood with their right hands resting on the top buttons of their coats. At the entrance to the VIP suite were more policemen, who reported his progress from the car to the doorway via hand-held radios and who failed to meet the smile, almost of apology, that he gave as he walked by them.

They sat him down in a low-slung settee far from the door, and a lady with a white apron brought him tea and a plate of biscuits. She at least returned his smile. The man who'd sat next to Elkin in the front of the Mercedes was moving across the room towards him. Sokarev could see that his suit was old, not cared for, there was a nick of blood on his collar, his tie was loose.

"The name's Jimmy, sir. Security. I'm to be with you right through your stay here. I hope we'll get along."

"I am glad to meet you . . . Jimmy." He waited for the other to offer a surname but none was forthcoming. "I was told I'd be offered help on the visit. I am grateful to you."

"There's more than just me, sir. Several hundred. But I'm the one you'll be aware of. I'll be beside you the whole way."

"You'll have competition," Sokarev quipped, warming to the man. "Mr. Mackowicz and Mr. Elkin, whom you met in the car, told me they had booked that place for themselves."

"Well, it should be crowded, then. Which is just about right."

Be grateful, thought Sokarev, this one at least one can talk to. He watched Jimmy go over to Mackowicz, watched folders pass between them. The room was full of men in huddles, chattering like sparrows. And I am the supernumerary. Nobody talks to me, nobody even has time to say hello or welcome. If I wanted to attract attention, I would have to shout, throw an epileptic fit. I am an exercise in strategy until I am packed up and shipped home, forgotten. For some of them I'm a source of anxiety. Not that they would mourn David Sokarev if his body lay in the gutter; they would mourn their reputations.

He was rather enjoying the self-pity when the security attaché spoke to him. "We are ready to leave now, Professor." His tea was half-finished in the cup. But that mattered to no one.

Immured between the security attaché and Mackowicz, Sokarev

saw little of the countryside bordering the M4. He could sense the tension in the crowded car.

In thirty-five minutes they were at the door of the hotel that had been chosen for him. Mackowicz spoke in his ear. "Don't hesitate, straight inside." Arms bundled him through swinging doors, across a lavish carpet, and into a waiting lift. As the doors closed he found himself pressed by the shapes of his own men, the attaché, the one who called himself Jimmy, and an elegant dark-suited fellow he presumed to be from the hotel. They went to the fourth and top floor. At the extreme right-hand end two men rose out of chairs, one of them turning to unlock the corner room. The pace was maintained till the door slammed shut behind him.

"Welcome to our hotel, Professor Sokarev," intoned the man in the dark suit. His formality did not quite conceal the management's displeasure at having responsibility for such a guest. "There is a connecting door to the room for your two colleagues."

"One room for the two of them," the attaché explained, "because one only will be sleeping. They will take it in shifts. In addition, there are the men outside."

The crowd made its exit—management through the main door; Mackowicz, Elkin, Jimmy and the attaché into the adjoining room. Sokarev was alone. Able to unpack the clothes his wife had folded with such care only hours ago in Beersheba. He could reflect that whatever fears he himself entertained were matched by the anxiety of the security services of Israel and of Britain. The realization chilled him.

Next door, Jimmy was on the telephone to Jones. He listened, face poker-straight, and rang off. He then relayed the latest information. "There's been a flap since Friday morning, but it's really buzzing now. Bit over an hour ago one of them called the contact man. We've traced the call to Richmond. Nice, comfortable, posh place. Now crawling with coppers. They think there's a chance they have our boys bottled up."

"How many of them are there?" Elkin asked.

"Just two," said Jimmy. "One from Northern Ireland. Cut above the usual grade. The other from your part of the world. No name, but we've a drawing of a face. Homesick, made a telephone call he shouldn't have. Special Branch will be round in about twenty minutes, he'll have files and pictures for you."

Jimmy sensed he was the odd man out in the room, that they wanted to talk out their problems among themselves. It was time to assert himself, make the position clear. "My orders, gentlemen," he said, "are explicit. I have to be beside your man every moment he's out of that room. Not three yards away from him, right beside him. This isn't a scene you'll run yourselves. We are in charge, and you will listen to us. And a final point. If I see something out on the street, open fire and hit the wrong target, there'll be a hell of a row, but it'll blow over. If one of you does it, you'll be in court before you know what's hit you; it'll stink for months. So go a bit careful."

Jimmy went out into the corridor to have a smoke and to allow them to vent their feelings. With amusement he heard Mackowicz's voice, rich in aggrieved anger, Elkin's quieter but in a harmony of protest, and then the attaché's, soothing hurt pride.

Poor little professor, Jimmy thought. He's going to stand out there like a tethered goat, great bait, with nothing to do but pray we get the killers before they get to him. Jimmy went back into the room and found Mackowicz and Elkin still uptight, but settling in. The attaché had done a good job.

"No appointments tonight, right?" Jimmy said to the attaché.

"Correct. He was to have dined at the university. We've put that off. He'll eat in the room. Tomorrow he stays in till evening."

"And Wednesday to New York?"

"His booking is for Thursday. We haven't changed it."

"I hope he likes his room, then," snapped Jimmy. "If he's going to be here an extra day, that's where he stays."

THE wind swept across the great open spaces of the park, sought out the body of McCoy where he lay. And awoke him. He looked at his watch. Past seven. He saw the girl beside him still in disarray, arms behind her head, staring into the deep distances of the sky.

"Come on, girl. Time to move." There was a cutting edge in his voice, sharp, unfamiliar to her. She reacted, twisting away from him, fastening the buttons of her blouse. He brushed the grass and dried earth from their clothes, and together they started towards the heavy iron gates of the park. They walked in silence, Norah with her head down, avoiding him.

They were a clear hundred yards from the gates when McCoy saw the roadblock. He counted six policemen and he understood that it was too heavy a force for anything routine like local crime. He thought of Famy, nervous at being abandoned, suspicious of where McCoy had gone. And now the roadblock. He had to find the Arab.

Stretching on either side of the gates were the eight-foot-high walls of matured brick that ringed the park, "I can't go through the check," he said. "I have to get over the wall, somewhere near the town." The girl hesitated. One scream and the policemen would be sprinting towards her. And then what would she say? Tell them the man they sought had lain with her?

She was not long in deciding. She took McCoy's hand and led him across the grass to a spot where the wall dipped down following the contours of a gully. He levered himself up for a look. It was perfect, the far end of a cemetery where big yews grew close together and leaf mould and grass cuttings had been piled against the bricks. He slipped over the wall, reached back and heaved Norah across. They crouched behind one of the big yews till he was certain they had not been seen.

"I want somewhere safe to lie up," he whispered.

"Just out of the cemetery, there's a building site they've cleared. Nothing there but scrub."

She led him to the cemetery gate. "Across the road, see?"

"But there's a fence round it. I can't climb it right on the main road."

"Down at the side, the second turning, no one'll see you." She was involved now. Part of his team. A possession quite priceless. Someone who would run for him, be his eyes and his ears. Don't know why the girls want to dip their fingers in. But they always do, he thought. He had his arm around her shoulder as they crossed the road. Boy and girl, out for a walk, and anyone who saw them would have imagined it was endearment he was whispering against her hair.

"Do exactly as I say," he said. "Near the station there's a tea shop, on the far side of the road. You'll find a man in there, a dark man. Taller than me, short hair. He'll have a grip-bag with him. Just say Mushroom and tell him to follow you. Take him down side streets and get him here. If he's not there, wait."

"Is he the other one?" Excitement was in Norah's voice.

"You don't need to know. Just get him here."

FAMY heard the sirens in the street outside and bit at his finger-nails. The images on the movie screen meant nothing. What preyed on him was his immediate survival. The bag was there against his legs, reassuring. He quietly slid open the zip and felt for the angled shapes of the grenades. He lifted one out, the size of a shrunken apple, and put it in his coat pocket. It could stave off immediate pursuit, and it gave him the confidence he would need to walk out of the theatre.

His thoughts wandered back to the men he had hardly known but whose companionship he had come to value, Dani and Bouchi. Their laughter on the plane out of Beirut, the fear that had bound them on the route to Boulogne. He recaptured again, so that it overwhelmed him, the sight of their blood that had soaked the seats of the car. He could hear Dani's dying exhortation: "Remember Palestine, and remember me, when you meet with him, with the Mushroom Man." The words knifed through him, providing the momentum he needed to go on.

He left the cinema before the end of the second film. He wanted to be away before the rush for the exits. With the bag in his hand and the grenade in his pocket, he slid back the iron bar that kept the fire door shut and slipped out into the middle light of evening and the unknown.

He made his way to the rendezvous with a shuffling gait, ready to spin towards the shopwindows when squad cars cruised past. To avoid police who walked the streets he entered shops, mingling with people at counters till the danger was gone. Each step gave him confidence. They're stumbling, he told himself, uncertain whom they seek. In the tea shop, he took a seat at the back to wait.

Finally he saw the girl come in, noticed the nervous eyes that

89

took in all the customers. The look of recognition she gave him stiffened Famy. He stared at her, hand clasped around the grenade as she came closer.

She bent down towards him, trembling. "Mushroom," she blurted out. "You're to follow me. I'll take you to him."

And Famy understood. Why had the Irishman been so anxious to split up? Needed a girl. One who would follow blindly where he led. Dangerous plan, but not bad, McCoy. A roll in the grass and you have the girl's loyalty.

She took him through the back streets of the old town. At last, in front of a tangle of shrubs, she spoke. "That's where he is." Her voice was detached, as if she realized, thought Famy, that her usefulness was expended. "It's time I was getting home, my mum'll be out of her mind."

"Where do you live?" asked Famy.

"Chisholm Road. Just round the corner. At twenty-five."

"I hope we see you again. You have been very kind to me."

CHAPTER EIGHT

In the ground-floor pressroom at Scotland Yard the crime correspondent of the *Daily Express* heard the first whisper of the major security operation being mounted to protect an unnamed Israeli. The paper's science correspondent was able to shed light on the identity of the man: he had received an invitation to a lecture by Professor David Sokarev of the Nuclear Research Centre at Dimona and had called the Israeli embassy for information on the professor's itinerary. He was met with a flat refusal, which served only to confirm that Sokarev was the man being subjected to intensive security. The chief sub-editor's intuition then turned the story into a front-page splash. He began to shuffle together what had been quite separate material—the stories he had catch-lined Sokarev and those on which he had scrawled Manhunt. The connection made good sense. And so the headline ARAB DEATH THREAT TO ISRAELI H-BOMB SCIENTIST blasted its way across the top of the paper's front page.

The Prime Minister's anger when he read the story was stonily put aside by the Director General of the Security Service. "No leaks from this department. I think you'll find, sir, that it's straightforward reporting of facts visible to any trained eye."

"Nevertheless," said the Prime Minister, "if anything happens to this man Sokarev now, we are going to look almighty stupid."

"That's a fair point, sir," the Director General replied. He wished the Prime Minister a good night's sleep.

BEFORE they set out into the darkness of the park, there were fierce words between Famy and McCoy. Famy was impressed by the deserted building site where McCoy had been waiting, and wanted to stay put. "We have to sleep somewhere. This is a good place," he had said.

"With police about, we have to get out fast." McCoy was accustomed to command without arguments. And he had assessed his colleague, felt the time of deference had died its death. "In the morning there'll be dogs, helicopters, the whole works round us. They know we're here. Don't know how, but they do."

"You have risked us." Famy threw his ace card, unwilling to let McCoy dominate. "And what for? To lie with that girl—"

"Shut your face," McCoy spat. "And just think back over what you've done today, try and remember where they picked you up."

The memory of the agitated diplomat on the telephone scared Famy's mind. The shame was too great for him to tell the Irishman what had happened. He was defeated. "Where do we go?"

McCoy made no capital from the submission, applied no salt, and spoke with the heat gone from his voice. Silently, Famy thanked him. The pivot that controlled who dominated the team had shifted—it was inevitable, also irreversible.

"Across the park and another couple of miles beyond. If we're lucky, we'll get ourselves a car," McCoy said.

Famy followed as McCoy led. The truth was clear to him: without the Irishman he and his mission were doomed.

They blundered across the rough ground, tripping and stumbling, always seeking the total black void away from the lights of cars. They climbed the fence that demarcated the park and a golf course, handing over the weighted bag one to the other, and made their way across the greens and fairways till they came to another fence, which shielded a neat, tended row of back gardens. They went with care over that fence and then were out in a short and rounded, well-lighted cul-de-sac.

McCoy said, "I'll go ahead. You take the bag. And go slow. Look as though you belong."

They walked another hour and a half till they were in the wide and deserted Wandsworth High Street. "Somewhere off here," said McCoy, "we'll collect an old car. The new ones'll have locking devices on the wheels." They were together now, mutually belonging, the threat of the police cordon far behind them.

"It was easy, as it turned out." Famy smiled, shy still.

"There's no way they can stand shoulder to shoulder round a town that size. All they can do is block the main routes and hope for luck. If you keep your cool, you'll win."

McCoy didn't regret their clash. Be something wrong, he thought, if we weren't at each other's throats on a caper like this. Not enough sleep, not enough food. We've less than a full day to go, and then . . . the mad scramble to get clear of the place. Not like it had been planned. And now . . . where to go now? One thing at a time, my Provie boy.

But this is not the way you do it. You don't stand up in Crossmaglen market square and blast a paratrooper and then wonder which way you'll run. You plan it all out. Don't leave it to chance. You don't survive in this business if you're in a hurry. They'd expect something better of you, Ciaran McCoy. Laugh themselves silly and think, Stupid little bugger. Off on the big one, off on the spectacular, and no plan out.

At least there'd be no more trouble from the Arab. He saw that, the way Famy followed him, half a step behind, down the dark, deserted locked-up streets. And no one curious of the sounds as McCoy prized open the hood of an aging Ford Cortina. His fingers found the vital terminals and the mechanism shook into life. He took the grip from Famy, unzipped it, and pulled out a shirt. He placed it against the glass of the quarter light, then smashed his hand against the cotton. The blow was muffled and the glass tilted on its axis with room for him to insert his hand and open the driver's door. A moment later the Arab and his bag were in the car and McCoy had edged the Cortina into the road.

He headed east, away from all the policemen shivering at their roadblocks. "Piece of cake," he muttered.

"Where now?" Famy asked.

"Across the river, where there are woods and we can lose ourselves. We'll need a garage when its light, to get some keys to this bloody heap. We don't come back to town till evening."

Famy nodded. He was conscious that he was being told what he needed to know, nothing more. No frills, no discussion.

McCoy sensed the mood. "Don't fret yourself, lover boy. This is your day, not mine. I'll get you there, just when you need to be. You and your man. It'll come soon enough. And don't go lousing it up on me."

McCoy laughed, selfish and introverted, and began to sing, privately, ignoring his audience. They were the songs of his move-ment—songs of death, martyrdom, adulation for the fallen hero. And there was a bitterness in them. You need to be stiff and shrouded before the music men get around to you. Let some soldier gouge your guts out and they'll be strumming and croon-ing your name. Never a song about the living, only when the grass is sitting on you. He'd walked at such funerals. Tramped his way far behind the families, and made a lone exit from the graveside while orations and epitaphs were in full flow. But they had an effect on him, those processions of silent men and women behind the cheap box draped with the flag and mounted by the black beret. An emotional dragnet that caught him up and wielded him farther into the cause. When they buried one of his men, there was immediate retaliation, a soldier died. It followed like night after day. Clear, easy to understand. But the death of an Israeli, some-one he'd never heard of, from the other side of the world—was this worth the journey across the churchyard? It's an order, McCoy. Do as you're told, soldier boy. Leave it at that. Somebody else's war, this one, but can't be fought unless McCoy stands in the line. Famy would die, no hesitation. Ciaran McCoy, though, what would he do? How hard would he press home his attack? Pray Jesus . . .

He glanced at the stranger beside him. Famy was asleep.

THE LEADER of the General Command was alone in his tent. On the table before him was a solitary piece of paper brought by the journalist from Beirut. He had read it over and over, savouring the news: the one they called Saleh Mohammed was there, on target and meeting his contact. The best boy he had, the one he had willed to survive. It would devastate them, twist behind the State of Israel's rib cage. . . .

The old man who acted as his bodyguard came into the tent.

"Some food for you, Ahmed. It is time to eat." He was the only one in the camp who would call the leader by his given name. It went back eight years, when, after the Six Day War, the Palestinians for the first time had stood and fought. The two of them together, leader and follower, had held a house against a brigade, and afterwards, among the Palestinians, there had been heady praise and the start of resistance.

The old man put the plate in front of the leader. A mess of beans and rice and sauce with lamb's meat cut in small squares.

"They have had their day, the Israelis. We will have ours," he said. "This blow will make them yelp like dogs."

The old man arranged a spoon and fork beside the plate. "Across the border?" he asked, with a burden of sadness. He had cleared too many bundles of possessions left behind by suicide squads.

"Across many borders. Far from here. Bouchi, Dani and the third one, you remember? Bouchi and Dani are dead, the other alone has gone through. He is on target. Today or tomorrow he will move, and then the world will know of him." He spoke the words hurriedly, as he scooped up the food. "His target is a man of the utmost importance to them, one who concerns himself with the breaking of the atom and the release of its energies."

The old man saw the excitement in the leader's eyes. It was a look he recognized—the fanatic awaiting his fulfilment.

"Eight bombs they have, perhaps more by now," the leader went on, his voice quavering. "In a city they would kill up to one hundred thousand. Burn the bodies of our people, blind them, maim them, infect them so that those that live would breed grotesque mutations. This bomb is a weapon of filth, their ultimate defence. They hide behind it in the knowledge that the very mystery of its

94

existence gives them strength. The man we will shoot is the man who has created this bomb for Israel: David Sokarev."

"And when he is dead, what will have changed?"

"The elimination of Sokarev will awaken the world to the Israeli power. We will tell the world why such a harmless-looking little man was chosen—we will tell them of Dimona, of the plutonium schemes. And with that will come fear of a mushroom cloud settling the 'Middle East problem', as they call it. Fear of an annihilation more ghastly than the world has experienced since its cleverer men developed this horror. If the governments demand to exercise control over this weapon, demand inspections and controls, then Israel will go down stripped of her last defence. That is why we will kill Sokarev." The leader smiled like a man who has outlined to his friends his plans for the conquest of a woman they all consider unattainable.

The old man had not heard him talk that way before. "It is strange," he said quietly, "how the death of a man can move the world more than the life he has so long striven to perfect." And he let himself out of the tent.

IT WAS past three on Tuesday morning when Jimmy returned to his flat. He'd had nothing to drink. He'd been to Leconfield House to report to Jones; he'd seen Sokarev in his bed. He'd padded around the hotel checking the fire doors to convince himself they were closed to outside entry and that the Special Branch men were in position. He'd told Elkin he'd be back by early morning, repeated that under no circumstances was Sokarev to be allowed visitors or to leave his room.

There was a Branch man in the corridor, another beside the lift, two more in the ground-floor lobby. Hopeless outnumbering for the opposition, thought Jimmy. Easy in his mind, he'd driven to the Richmond police station. He'd walked into a bustle of activity —lights blazing, corridors noisy with hurrying men, teleprinters chattering messages to and from Scotland Yard, telephones ringing. The senior officers who sat around a table littered with maps and plastic coffee cups didn't waste Jimmy's time. They explained crisply what they planned for the morning. They showed him exactly where they had searched and where their roadblocks and mobile forces were operating. Painstaking effort. But he could read the answer he was looking for in their drawn, humourless faces. There were few in the room who expected the night's efforts to be crowned by success. Not without extraordinary luck, and policemen don't count on luck, Jimmy knew that.

As he let himself into his flat he reflected that they were loose, those two, free, with their guns and their plans, inching their way closer to the target. And that he, Jimmy boy, was enjoying that state of affairs. No doubt about that. Nobody likes it when a fox won't run, goes to earth too fast. And Jimmy was looking for a good long ride before the kill.

He found Helen asleep, and he took off his shoes and tiptoed, careful not to wake her as he eased his way into bed.

Sleep came fast to Jimmy. It always did, even on the nights he might later be required to shoot or be shot at. There was no tension. Which was why Jones championed him, which was why the Director General tolerated his presence on the payroll.

THE COLD woke Famy. He had been in a half sleep for some time, wriggling under his coat in the back seat of the car, trying to escape the chill. For a few moments he could not place where he was; then he swung his head up to peer into the front seat, anticipating the sight of McCoy's huddled shape. It hit him a cruel, winding, sledgehammer blow. The emptiness that he saw. He sat up abruptly. There was a tremble in the fingers, weakness in the legs. With a quick movement he felt for the grip-bag and ran his fingers over it. The guns were there. But where was the hateful Irishman?

The hard words of the previous evening came back to him, and the long silences. He should have known. Putting trust in a stranger—it had been madness. But now, on his own, how could he go forward? Tears drove their passage across his cheeks and he had no strength to fight them. He had not wept for many years. Since adulthood he'd prided himself on his ability to keep his emotions tight. But that the Irishman had left him asleep and defenceless, had not had even the courage to face him directly . . . that was a total wound, painful and throbbing.

He eased himself out of the car. His watch showed past eight.
The sun was coming high from behind the houses that surrounded
the junkyard where the car was parked. He walked warily away
from the vehicle, through the gate to the road. There were
people there, but none concerning themselves with the tall young
figure who watched them. He had no knowledge of his where-
abouts and could not ask. Then he remembered his *A to Z* street
guide. If he could find a street name, he could identify his exact
location. The sign would be at the far end of the line of houses,
where the junction was. Later, when things settled into a midmorning listlessness, he would walk down the street to find its name.

By the time he turned back towards the car, his mind was made
up. When the men of the General Command went across the
enemy's border, there was no retreat. If they were cut off short of
their target, they stood and fought and died where they were
trapped. None returned to admit failure. If we lose our courage,
he thought, we can lay down our rifles and go back to ploughing
the fields of Lebanon and Jordan; we will never see the hills of
Nablus and the groves of Haifa.

It would be a sentence of death for him to go on. A conscious
decision. But it had been so for his brothers at Bet She'an or on
the sea front of Tel Aviv. He felt a great calmness now. The
tears ceased to fall; the tightness in his belly had gone.

MACKOWICZ did not inform David Sokarev that a visitor had
arrived at the hotel expecting to take breakfast with him. When
the tall, white-haired, upright figure of Sir Humphrey Talbot,
Fellow of the Royal Society, had stopped at the reception desk to
ask for the Israeli's room number, a Special Branch man had
walked over to him. "Can I help you, sir?" His voice was low.

"I don't think so." Sir Humphrey turned to the receptionist.
"Young lady, I was asking for Professor Sokarev's room—"

"He's not taking visitors, sir," said the detective.

"And who might you be?"

"Detective Sergeant Harvey, Special Branch, Scotland Yard.
Our instructions, sir. I hope you haven't been inconvenienced."

"Of course I've been damn well inconvenienced. I've come up

from Cambridge to breakfast with the professor. He invited me."
Sir Humphrey rifled through his faded leather briefcase and produced a single-page letter. "Read that. Clearly typed and with his signature at the bottom, on headed paper from Dimona."

The detective read it, motioned for the visitor to wait, and picked up a house phone. He spoke quickly and out of earshot, then returned to Sir Humphrey's side. "One of the professor's colleagues will be down to see you directly, sir. To explain the position."

"But he's travelling on his own. He says so in the letter."

"I wonder, sir . . . have you seen a newspaper this morning?"

"Of course I haven't. Been travelling, haven't I?"

"If you had, perhaps things would be clearer to you, sir."

The lift door opened and Mackowicz emerged. He took the letter, read it, and handed it back. "I regret that your journey has been unnecessary. Professor Sokarev is receiving no visitors before his speech. I am sorry."

Sir Humphrey's voice rose in anger. "I've come at the professor's invitation, and you, without even the courtesy of introducing yourself, turn me away. What nonsense is this?"

"My name is Mackowicz, I am with the professor's party. I can only repeat my apologies that you were not forewarned."

"When in heaven's name will I be able to see him?"

"You are going to the professor's speech this evening?"

"Of course I'm going. I'm chairing the damned thing."

"There will be an opportunity then," said Mackowicz.

"And perhaps you would be so kind as to inform me the reason for this lunatic carry-on."

The detective handed him a morning paper. "If you will read the headlines, sir, perhaps you will see our problem. Because of this situation, the professor is to receive *no* visitors." He stepped abruptly back into the lift. Flushed with embarrassment, Sir Humphrey walked to the door.

Four floors above, Sokarev paced his room dejectedly. It was Elkin's turn to sleep, and Mackowicz made poor company. More than an hour to go before the typist came from the embassy to take down his speech. That at least would distract him from these young men with their submachine guns and their fixed, humourless stares. The speech would take the morning to prepare. Then perhaps he could sleep. There would be many distinguished men of learning to hear him in the evening; he wished to be at his best.

WHEN Jimmy woke, Helen was still sleeping. That one of them was always asleep seemed the most consistent fact about their life together. They laughed about it with each other, and cursed privately. She looked good, always did when she was sleeping and vulnerable. She'd be late, but he wouldn't wake her yet. Jones could wait for one morning, might not take her so much for granted.

From the bedside table he telephoned Sokarev's suite. Jimmy recognized Elkin's voice. He sounded cheerful, said they'd had an uneventful night. "A guy came and wanted to see him, a scientist. Mack dealt with it. The man was a bit bothered, but left."

Jimmy shuddered, imagining the tact that gorilla would have employed to make his point. He said, "I'll be down well before lunch. And no room service. Nothing sent up. If he wants something, you go get it yourselves."

After Jimmy had shaved and dressed, he put on the holster apparatus that had been made to fit him and the pistol he had drawn from Leconfield House. The holster straps lay smooth and tight across his upper back and chest. When he had his jacket on, the PPK and its props were decisively hidden.

He shook Helen's shoulder with a gentleness that few who knew him casually would have guessed he possessed. "Wake up, girl."

"What time is it?" she said it sleepily, eyes squinting.

"Bit after nine."

"You pig," she shouted, scrambling out of the bed. "You're a mean, miserable pig, Jimmy. All dressed yourself, and not waking me. Jones'll be off his rocker."

"Won't do him any harm, let him sweat a bit," Jimmy said.

She said nothing else, fiercely concentrating on her dressing and then the application of makeup in front of the mirror.

"Are you coming down to the speech tonight?" Jimmy asked as he walked her to her Maxi car.

"Only if I'm needed. I don't want to just rubberneck."

"I'd like you to come, might want the car there. If I have a department car, I'm saddled with it. If you come, when we've dumped the little guy back in bed we can shove off."

She got in and started the car. "Want me to see hero boy in action? Roy of the Rovers defies amazing odds. Triumph of virtue. That it, Jimmy boy?"

When it came to needling him, she was the great expert.

"Get off to your boring office," he shouted. "I'll call you. I want you at the speech. If you want a meal on the house, that is."

Jimmy hailed a cab and sagged deep into the back seat, peering at the scurrying masses. This was ideal guerrilla country, perfect territory on which to wage that sharp and cruel form of warfare. In this huge, diverse capital, what hope could there be of finding just the two men who were different from the rest by virtue of having declared hostilities? Impossible, thought Jimmy.

There can be only one killing ground. The one right beside David Sokarev. Not ten yards from him, or even five, but right up against him. Jimmy felt no fear at the prospect of physical injury. What caused him a cold, mindless state of apprehension was the possibility of failure. It always dogged him, that horror. He could picture the little man with the blood on his face, and the look of betrayal that would dominate his eyes. That would be the awfulness for Jimmy. The unspeakable disaster, if he lost Sokarev. The very thought of it rendered him irritable and tense.

FROM where he crouched inside the small car Famy saw McCoy appear around the corner. Twice the Irishman looked behind to satisfy himself he was not under surveillance. Under his arm was a brown paper bag, and he was reaching into his trouser pocket when he saw Famy staring at him. McCoy took in the numbed astonishment in the other's face.

"I've got car keys, good on any car. From an old fool in a garage up the road. Said I'd return them later. I've got us gloves for the lecture-room window, too, motorcycle sort, with protection halfway up the arm. Made of leather, and bloody expensive. Hope your mob are good on expenses." His laugh dissolved as Famy's face failed to react. "What's the matter? You look like someone's just parachuted you into Jerusalem."

100

"I thought you'd gone," Famy whispered, frightened of the words, but with no option but to speak them.

"Course I'd gone," said McCoy. "I told you last night we'd need keys. You said we'd need gloves. What's special about that?"

"I thought you'd gone and were not coming back."

McCoy spat back at him, angry. "How many times do I have to say we're in this muck-up together. For once in your suspicious, miserable life, try believing what you're told."

Famy climbed out of the car. "I'm sorry. It was shameful to doubt you." He paused, let the seconds of confrontation flitter away. "How do we spend the rest of the day?"

McCoy had the imagination to feel the Arab's sentiments on waking to find the car empty. "I should have woken you when I left. Now we'll stay put for the rest of the day and go direct from here to the university. No sense in moving about unnecessarily. What we need is sleep."

THE FEW tourists who had gathered across the road were all unaware of the identity of the man who stepped from the black Humber and hurried into 10 Downing Street.

The Director General was taken by lift to the top-floor flat that the country's senior politician had turned into a home when the pressure of work kept him from his own town house.

The Prime Minister was at breakfast. As he spread marmalade onto a square of toast he motioned to the head of the counter-espionage force to take a chair opposite and pushed a china coffee jug in his direction. "I've seen the Home Secretary this morning," he said. "He's told me what the police are doing. I wanted to know your feelings about this affair as we go into these crucial hours, and what your own department's state of readiness is."

The thought of memoirs that political leaders wrote with such enthusiasm on retirement kept the Director General on his guard. He regarded the Prime Minister's request for information as legitimate, but cautiously chose not to expand beyond what the other man already knew. He started with the police operation at the hotel, listed the precautions that would be taken to transport Sokarev across the city. Official-style decoy car driving from the

101

hotel at high speed, while the target left via the kitchens in a police van, switching to more formal transport in the concealed yard of Tottenham Court Road police station before being delivered to a side entrance to the university's main building. He spoke of the scale of the escort, of the numbers of men on guard at the hall where Sokarev was to lecture, and of the search procedures that had been adopted there. The gelignite-sniffer Labradors and the metal detectors that plainclothes troops had employed before the room was sealed the previous night. He went into the degree to which invitation holders to the lecture had been vetted, and lingered on the problems of body searches without giving offense to the learned guests.

Then he stopped and waited. The Prime Minister's question was not long in coming. "That covers the police side of things. Everything, in fact, that the Home Secretary told me. What are your people doing?"

The Director General was in no hurry. His long pauses could be infuriating and he knew it.

"I have the heads of the department involved in constant meeting, and they have a liaison line to Scotland Yard. We have endeavoured to provide the Metropolitan Police with all relevant information at our disposal."

"Do you have a man on the ground with Sokarev?"

"I have a man right beside him. He is my direct liaison with the police and with the Israeli Foreign Ministry's protection team."

"What sort of man?"

"Experienced," said the Director General.

"Experienced in what? Liaison, Arab affairs?"

"He's a marksman."

The Prime Minister lifted his head to stare directly at the DG. "There are enough police there for that, surely? I'd have thought you'd have used a senior man with liaison capabilities rather than a gunman."

The Director General was patient. "I have placed a gunman alongside Sokarev because the greatest risk to the life of our guest is close-range shooting. My man is far in advance of anything the Metropolitan Police can provide."

"It would seem," said the Prime Minister, "that you regard an act of violence as a major possibility."

The DG poured himself a cup of now lukewarm coffee. He said, "Considering the opposition, I regard it as an inevitability."

CHAPTER NINE

David Sokarev walked through the door of lecture room D in the main building of London University and was close to halfway down the side aisle before any of the waiting nuclear physicists reacted to the short figure in the grey suit hemmed in by body-guards. There were few who had come to listen who had not read or heard that a major terrorist plot existed with the sole purpose of assassinating the scientist about to address them. Those who first recognized him from pictures, or who had met him, rose from their seats and began to clap. Within seconds the entire room had joined in. The noise spilled into a cheer, self-conscious at first, from men unaccustomed to venting their feelings in such a public manner. Those that were close enough saw the sad eyes of Sokarev, saw his tongue run with anxiety over his lips. Perhaps the acclamation confused him, but as he turned to look behind to gauge the size of the room, his feet tangled one with the other and he pitched forward a few inches before the hands of the men who surrounded him arrested his stumble.

By the time he reached the raised table, everyone was standing, pulping their palms together in a gesture of solidarity. The smile that dawned on his face was one of helpless gratitude. He tried not to look as they beamed and shouted their support, instead cleaning his spectacles and sorting his notes.

It all meant little to Jimmy.

He had permitted Mackowicz and Elkin to flank the scientist and had positioned himself a pace or so behind. Beyond had been the Special Branch men, six of them, who could get no closer than five to six feet from their charge. Now the shell around Sokarev fragmented as the guards moved to their appointed places, where they would stay for the time he was in the room. The door had been locked behind him, plainclothes guards on either side equipped with walkie-talkies. There could be no surprise entry from that quarter.

The two Israelis were with Sokarev at the table, Elkin on one side, Mackowicz on the other, close to the windows draped in long brown velveteen curtains. Jimmy saw that Mackowicz held a raincoat across his thighs; on this warm summer evening, clear sky, forecast of sunshine for at least three days, the coat would mean the Uzi was concealed there. Wonder if the catch is off, thought Jimmy, if he's cocked it. Along the side walls were four of the Branch men, two on each side. The remaining two were at the far end, facing Sokarev and the committee that hosted the meeting. Nine armed and trained men. Has to be enough, Jimmy said to himself, has to guarantee it. But the knowledge that Mackowicz had the submachine gun grasped in his right hand aggravated him. Swiftly and unseen, he drew the PPK from his holster and held it low behind him against the wall, positioning himself so that he faced the windows and could see Sokarev to his left.

When the silence at last settled on the hall, the chairman, Sir Humphrey, rose to speak. He glanced at Mackowicz with anger, still stung by his experience of the morning in the hotel lobby.

"Ladies and gentlemen. It gives me the very greatest of pleasure to welcome this evening that most distinguished of colleagues from the State of Israel, Professor David Sokarev." The clapping began immediately and continued with fervour, till he raised his hands to quell it. "We are all aware that the professor has done us a great honour in keeping this engagement. And there is no doubt in my mind that he has also displayed great courage. I think we can accept that in the highest offices of our land the dangers that Professor Sokarev is running are believed to be genuine. Witness the number of gentlemen with us this evening who are, I regret, going to find the lecture extremely tedious." There was a ripple of brittle laughter.

"Because of the difficulties that have surrounded Professor Sokarev, I myself have not yet had the opportunity of speaking to him. Whether he plans to discuss in our company his distinguished work with lasers, I do not know. . . ."

The speech of introduction droned on, Jimmy's attention lost.

104

The gun, he had now decided, was unnecessary. It could rest as easily in the holster, enough of the bloody melodrama. He turned to the wall and placed the PPK again against his chest. He felt himself beginning to relax. Two moments of priority danger, and one already negotiated. Arrival and departure. Those were the hitting times for the opposition. Not in here, not with the screened and searched and checked-out audience. The departure would be the time for maximum vigilance. And then there'd be Helen out there waiting. She'd follow them to drop Sokarev at his hotel; then they'd be together. Soft and comfortable.

The policemen who were beyond the locked door, out in the corridor, shared Jimmy's feelings. They were sufficiently at ease to light up cigarettes. And those outside, in the creeping darkness, also felt an easing of the tension. There would be ample warning of the professor's exit for them to return to their closely chosen watching points. But for now one group had gathered at the main entrance, another by the side door through which Sokarev had entered. From neither position was it possible to view the windows of the lecture hall, as that part of the building butted out too far for them to see beyond its corners.

THE POLICE officer who had been assigned the duty of watching the windows lay now at McCoy's feet. He had not been armed—it wouldn't have mattered if he had been—nor had he spoken into his radio before the crashing blow hit below his helmet, where skull base and vertebrae come together. It had been mercilessly simple: Famy advancing with a tourist map, distracting the policeman as they peered together at the street divisions, while McCoy moved cougar-quick with the plumber's piping. McCoy's borrowed keys were next employed, a parked car opened, the vehicle pushed in silence to where Famy had scratched the star.

Famy saw that the Irishman never looked at the sprawled figure beneath him. Obliterated without concern, as with the girl. It was as Famy himself would be when the time of firing came. He was aware of the flooding excitement bursting through him. At last they would savour victory. Triumph. It was the ultimate moment of his mission.

105

McCoy said, quietly and slowly, so that he would not have to repeat it, "There was one round of clapping when he went in. The next round means he's on his feet. We go, straight then."

Famy extended the shoulder rest of the M1, locked it in its extended position, checked the magazine, cocked the gun.

McCoy pulled the heavy black glove onto his left hand, grasped the plumber's pipe in his right. But no gun, Famy saw. "You should have the other M1," he hissed.

"No need. Your pigeon now, remember? I give you the clear shot; then it's all yours, baby boy."

"It will be a famous success for our people. . . ."

"Keep that nonsense till you've hit him."

They heard the swell of applause build. Famy climbed onto the roof of the car. Needed to steady himself with the free hand, nerves gripping at his legs. McCoy climbed over the hood and up past the windshield till both stood together, uncertain of balance on the buckling, heaving platform. They were exactly above Famy's mark and level with the join of the curtains.

"Remember," McCoy whispered, "when I've done the window and got the curtain back, he'll be forty-five degrees to you. And if they all start blasting, chuck the grenades. Right?"

He waited till Famy's rifle was snug against the shoulder and the right cheek, then smashed the tubing into the glass. Famy winced away from the noise, as McCoy's gloved fist beat at obstinate slivers still fastened in the frame, then pulled the curtain back. Instinctively, Famy lunged forward, still in the aim posture, raking the brightness of the room for his target.

Where was he? Which was the one he sought? Which of the blank faces, transfixed, peering at the source of the commotion? The clarity was not long coming. The man who stood at the table while all around him sat, the man who had begun to cower, who knew the blow was near and sought to avoid it, who could not make his muscles follow the orders of his brain—that one was Sokarev.

Famy steadied to fire. Aiming for the white shirt.

"Speed it up," screamed McCoy.

As Famy began to squeeze the trigger as he'd been told, he

twisted his gaze to the agony of impatience on the Irishman's face. When he looked back, he saw one man thrusting his way towards Sokarev and one swinging the billowed shape of a raincoat.

Famy fired.

AS THE curtains exploded with the noise of the breaking glass, Jimmy's hand had moved to the holster under his jacket, found the handle. Then he saw the gun barrel protruding through the window barely thirty feet from him. His pistol was coming fast, arm extended, level with the eyes as he heard the yell from out in the night, and then the first shot. Fractionally later Jimmy pulled the hair trigger, conscious of the need not for accuracy but for a volume of shots. He fired six times, shouting all the while in the direction of Sokarev. "Get him down. Get the man on the floor. Under the table."

Elkin reached Sokarev first, taking off in a leap from five feet away, pinioning him among the tangle of chair and table legs. Jimmy saw the chairman sag and his upper torso fall forward, casually, onto the table.

Again and again the rifle at the window fired, and with each shot Jimmy was surer that the marksman was missing and knew it. Half smile playing on the mouth, but the eyes—cold, focused.

The two Special Branch men along the wall on the same side as Jimmy had begun to fire, not standing but crouched in the taught posture, classic but slower. Jimmy saw Elkin covering Sokarev under the table, saw Mackowicz bring the Uzi out from under that raincoat. He made for the door, was shouting for it to be opened, above the nerve-shattering noise of the long burst fired by Mackowicz, when from the corner of his eye he saw the dark-grey and rounded shape loop its way from the window towards the table.

Mackowicz yelled the one terrifying, choked word: "Grenade!"

It bounced on the floor between the table and the front-row seats, made a gentle parabola before bouncing again and then rolling unevenly, because it was not a perfect sphere, towards the table where Elkin protected Sokarev. Mackowicz jumped for it. Jimmy could see it disappear underneath the big body. Complete stillness. Then Mackowicz was lifted high towards the ceiling.

Jimmy did not see him fall; he was through the door, now unlocked, and running, the detonation battering in his ears as he forced his way past a charge of advancing policemen. He knew where to go. As he swerved along the side of the building to the marksman's position, he saw two men jump from the roof of a parked car and run for the low wall that separated the university from the street. Still sprinting, Jimmy fired—stupid really, carried away with the cowboy game—only one shot, and the magazine was expended. There was a shot in return, wide and high. Jimmy couldn't get close now, not with an empty shooter. Across the road he heard the frantic sound of dispute, and the noise of a car being revved. And he was panting, out of condition.

"Helen. Helen. Where the devil are you?"

It seemed deep eternity before the car pulled up beside him.

"Get out. Get out." His voice came in short staccato bursts. She hesitated, disoriented by the sound of gunfire and now the wild-eyed form of Jimmy wrenching open the door. In one action he pulled her out, took her place, and was already spinning in a half circle towards where he had seen the men and the starting car.

Seventy yards in front, the Cortina struck out into the main-stream. Jimmy heaved with relief. He was in contact; the space between the cars would lessen. He cut from the centre of the road to avoid a police car racing in the other direction. Flashed his headlights, but it was past him, his gesture unseen. No system of communication from Helen's car, no radio telephone. The Cortina went through the traffic lights on red and was in Goodge Street, heading south, Jimmy following. Not close enough yet, Jimmy, but it'll get better, and they'll wonder up front what hit them. The PPK rested on his lap. Another magazine was in his jacket pocket. He could reload fast.

THEY HAD run from the window close together. Famy with his head bent around, covering the area behind them with the rifle. McCoy leading, with his right arm pressed hard against him. Famy had fired once, and McCoy had savagely pulled him forward.

"It's distance we have to have or we're finished." The words sobbed out, emerging from the clamped, pain-creased mouth.

When they reached the Cortina, McCoy had thrust his left hand across his body into the opposite trouser pocket and pulled out the laden key ring. He selected one and tossed it to Famy.

"You drive," he said, and flung open the passenger door.

Famy still had the rifle to his shoulder, watchful of pursuit. It was small, too insignificant to be a killing weapon. He saw that the people who had paused on the far pavement now stood and watched. Not with fear, curious.

"Drive, you stupid eejit," McCoy hissed.

Famy lowered the rifle and held it at his side. "I cannot drive," he said slowly. Humiliation, abject and total.

"Course you can drive." McCoy's voice rose. He shoved his right arm in Famy's face. "Can't you see, you've got to, there's a bullet in there. Move the car off."

"I don't know how. I have never driven. I cannot."

The recitation slid home to McCoy. The obscenity he yelled at the Arab was vicious and wounding. He ran around the car and draped himself into the driving seat. He laid his right arm along the wheel for support. With his left hand he inserted the key, then put the car into gear.

Famy could see the whitened face and the sweat bead of deep hurt on his forehead, and he wondered whether the Irishman would faint. He wound down the passenger window and looked back, rifle aimed again. In his jacket pocket, three grenades. Grip-bag in the rear, more ammunition, more grenades. Needed the reassurance. He cringed as they went through the red light, bracing for collision. And another car came through the light, unmistakable. "A car followed us." Near panic, near hysteria.

"If it gets close, blast it. If not, forget it." McCoy felt the weakness drifting uncontrollably over him. He glanced obsessively at the wound. Just the neatly driven hole that lay in the centre of the bloodstained cloth on the upper forearm. The pain rose when he tried to use the hand, ebbed into numbness when he rested it again on the wheel. If he did not have to drive fast, he could manage. If there was pursuit . . . "Did you hit your pigeon?" he asked.

"I don't know." Little more than a whisper. Famy wanted to explain, wanted the other man to understand. "I was about to fire

110

when you shouted at me to hurry. There was distraction. As I fired, a man across the room began to shoot. One of the men pulled Sokarev under the table. I was firing all the time, but he was out of my sight. The man who sat beside Sokarev, he was hit. . . ."

"Big deal, they'll be singing and dancing in Beirut if you've drilled a Brit geriatric." The man's discomfiture almost amused McCoy. Without his wound he would have felt savage hatred at association with the fiasco, but the injury dissipated anger.

"There was shooting from the wall facing us. Three or four men. And the tall bodyguard near the table had started to fire the small machine gun when I threw the grenade. The grenade would have taken Sokarev, but the man fell on it. Then I could see nothing. He just exploded, and then there was smoke."

"One of those bastards took me." There was finality in McCoy's words. To Famy it seemed the pain of the inquest was over, and the car was still moving; McCoy could cope with the disability. He glanced behind, but could find nothing to sustain his earlier anxiety. He put the M1 on the floor under his legs.

McCoy said with a trace of a smile, "I thought this was the one where you took Sokarev, or they took you. Bugged out early, didn't we?"

"It was impossible to continue shooting with all the firing."

"Handgun stuff, not accurate. Lucky shot hit me."

"You started to run."

"It's not my war, remember? You could have stayed. You were the bloody marksman. Me, just the chauffeur. So why did you do the scamper?"

"I couldn't aim in the smoke." But there was no recollection of a decision to run. Already moving, never a moment of choice between life and death.

They had swung to the west now, and the traffic was lighter as they navigated a bypass route, avoiding the heart of the city. McCoy was able to keep down to twenty or thirty miles an hour.

"They won't react well, your masters. Won't want you hanging about and Mr. Sokarev coming out clean." McCoy was turning the screw. Knew and enjoyed it. Retribution for his pain.

Famy had his eyes closed, but was unable to shut out the

111

message. He said, "There was one who went into Israel and came back alone. His Kalashnikov had not been fired. They took him with ten of his friends to the open ground. They all had to shoot, and the guns were checked afterwards. That happened only once."

"You'd better think of something good to say," said McCoy. The game had gone far enough. Blood sports when the chase is over are seldom savoured, and he had other preoccupations. What to do about the wound. All men who go to the lonely war, the guerrilla's war, have a common fear. It is the horror of gangrene, of the putrefaction of their flesh. Needed a den, where he could be safe, with hot water and clean towels. . . . What to do with the Arab? Perhaps kill him, easiest solution. Half an hour more of driving, a decision by then.

FOR A FULL three minutes after the firing of the last shot, Elkin covered Sokarev's body. When the scientist tried to move, the security man firmly pressed him down again. Elkin's eyes were very clear, traversing for any further threat, and outstretched in front of him like an antenna was his service revolver.

The nearest Special Branch man had bent down and asked if Sokarev was hurt. Elkin had shaken his head.

"Keep him there," the detective said. "We'll clear the casualties. Empty the room. Then work out how to shift him."

Sokarev was aware that his legs were trembling uncontrollably. He remembered the noise of the window and the sight of the rifle in the curtain gap. Elkin had pulled him down, and there had been that horrific exchange of gunfire. He had seen Mackowicz dive, lie still and then lift off into the air. His ears still felt pierced by the shock wave of the grenade. From under the table he saw them cover the chairman's body on a stretcher. He could not look at what remained of Mackowicz.

Seven casualties in the lecture hall were rushed to University College Hospital. Outside, detectives examining the fire position under the window stumbled on the body of the policeman. When they lifted him onto the stretcher, it was with special gentleness, conscious that they were handling their own.

In strange, shuffling silence the guests were ushered from the

112

room and across the corridor to a similar lecture hall. Their patience was requested. They would not be detained for long, but they could not be allowed to head for their cars and public transport while the large-scale search of the university area was still under way. After the door had been closed on them, few had anything to say. Briefly they had been exposed to the unfamiliar, but the experience would do little to aid their comprehension.

When all had gone Sokarev was helped to his feet. Someone brought him a glass of water. He found he could scarcely hold it, and Elkin took the glass and put it against the professor's lips.

JONES had stayed in his office alone that evening. Helen, vague about her movements, had been gone three hours. From a long way down the empty corridors he heard the footsteps of the messenger from Communications and bounced out to snatch the paper from his hand. It didn't tell him much. An attack on Sokarev—unsuccessful; rifle fire and an explosion. Casualties. Large local hunt started for two men—no immediate result.

In his office, he sagged back in his chair. And nothing from Jimmy. Why hadn't he called? Half the reason for putting him there was so the department needn't rely on the police for information. He swivelled around and looked at the artist's picture of the young Arab, seemed as harmless as a butterfly. But bloody near pulled it off, him and that Irishman. Jones felt a great sadness. All the king's horses and all the king's men could be pushed off centre and laughed at by a little rat like that.

Brave, Jones acknowledged that. The Arab had been prepared to die for his army, whatever bunch of twisted idiots they might be. All such a terrible waste, and everyone scared out of their wits by the implications of it all, everyone except his Jimmy.

The telephone broke in, shrill and insistent. Helen on the line. Jimmy in her car—don't know where—hot pursuit—a getaway vehicle disappearing from the scene—shots in the street. She was coming back to the office. Staccato statements, and she'd rung off. Jones put the receiver down. Funny the way she'd used Jimmy's name; usually the laugh when she mentioned him, not this time. What was she doing there, he wondered, then put it from his mind, his thoughts surging with Jimmy. Just what Jimmy would have wanted, the big chance to prove himself where all else failed. Jimmy'd have to kill the Arab, wouldn't he? Only option.

Jones had no function now; all out of his hands. That's how far down we've been taken, he thought, right down to the base area, where the Jimmys are waiting.

THE PRIME MINISTER, called from the dinner table, suffered three agonizing minutes of uncertainty. The first message from Scotland Yard had stated merely that there was heavy shooting and an explosion inside the lecture hall. More details would follow. He had waited in his office, unwilling to face his guests before he knew the worst. When the telephone rang again, he was told that, whereas there were casualties, Sokarev was not among them.

He had barely resumed his meal when his parliamentary private secretary brought in a note. The Israeli ambassador demanded a meeting at once. "Put him off till the morning," the Prime Minister said, and motioned for the butler to replenish his glass. "Right to the top," he urged.

IT SATISFIED Jimmy that the car he tailed should be unaware of his presence. Eventually they would stop, and then he would make his presence known. Because of their low speed, they were not hard to follow. But their lack of urgency confused him.

The PPK was reloaded now. It had been easy to do when the men in front stopped for a traffic light. He was but two or three car lengths away from them when the traffic closed, and he could see the two heads—the driver's bent low over the wheel, the other turning every two minutes or so to look behind him. How did they rate themselves? Jimmy wondered. He knew where he'd have put it. Fifty-fifty, at best. Escaped, but hadn't taken the professor. No, not as good as even, if only the professor counted. Buggered it, hadn't they? Yet for all the security, they had achieved their surprise. Good groundwork, but the rest screwed up. Not like McCoy that, Jimmy thought, not if you read his file. Couldn't have been him on the gun.

Jimmy could see they had slowed in front of him. Nearly there, he told himself, in the side streets, but unsure of the turning. The pistol was in his right hand, flat against the wheel, ready to fire. His window was down. "Not long now, my little darling." He muttered it casually, but would not have denied the excitement.

TO KILL the Arab or not. It kept bouncing around McCoy. Famy was expendable, and from the way he fidgeted in his seat he was aware of it. Knew what his own people would do to him if he crawled home. The alternative, to rot in a cell here with no one coming in a hijack jet to lift him out. A bloody great beacon of fiasco; McCoy liked that, rolled off his tongue well. And the bugger knew it all; he could see that from the way he sat, misery from ear to ear. His chances of getting clear on his own were minimal to nil. If he'd needed his hand held for the attack, how much more would he depend on nanny for escape.

McCoy was close to resolve when Famy broke the long silence.

"You are going to the girl's home, right? At that place I will leave you." There was no reaction from McCoy. "There was an idea when we were planning the mission at home, that the attack should be mounted at Heathrow airport before he flew to the United States. It is the only possibility left. I will go on foot to the airport. They told us that it was not difficult to gain entry to the perimeter, and I will see the El Al land."

"Impossible." McCoy never moved his head.

"Not impossible, only difficult. I have the resolution now, the will I should have possessed earlier. But it was the first time I had ever fired on a man. It is not easy the first time. Not simple to expose oneself to gunfire. I have learned much in the last hour, more than they ever taught me in the camp."

"They'll gun you down before you're within two hundred yards of the plane, and you don't even know which one it will be." The quietness of the Arab disconcerted McCoy. The strange confidence, something new and delicate that he did not wish to fracture.

"The plane will be the one that is most heavily guarded. I have ideas, and many grenades. The Israelis say, and they are right, that if you intend to kill, you have to be close, body to body, not relying on aim or the steadiness of the hand. And prepared to die yourself."

115

"We part company, then. It's not part of my game."

"You carried me to the target. You have fulfilled your order. As long as I live I shall remember you with friendship."

No risk of that being long, thought McCoy. But if the boy wants to go gloriously, his concern. "I'm going to her house," McCoy said. "She'll put me up somewhere. I have to clean the arm."

"Where will you put the car?" asked Famy.

"At the end of the street by the house. It's a dead end."

He'd hesitated at several turns in the last half mile, searching for landmarks known from the one time he had walked the girl home. And then there he was, in the right road. After he stopped the car he reached awkwardly back for one of the M1's and another magazine. From the cloth sack he took three grenades, which he slipped into his pocket, crooked the gun under his arm as, with his left hand he opened the car door. Famy waited for him, then got out with the grip-bag. Simultaneously, both were aware of the lights of another vehicle that turned into the street.

"Stay still till he's parked and switched off," McCoy snapped at Famy. They were both illuminated by powerful beams that blazed at them from twenty yards down the road.

"As soon as he's gone, disappear." McCoy's pride dictated that, even relieved of his commitment, he should still lead. "Not much to say now . . . but I'm sorry for your sake . . . sorry it loused up. Why aren't those bloody car lights being killed?"

McCoy felt the searing surprise of pain as the first bullet struck his shoulder. It spun him half around in the fraction of time that it smashed into the boned strips of his upper ribs. Famy reacted well. Crouched beside the car door, he fired six aimed shots to destroy the lights, and when that was complete, blasted into the darkness above them. He grasped for a grenade. Pin out, lever free. Then he hurtled it towards the car. The moment before the blast he saw a shadow, down low to the pavement, scurry for the nearest front garden.

Drunkenly, McCoy regained his feet, lurched through the wicket gate to the girl's front door, and hammered at it with his rifle. There was one more shot, wide. "It's a pistol. Out of range," he gasped. "Give him a few more to keep his head down. And

116

listen. When we get inside, just do as I say and don't argue."

The door opened, showing a hallway that stretched the length of the house. Silhouetted in the light was the girl, behind her an older woman and a man, staring without understanding. McCoy pushed the girl savagely to one side, sending her spinning onto the floor. Satisfied that Famy had followed him in, he kicked back with his heel and heard the door slam, the lock engage. "Whoever that is"—and McCoy was speaking to the Arab as if the others did not exist—"he's seen us both go in. Double yourself out back, through the kitchen door, and run till your legs won't carry you. I'll hold here. It'll take the fuzz light-years to work out what to do, and give you hours of start. But move yourself—" The pain came in a great spasm.

Famy ran. Past McCoy, the girl, the parents. In the light from the kitchen he saw the garden fence, five feet high and sixty feet away. He trampled through some plants, then swung himself onto the wattle-embroidered barrier and was over.

When McCoy spoke again, it was with great deliberation, his defence against the flowing agony. "I have a rifle, fully loaded. And grenades. No hesitation to kill you if you do not do exactly as I say. The women get it first. The old one right at the start." The girl, upright now and joined in fear to her mother, began to weep, quick, choking sounds. "You, father"—McCoy gestured with the rifle to the man—"go round the house. I want all doors and windows locked and every curtain drawn. And I want the keys."

He looked at them, one at a time, with deep, hate-consumed eyes. "Don't mess me about. I've said what it means if you fool with me."

As he took the mother and daughter upstairs, he could hear the noise of the locks being turned, the bolts driven home. He was near to sleep, yearning for it, and for an escape from the pain and the awful hallucination of fighting another man's war.

ON ALL fours Jimmy edged his way towards the house. Helen's car was alight with flames. When the heat reached the petrol tank it would explode. Shouldn't have happened to her, only girl he knew who washed her own car. He went without haste, without

117

panic, watching the house, expecting all the time the gun, the black barrel. Next round due. He saw the curtains in an upstairs room abruptly jolt across the window, noted it as an essential precaution against siege. Nothing else he could register on, and then he smiled, nothing but that pool of blood by the front gate. The Irishman's, it would be. The one he'd aimed for, and the blood, the amount of it, meant an effective wound. Incapacitating. Cuts the odds, getting onto an even chance now, Jimmy. The front door of the nearest house opened, and Jimmy saw the man who came out and peered at the burning car. The man backed away when he saw Jimmy's gun and hurried to his door to shut out the threat. But Jimmy was faster, had his foot there, his worn leather taking the force of the swinging woodwork.

"I want the telephone," Jimmy said. "And write me the names of the people in the end house. Don't go back on the street unless you want to make the front page of the papers, picture and all."

For the man it was instant nightmare, too consuming to question Jimmy's identity. He led him to the phone. Fingers spun the dial.

"Jimmy here, Mr. Jones. They're holed up in Richmond. Chisholm Road, just by the park. One's in bad difficulty, but not fatal. They've rifles and grenades, are taking correct precautions. Police'll be coming when the local worthies report gunfire—"

Jimmy heard the penetrating wail of a siren. He dropped the telephone and ran out to wave down the patrol car. He saw the officers inside flinch away, remembered then that he still held the PPK, showed them his identity card.

"First thing, one of you get round the back, the other clear the street," he snapped. "Boyos from the London effort tonight are in the end house. They're littered with hardware, so go careful."

Within a quarter of an hour the house was surrounded by police marksmen. The local force's two attack-trained Alsatians were at the back, and a searchlight projected its high-intensity beam against the house. At the bottom of the street were the fire engines and ambulances. The home was eerily still. In the ambulance zone the other residents of Chisholm Road had gathered, wrapped in anoraks and overcoats against the chill, silent in their shock that such things should happen in their street.

118

Orders had been issued that no word of this operation should go out over police radio or be issued to the press.

"We have to cocoon them," said the local police superintendent. "Cut them right off till the VIPs arrive and announce the plan."

"Who's coming down?" asked Jimmy.

"Half of London. Assistant commissioner from Scotland Yard, Home Secretary, Defence people, a man called Jones from your crowd, scores of them."

"Let's hope they bring some changes of socks," said Jimmy. "They can take a long time, these things."

"It can take a long time, or it can take five minutes. That's the political decision." The superintendent walked away.

THE PRIME MINISTER sat at the end of the table. On his right the Commissioner of Police for the capital and the Permanent Under Secretary of State for Defence; on his left the Director General of the Security Services; and a young man, a middle-ranking civil servant from the Home Office. The Prime Minister had opened the meeting by asking the police commissioner to report on the situation at the house.

A detailed, clipped account concluded, "They have three hostages, they are proven killers. As yet we have no demands. They're likely to be wanting a plane out. These men are liable to be in a highly unstable condition after their earlier failure. I submit that time, as much as anything else, will calm them down. Otherwise you have a potential bloodbath."

The Prime Minister turned to the Director General, who said, "I've not much to add. We believe that our man has wounded the Irishman, McCoy. Our assessment is that McCoy would be the more skillful of the pair but that his resolve may not equal the Arab's. We believe that if it came to a shootout, the Arab would be the greater threat to the hostages."

"Mr. Dawson." The Prime Minister was looking to the young man from the Home Office. "What do we have to weigh in contemplating the storming of the house?"

Dawson spoke at length, for he was the expert on a vague and untested subject: the handling of siege situations when terrorists held hostages. He reviewed with precision the German tactics in the Munich Olympics attack, compared American and Israeli experiences, went on to the Dutch. "In the prison siege at Scheveningen in the autumn of 1974, the Dutch authorities determined to enter one heavily locked door, the only point of access. They waited till they were satisfied the terrorist faction had been lulled into false confidence, then used a laser beam to burn out the lock, while employing massive diversionary noise. That operation was completely successful."

The Prime Minister wanted it over, completed. And the laser idea appealed to him. He talked frequently in public of the need for technological advance. "How soon could we mount an effective attack on the house?" The other men could easily recognize the fear of a long drawn-out bartering for life. Endless negotiations, then government capitulation to the power of the automatic rifle and primed explosives.

Dawson said, "It's well documented that the most favourable time for assault is just before dawn, around four o'clock. Medically this is the time of least resistance, it's when the elderly die. The blood gets colder. And we start with the advantage that these men are extremely tired already. If one is hurt, that puts greater stress on the other, but he, too, must relax at some stage. It could be done as soon as tomorrow morning. But the sooner you attack, the greater the risk. The two men will still be attempting maximum performance. You would be leaving no time to wear them down."

The Prime Minister was close now to decision. "Two questions, Mr. Dawson. Could we obtain the laser by four a.m., and what sort of diversions would you think necessary?"

"Probably we could get a laser from industry, certainly from Imperial College. It does not have to be a particularly sophisticated model. Whether the necessary authorization and personnel could be obtained in the next five hours . . . ? As for the diversions, I would suggest considerable noise for five-minute periods, every twenty minutes or so. Engines revving, sirens, radio chatter. Build it, let it fade, but keep up the pattern all night. They'll be accustomed to it, and when we use the laser, its noise will be covered. It will take about fifteen seconds to open the front door."

120

"You have the authorization, Mr. Dawson. Get the damned thing." The Prime Minister was bubbling now, decision-making, the broth of politics. Facing the Permanent Under Secretary for Defence. "Mr. Harrison, I want the Special Air Service Regiment to assault the house at four a.m. I would be unconcerned if the Arab should not survive the entry."

The police commissioner reacted quickly. "With respect, this is a Metropolitan district, sir. It's a slur—"

"Commissioner," said the Prime Minister coldly, "I am interested in results, not sensibilities. One of the few useful legacies handed down by the Munich police after the Olympics was the certain knowledge that in future all similar operations should be placed squarely in the hands of the military."

And so the messages went out, coded and fast. Thirty-five minutes later, and still short of midnight, the Special Air Service anti-hijack force had been lifted by helicopter from their base camp in Herefordshire. They represented some of the most highly trained and resourceful troops in the British armed forces.

THE spasms in his shoulder came and went with increasing frequency and severity as McCoy moved about the house, but there was much that he had to do. He took the parents upstairs, one at a time, and laid them face down on beds in different rooms. To rip up a sheet into the strips he needed to tie them, he had to use his teeth. The elderly people, separated and horrified, did not resist him, but if they had, one well-placed blow would have won them their freedom. As it was, he left them tied up, threatening each that if he heard a sound, he would kill the lifetime partner.

His strength drained, a rising nausea mingling with the pain, he flopped on the bed in the girl's room. He laid the rifle across his lap, pulled out the grenades and placed them beside him, then resumed hold on the trigger guard of the M1.

Till she followed him into the room she had not seen the wounds, but when he shifted on the bed, seeking comfort that the pain denied him, the bullet holes and the blood were visible.

"Why did you come here? What do you want of us?"

"Time, my little girl. Time for the Arab. This is where I finish.

121

He has the whole course to run. Big Ciaran ensures he starts out ahead of the bastards."

No need to talk to her. Time to think of yourself, Ciaran boy. We held all the cards, he thought, now none of them. He's gone on to his death, and he's taken you with him. McCoy had never thought of death coming like this, not in a room eight by ten with rabbits and daffodils on the wall. But even as pain spirals to hideous levels, the preciousness of life remains hard to pass up. He waved with the rifle barrel for the girl to come closer. "Get some water to clean the wounds." She barely heard the words.

He opened his eyes when she switched on the light and came back with a steaming saucepan. She took off his jacket and shirt. The blood had caked far down his chest. She swabbed the arm, then the shoulder. She felt the skin tighten as she neared the place of the last bullet's entry. She leaned him forward to clean the exit wound in his back and saw only unbroken skin. "It's still in there. It has to come out. It'll kill you."

He nodded, and for the first time she saw him smile.

"All in good time. I want the lad far on his journey before the heavies find it's just wee McCoy that's holding the baby."

"What will they do, the police?"

"I don't know," said McCoy. "I don't know."

CHAPTER TEN

Once the embassy doctor had gone they left David Sokarev alone in his room. The tablet he had been given brought on a drowsiness that conquered the terror. Elkin had hovered, close and maternal, as the doctor bent over his patient, but Sokarev could see that the bodyguard's calm was waning, like a lion that had lost its fellow hunter and with him his assurance. The Englishman should have been there, the one Sokarev had trusted above all others, who had promised to be beside him. "Where is the Englishman, the one who called himself Jimmy?"

"He left in chase," said Elkin. "After Mack was killed. Running the streets, no doubt, trying to pull back something from the chaos. A shambles they made for us." He came close to the bed,

spitting the words in anger. "From now, Professor, there will be no more outsiders making decisions. The Englishman you want made a grand speech about responsibility to Mackowicz. Where is Mackowicz now?"

With the arrival of the Israeli ambassador at that moment, Elkin withdrew to the adjoining room, along with the security attaché and two more men from the embassy that Sokarev had not seen before. They closed the door after them. I'm just a specimen to them, thought Sokarev. To be displayed and shifted when convenient. Not to be consulted. In the minutes before the pill took effect he could hear the raised voices.

THE POINT at issue was simple enough. The movements of Sokarev. Elkin insisted on his immediate return to Tel Aviv. The ambassador, without specific responsibility for Sokarev's safety, required clearance from the foreign ministry in Jerusalem before the visit to New York could be cancelled.

"It is impossible to justify that journey," shouted Elkin. In the Israeli community title counts for little when security is at stake; Elkin could browbeat a senior diplomat in a way unthought of elsewhere. "One of our men has died already. How many more do you want to lose, and for what?"

"For the same reason we came here. We do not bow to threats."

"He is a scientist, not a damned target dummy."

"The decision was made at Cabinet level. We will not be cowed by these people."

"Before, that was a reasonable risk. Not now. That they missed tonight was our luck. Luck, and what Mackowicz did."

There was a purple flush high on the ambassador's cheeks. He turned to the door. "The decision must come from Jerusalem. That is final."

"And what of Sokarev himself? What of his ability to go on?"

But the ambassador and the security attaché were gone. Elkin looked at the two new men, who were to share the room with him, then twisted away lest they should see the tears. A brother to him, Mackowicz. An elder brother. He crumpled on the bed.

The decision from Jerusalem arrived in the embassy

124

communications room within two hours. Decoded, it ordered Sokarev to return on the first available nonstop El Al flight and demanded fullest security, particularly at Heathrow.

ALONE IN the flat in Beersheba, the scientist's wife heard over the radio of the attack on her husband. The information came without warning. In desperation she tried to telephone her son: on operational standby and not available to take messages. Next her daughters: both out of their student hostels and not expected back till later. That she knew her husband to be safe was of some small help. What caused her to sob soundlessly into the darkness of the room was the knowledge of the deep fear he would have suffered. So mild, without enemies, with a voice never raised in anger. Would his work, the implications of the bomb itself—awful, grotesque, multi-destructive—would that have prepared him to confront this vicious obscenity? But it had not been his way to see his work as an article of war. He would not have understood. He had been too long insulated from the world. He would be alone, defenceless. For that she wept.

THE SPECIAL AIR SERVICE squad was brought from the helicopters to Chisholm Road in two Black Maria police vans. Jimmy stood and watched them. The killing squad. Not self-taught as he had been. Taught not to act independently, but in the pack, deadly when the leash was slipped. If they felt excitement, they did not show it, just trooped after their leader to where the Home Office man waited.

William Dawson was a thorough man. He took them through a scale diagram of the house, inside and out, red marking all windows and doors, with blue crosses on those that neighbours reported to be fitted with locks and bolts. Dawson talked, fast and coherent. The attention that the SAS squad gave him was the ultimate accolade—for he was as expert in the planning as they would be in the execution.

When the group broke up, it was to appointed tasks. Four to lay out and load their weapons. Four to scrounge ropes and axes and ladders from the fire brigade. The officer and his sergeant

125

and the chief inspector traversed the front gardens of the houses along the street, working closer to the house that they would storm. When they had studied the front they moved, silent and catlike, across the back garden of another house, till they came without warning on the police who watched the rear of Number 25. From the outside, there was little to tell them of the situation within. All curtains drawn, all windows dark.

"They had a light on for a minute. Upstairs, in the girl's room. The men out front think the curtain there moved when we first started that diversionary noise. We've used the noise three times since then, and nothing's happened." The chief inspector was depressed. The competent hardness of the new arrivals had shaken him. "What chance have you got of getting those people out alive?" he asked the SAS officer as they headed back.

"Can't say. Depends where they all are. What state the wounded fellow is in. If we're fast enough, there's a good chance. As I see the priorities—if we get the family out, that's a bonus. Hitting those two blokes is what we're here for."

Jimmy's eyes had seldom left the house. Its very ordinariness fascinated him. Lived in by people who were unremarkable, undistinguished. And their visitors, they also were mediocrities, without significance—except for the guns and grenades. But that to Jimmy was muscle, the centre core of terrorism, the power that lifted the nonentity onto the pedestal. Behind Jimmy were the Home Secretary and the assistant commissioner, looking solemn. It's the hardware that brings the big men out, too, thought Jimmy. To all of them standing around, McCoy and the Arab were just pictures, two dimensional. Not to Jimmy. Jimmy had seen the character of their faces, the slouch of their movements. And they had seen him. Jimmy had tried to kill them that evening, counted himself unlucky that he hadn't. It tied them together, Jimmy and McCoy and the Arab. Perverse but brutal liaison. There had been the rifle fire and the thrown grenade. So they knew each other, understood the stake.

Jimmy walked across the road to where the SAS captain stood, and showed his identity card. "Jimmy's the name. Security Service. I've been on this one. Full time. Since the flap started.

I'd like to go in with you. I know what they both look like."

The captain smiled. "Sorry, father, no passengers this round."

"Listen," said Jimmy, "don't give me the father crap. I'm in the protection team. Right beside Sokarev, the Israeli, this evening, appointed to guard him."

"You're a touch off course, then. I'd have thought your place was at the hotel holding your baby's hand. Must be looking for a bit of a lullaby after the hoop you put him through."

Cool's going, Jimmy. Like always with these uptight swine. "If it hadn't been for me, he'd be in the morgue. You'll find one of those boys in that house with my bullet in him."

"I don't hand medals out. Right now I'm busy, and no one goes in alongside my team. Understood?"

"You stupid jerk," said Jimmy. It took him some minutes to find Jones. He was in a group among men of equal status, discussing the merits of various electronic surveillance devices. Jimmy was at his side, drawing him away. Jones saw the warning signs, noticed the blink in Jimmy's left eyelid.

Jimmy launched off on the army. "I did you well tonight, and now I want to go in there and finish the thing, and that little army prig treats me like I'm out for some Cook's tour."

"You want to be in at the kill, Jimmy? That's what you want?"

"Right. I started with this one and—"

"It's not a quota job, Jimmy boy."

"You're not going to tell them to count me in?" Jones had always backed him—why different now?

"Of course I'm not. You've had your scene, Jimmy, done well. Now be off home so you're not knackered in the morning."

"I hoped there'd be some bloody clout from you," Jimmy shouted. He swung on his heel and walked through the rope cordon, sidestepped the press and TV people, past the sightseers and on to find a taxi. The tin that he kicked in his fury careered raucously down the road in front of him.

SHE KNEW that if she moved McCoy would wake. It was awkward, lying across the narrow width of the bed, with the weight of his shoulders and head on her stomach. He had told her that they would come with rifles, bullets, bursting through her door. And what would he do then? His rifle was half under his legs, still held close to the trigger guard by the left hand. He'd try to fire. They'd be quicker, organized, without pity. When they came, it would be to kill, not to capture. Norah knew that.

She could not analyse her feelings for Ciaran McCoy. Love was the word written in stories with windswept hills, boys who were dark and tidy, and girls with wasp waists and long hair. Infatuation she understood, real enough, able to match it with her own emotions; the boy last year who worked under father at the factory. Temporary and heartrending . . . nice. But McCoy was something unique for her, surpassing her vocabulary. She could not envisage herself in love with a man capable of such horror. Yet she had lain with him in the grass of the park and taken him in her arms. And he was to die. Snuffed out. Shot dead by the guns of men in uniform.

Norah reached down and felt under her bed for her shoes, careful not to disturb his sleep. Two pairs were there—her evening going-out ones and the flats for work. Farther under was a pile of magazines. She straightened, gently and slowly, till she could ease out the pillow that had nestled in the small of her back. Together they would be sufficient. First the magazines, then the shoes, then the pillow. With one hand she steadied his sleeping head while she wormed her body out from under him. Then there was the space to build the counterfeit lap. When she eased his head onto the softness of the pillow his eyes stayed tight shut.

It was not that she was betraying him, she told herself, but offering him salvation. This way he would survive. On her window sill were the keys he had brought upstairs with him. She took the one for the front door. Past three, she saw on her watch when she went barefoot to the staircase. Pray God he doesn't wake.

FAMY had gone over the wall into the park. He ran till his legs would carry him no farther. Fast, hard, and direct to the southwest. The Irishman's sacrifice clinched his motivation, and he rested only for the leg muscles to tighten before starting once more. When he came to the river he was anxious lest he should miss the bridge

128

marked on his *A to Z* map. But when he had found it he quickened his step.

There were now no more barriers separating him from the airport. Every time an arriving jetliner roared above him on its descent to the tarmac, red and green belly lights flashing the message to the Arab far beneath he knew he was on his course.

IT WAS the policeman crouched in the doorway across the road who first heard the whisper sound of the bolt being withdrawn behind the door at Number 25. He stiffened into an aim position, talking all the time into the radio clipped to his tunic. Within seconds he could hear the scraping of activity, others preparing themselves. The superintendent's voice over the miniature loud-speaker sounded unreal. "If the men come out, shoot. Only if their hands are up and they are obviously not armed do you hold your fire. Even if they have hostages with them, shoot. Under no circumstances are either of the men to reach the darkness."

The door edged open, two inches at first, time for the sweating policeman to ease off the safety clip on the right side of the rifle. He'd only fired in practice, the last time eight months before. Then the door swung back on its hinges, revealing a black rectangle of darkness. They'll all come in a rush, he told himself, the parents and the girl in front, the men behind. And his orders were to shoot. God help us, he thought, his finger tightening around the trigger.

Then he saw the girl come from the shadow and hesitate on the step. Relief surged through him. At least they were not right behind her. It would give him a chance to miss her. Very quietly he broadcast her progress to the front gate. Here again she stopped, and the fifteen rifles that had covered her as she walked forward traversed their aim back to the dark recess of the doorway.

At the control van, and watching through binoculars, the superintendent called into his microphone, "Tell her to get into the middle of the road."

The policeman straightened his legs against the stiffness of his crouch. "Keep walking," he said, staccato with nerves. "Into the street, hands high."

The girl seemed unaware of his presence, simply obeyed the

commands. "There's a rope across the road about a hundred yards down. They'll meet you there. And don't run."

When she reached the rope a host of hands greeted her, lending support. She felt weakness till two detectives frisked her, and she was alive again, backing away from the fingers that ran over her body. "Just formality," said the voice behind her, but close and reassuring, and then there was one arm around her, strong, protective. She made no effort to stem the flow of tears that shook and racked her as they led her to the control van. "Keep it very gentle," the superintendent muttered. "Rush it now and we'll screw it for all time."

They led her into the van and gave her a chair. "It's Norah, isn't it?" the superintendent said kindly. "You have to tell us what's happening."

She smeared her arm across the upper face, diverting the tears, snuffled, and started to talk. "He said you'd attack, and when you came in you'd be shooting. You'll kill, I know you'll kill him. You'll murder him in there." The faces of her listeners were impassive, showing no reaction to what she said. "I couldn't see him die, not like that. He's hurt, there's a terrible wound, blood . . . and he got me to clean it. He's sleeping now, he was when I left him. He's up the stairs, in the small room at the front. It's my room. He's on the bed there. Asleep. He doesn't know I've come. He'd kill me. . . ." The tears came again and her head sank forward on the smallness of her chest.

The superintendent spoke softly, paternal, a voice to be trusted. "Norah, listen, because this is very important if we are to help. You have to tell us where in the house is the other man. The one on your bed is the Irishman; where is the other one, the Arab?"

She wanted to scream her laughter. It was as McCoy had said. He was buying time for his friend. And they didn't know. All these coppers, and McCoy had done them.

"He's been gone a long time," she said. "Right at the start. Just ran through the house. There's only Ciaran. . . ."

"Bloody hell," said the superintendent, kindness evaporating. "And you haven't come to tell us this to save your father and mother, haven't mentioned them. Nor to help the troops who were

130

going to break in, risking their lives. Only thing that matters is that Ciaran gets his treatment. Makes you want to puke."

She was satisfied with herself now. Defiance coming to her.

"So where's the Arab?" Harsher tone, games completed.

"He didn't say. Left hours ago." The last spat out with relish. "Ciaran said the whole thing was to win him time."

"How long have you known him, this McCoy?"

"Two weeks."

"And you knew what he'd done?"

"I knew." And she smiled. Pretty face, the superintendent thought. Stupid, as they all are when they meet their McCoys. Par for the course. He climbed out of the van to begin organizing the manhunt that would get operational at first light.

THE split board on the stairs that Norah's father had so long meant to repair betrayed to Ciaran McCoy the approach of the SAS sergeant. He sat up sharply, a reflex before the agony jolted him down, and simultaneously realized the girl had gone. He felt the pillow and the shoes and the magazines. Confirmation, if he had needed it. There was a whisper from the stairs, then the drumming of feet, the moment of assault. He had a second to decide whether he would raise his gun or submit, but his mind was incapable of thought. When the sergeant came through the door, finger poised on the hair trigger of the Sterling submachine gun, McCoy lay where he had slept, gun barrel prone and offering no threat. That he lived through those first three seconds was due to the sergeant's training, his assessment of the crumpled figure, the barrel that pointed nowhere, the grenades harmless on the bedspread. And then there were others crowding into the bedroom, three and four and five more, standing high over McCoy. They ran their hands over his trousers, checking him for more weapons, and lifted him without violence before ripping the mattress apart. When they laid him down again, it was on the hard coiled springs.

Ciaran watched them as they worked quickly and with thoroughness around the room. End of the road, Ciaran boy, but not the end his imagination had ever entertained. He'd thought they'd shoot. Flattering himself. Couldn't take the great Ciaran alive. Too big just to finish up this way. He didn't care, though. Such exhaustion that you don't give a damn what happens. Just relief that it's completed. And the Arab had had his start, his opportunity to go through it all again, poor bastard.

The captain bent over him. "Get the doctor up here."

Through the door McCoy could hear the voices of Norah's parents, seeking reassurance. Then the arrival of the doctor.

"Make a habit of this caper?" The doctor's hand was on McCoy's pulse, but his eyes took in the healed scar in McCoy's side.

"You can shift him," said the superintendent. "But I don't want him under anaesthetic yet. He's got some talking to do."

The father and mother were on the landing when they carried the stretcher out. McCoy heard the mother, plaintive, appealing. "What's happened to our Norah? What did he do to her?"

You'll find out soon enough. Without the pain he would have laughed. He was still wondering why she had betrayed him, when the stretcher party carried him onto the street. There were television lights there now. Give 'em a show, McCoy. He shouted, "Up the Provos," and the policeman carrying one end of the stretcher jolted it hard, sending the rivers of pain flowing fast and deep. Pigs. Up to the bloody Arab to wipe the victory smile off their faces. And he lost consciousness.

THE FLAT had been empty when he returned to it. Helen not there, and hadn't been. Could hardly blame her, didn't know what time he might have shown up or in what state of tiredness. At least he wouldn't have to tell her about the car. Pride and joy . . . and up in smoke.

Jimmy unscrewed the top of the bottle, cheap brand. About an inch to start with, four gulps, blazed a trail through his guts. Sagged in the chair, loosened his collar, then reached for the first refill. So tired, wanted to shut it all out. Jones pulling his rank. It should have been your day, Jimmy, and sent home early.

At first the telephone was simply an accompaniment to his thoughts. It took time for it to communicate urgency, and even then he deliberated whether to answer, but discipline won.

"It's Jones here, Jimmy. It's all over down at this end."

"Congratulations." The word was slow coming.

"It's not like that, Jimmy. We have McCoy, but the Arab's gone. He's loose."

"Not so bright, then. Which of the clever brigade let him slip?"

"He went when you were there, so cut the quips."

"I was all on my own, wasn't I? Can't be round the whole house. He didn't come through the front." Bloody buck passers.

"No one's criticizing you, Jimmy. It's simple fact. He's loose, with five hours' start. We're keeping the surgeons off McCoy till he tells us what the Arab is at. Get to the hospital. Now."

"You've got others who can go and do it."

"Jimmy, stop waffling. The Yard's there. I'm on my way. I've sent a car for you. Put your head under the tap and be at your door in ten minutes. I want you to talk to McCoy."

Jimmy knew why he had been called. Just like Jones, the way his mind worked. Who'd be on the same wavelength as this Irishman? Not a copper, no bright lad from intelligence, not old Jonesey himself. Another thug. Put them together, two rats, both hungry, in the same hole. Two roaches disputing the one patch.

JIMMY sat up, breaking his catnap as the car drove through the wide gateway and into the hospital forecourt. Time now to regret the whisky. Head spinning, uncontrollable circles. The half-light was beginning to simper through, and the nineteenth-century buildings were heavily outlined against the dawn. He saw the police van as the car pulled up. Jones was waiting for him. He saw Jimmy's appearance and winced.

"We don't have long. The surgeons are impatient. Want to get their hands on him. Police haven't had anything out of him. Laughs at them. He's weak, but should survive. Reckons he's the cat's whiskers, probably the morphine." Jones led the way through the corridors, up the stairs to the first floor, and towards the ward entrance to their right.

Jones said, "Fifteen minutes maximum. You and me, I'll take the notes. Just get him talking."

There was a nurse sitting at McCoy's feet, waiting to remove a thermometer from his mouth, when Jones and Jimmy went into

133

the small private room. After she had written down the results on his clipboard she moved into the corridor. The detective who had been sitting in the room followed her. Jimmy sat on the end of the bed, Jones in the vacated chair.

Picking at his nose, Jimmy said, "My name's Jimmy. I'm here till we've finished with you. Not until we've chatted do you get patched up. Ten minutes, ten hours, ten days . . ."

"That's not what the doctor . . ." McCoy spoke faintly.

"The medics come back in here when we say so, McCoy. We've all the time in the world. You haven't."

McCoy turned his head fractionally towards Jimmy, so that he could see into the eyes, grey-blue and pitiless. There was a man like that in Armagh City, came to do the executions.

"I know about the bullet that's in you. I fired it. Not a good shot, should have killed you. Was ahead of you all yesterday. You gave me a good clear shot while you stood on the pavement. Pathetic stuff, McCoy, and you supposed to be a bloody expert. Short of men on your side of the water, are they?"

Good stuff, Jimmy boy, thought Jones. Kicking his vanity.

"Wasn't me on the gun."

"Course it wasn't you on the gun. That was the sharp end, wasn't it? Left the man's bit to the kiddie, did you?"

"Famy wanted to shoot, that's what he came for."

Jones started to write. A name at last to put to the face. And now they had it, not really important. They needed the face itself.

"He's worse than you, and that's useless." Jimmy's voice was casual. McCoy could follow the technique but was too tired, too hurt, to combat his adversary.

"He's not finished, the boy."

"Only because he's running."

"He'll bloody show you, you Britisher pig." The Irishman was struggling to shout. "He's not finished. What do you think I stayed behind for? To give him time. He's set to blast you, you and the Yiddisher."

Jimmy laughed, loud, ridiculing. "He'll never see him."

"He'll see him and he'll get him. You can't keep him close all the time. He'll have to put his feet on the ground. . . ."

134

"There's only one place."

"Right," hissed McCoy. Jimmy could see him quivering, chest shaking, in the emotion of the dispute.

"The airport. Up the steps the little man goes and your hero makes his last stand," Jimmy gabbled, maintaining the momentum.

McCoy was with him. "Right, right first bloody time."

Jimmy said nothing. Sudden, total silence.

McCoy's eyes closed tight shut. The enormity of what he'd said, slow in dawning, then overwhelming. Betrayed him. Ciaran McCoy, officer of the Irish Republican Army, had betrayed him.

"Holy Mother of Jesus, forgive me." McCoy's lips barely moved. In his life he had never known such abject misery.

Jimmy walked towards the door, Jones a pace behind him. He said, matter-of-fact, "The surgeon gave us fifteen minutes, we've four and a half to spare. So it's over to his tender hands now. Hope the knife's blunt."

THE pale shiver of light was spreading as Famy came to the outer perimeter of Heathrow. Now that he was alone, new confidence held him, helped by the new clothes—blue jeans and a pale green shirt—that a housewife had left out for the night on the garden line. A bonus for Famy that rendered obsolete the police description.

Famy recognized the danger of moving too far inside the airport before he had solidified the cover that he would need later. The details of it he had figured out as he ran. He must be ready when the first El Al landed. Surely they would send Sokarev home on the first flight. Easy to know, once he was there. Just be patient and observe—watch for the hard-faced security men who would tell him the quarry was close.

In the camps they would be waking now. In the tents, set among the scrub and the rocks his colleagues in arms would have passed a night dreaming of an opportunity such as he had been given. The new day would be coming over the camp. And in Beersheba the Jews would be waking, too. All would say his name when the next evening came. Some with adulation, some with detestation. The blow he was prepared to strike would shatter the

135

complacence of many millions, and to those who lived on the far side of the wire and the mine fields and who longed to cross over, he would bring hope and aspiration. There was a pounding of excitement, close to purest happiness.

Back in Lebanon they had told him about the tunnel that led into the heart of the airport complex, showed him photographs, pointing out the footpath that ran its length, separate from the vehicle road. If there was security, that path could be guarded too easily. He saw the bus queue not far outside the entry tunnel, a straggled line of brown-faced Indians in turbans and saris, many carrying bags that contained their working overalls, bags very like his own. Infiltrate where you will not be noticed, that is what they had told him; it is a time for camouflage.

Joining the bus queue, he appeared as one more from the ranks of the thousands of immigrant workers, the lifeblood of the airport, on his way to another day at work, washing, sweeping, cleaning. The bus would take him to the central terminals. He must look there for the canteens and rest rooms where the workers gathered for their breaks. He must look for a man whose job, appearance and identity card would give him the passport to the tarmac where the jet would refuel and reload.

One man, one man from so many who would be there, one alone was necessary.

FAMY followed the workers as they left the bus stop. The stream took him to the opened double doors of the red brick building surmounted by the octagonal control tower. There were signs beside the entrance, CANTEEN and ADMITTANCE TO STAFF ONLY, but no security checks.

There was no fear in Famy, not now that he was without the Irishman. And confidence is of critical value to the assassin. The killer has to believe in his prowess as in his God-given right to exact retribution. Those who saw the unfamiliar face sitting at the clothless cafeteria table by the window would have noted the great contentment on his features. He was now a more dangerous figure than at any time since he had landed in England. He had come to terms with his mission. He was ready to kill.

ALONG THE Great West Road leading towards London from Windsor huge queues of traffic formed up behind the military convoy. Alpha, Bravo and Headquarters Company. Grenadier Guards, trucks, Land-Rovers, Saladin and Saracen armoured cars. Four hundred men in all. Rifles, general-purpose machine guns, rocket launchers. There to protect one man from the hands of an equally solitary threat.

Police reinforcements were being mobilized from divisional forces in the Metropolitan area and from the Thames Valley. By nine in the morning the perimeter of the airport would be sealed, the concourses under guard, the tarmac patrolled. The Prime Minister had rubber-stamped the operation. Box the Arab out, deny him any chink of light, any opportunity to attack.

THROUGH the window Famy saw the deploying. It amused him. One against so many. So much rallied against him. No one to share the glory moment with him. After a while he became tired of watching the crisscross motions of the enemy, ordered a fresh cup of coffee and a cheese sandwich.

The sights beyond the window had fanned his confidence.

From the next table he took a discarded newspaper and read a version of the previous night's events. McCoy, though injured, would live. Famy was "fleeing", "probably on drugs", "a fanatic". The public was told to phone the police if he was sighted. That they did not understand raged through him. There is no word of Palestine, no word of the bomb, no word of the camps and the suffering. Why do they think we are prepared to die? Stupid goats, do we enjoy death? Can there be no sanity in what we do? Can we never be right, justified? And then his rage eased. In the centre pages was a photograph of David Sokarev. More recent, more detailed than the snapshot he'd seen in Lebanon. Now he could study the face. This time recognition must be instinctive. He will be hurrying, and there will be men around him.

He would know him. However fast he went, he would know him.

THE ALCOHOL that he had drunk in the small hours needed greater time to disperse through the bloodstream than Jimmy had

137

permitted. Splitting headache, wanted just to fold up, but no, he had to be with Sokarev. Back on course, taking orders again.

The Special Branch man in the hotel foyer nodded a greeting and described Jimmy's passage into the lift over a small radio transmitter. On the fourth floor, he was met by a man he had not seen before, who blocked his way. Jimmy fumbled for his card. The detective was clean-shirted, shaved, dressed for work. Jimmy found the card, the policeman examined it and allowed him through. Men outside the doors of the two rooms repeated the routine. Bloody coppers.

Elkin's greeting was cool. "We have taken charge. Any plan will be approved by us. After last night we make the decisions."

Hadn't expected the assault that fast. "You'll make the decisions when you're on that blinking aircraft."

"We left it to you, and it was a fiasco."

"You'll be told what's going to happen, and if you don't like it, you can walk to the airport." When Jimmy shouted, the sledge-hammer reverberated in his skull. All so childish. "Calm yourself down, will you." He spoke like a man who wants to end a domestic row. "Did you sleep last night?"

Elkin shook his head. Been in tears, Jimmy saw.

"We have the Irishman. The other one fancies himself at the airport when your man goes out this afternoon. Be out of his depth. They're working out our route. You should put your head down till we get it."

Elkin walked back to his bed, sat on it heavily. Jimmy recognized he would struggle to stay awake and lose. Poor fool, doesn't trust us, and why should he? Jimmy took off his jacket, lifted the pistol from the shoulder holster, and pressed it into the waist of his trousers before falling into a brocade-covered armchair.

Beyond the partition door David Sokarev, too, was asleep. For some reason Jimmy got up, turned the door handle, giving himself a few inches of vision. Dead to the world, blanked out. Pray the drug keeps him there. Cushion him from the carry-on. A weak face he had, unprotected.

By late afternoon Sokarev would be gone—and Jimmy boy would be back with his girl. But he'd be in lousy shape.

138

FAMY had studied the men who came into the canteen through the morning. It was nearly noon when he finally saw the man he wanted. Indian, a little below six feet, slender, early twenties. A turban, good because it distracted from the features. White overalls specked with oil spots, and with British Airways emblazoned across the chest. Maintenance. A man who worked on the engines when the aircraft were on the tarmac, on the big concrete open spaces. Access dominated Famy's thinking. The need to find an identity that ensured access to areas denied civilians.

Famy left his table and, holding his bag, moved across the floor of the canteen towards where the Sikh sat, solitary, unaware.

AS HIS CAR drove away from the cul-de-sac of Downing Street, the Israeli ambassador's acute concern was defused. He had taken his security attaché with him to the meeting with the British Prime Minister, but had left him outside the heavy oak personal office. "The Prime Minister put it to me," said the ambassador to his companion, "that his government could in no way be accused of dragging their heels on this matter. I cannot counter that. It was on his own order that the assault was prepared on the house the terrorists held and that the safety of the hostages was put at secondary priority. It is true also that they have been fast with the interrogation of the man they hold. They tell me that the Arab will attempt a final attack at the airport."

The security attaché was unconcerned with diplomatic innuendo. "What are their plans for the airport?" he asked.

"They have moved around a thousand men from their security forces, army and police to Heathrow. The Arab is in possession of an M1 carbine, with a maximum effective range of three hundred metres. Therefore they will put a cordon around the jetliner with a radius of four hundred metres. There will be no admittance inside that area other than for vetted personnel, our own people, and the security men. The plane will already be loaded when Sokarev boards—"

"How is he transferred to the airport?"

"By motor convoy. They maintain that it would be impossible for the Arab to know which of the many points of entry to

Heathrow they will use. Then, their hope is that the demonstration of force will deter the man, and Professor Sokarev will be safely in the air. After that they will concentrate on his capture."

"Again, we are not consulted." The attaché spoke evenly.

"They have consulted me."

"You are not expert enough to recognize flaws in the plan."

"That is offensive. Where are the flaws that your experience warns you of?" Knife-edge sarcasm from the ambassador.

"How can I tell without having seen the plans? Discussing alternatives, being told of contingency fallbacks."

The ambassador was silent, thoughtful of the way he had committed himself so few minutes earlier. Career, future, promotion to permanent position in the ministry in Jerusalem—all might rest on the agreement he had made with the Prime Minister. The attaché, too, was silent. He had made his point. They would do their best, the British. Only they were not experts. The Israelis alone were experts in the new science of counter-terrorism. Proud of their integrity, determined to make their own decisions. And mistakes. So there had been no talk of decoys or helicopters or military aircraft. Do they comprehend the resourcefulness of the assassin who is prepared to die to reach his target? He doubted it, and the belief tightened the muscles of his belly.

MOHAN SINGH was happy at the other man's company. It was rare for him to have conversation during his early lunch break. The stranger listened to his problems, to the description of his family—his wife and three small children—and how they lived in two rooms of an uncle's house. He was not aware as he talked that the man spoke little, just nodded and smiled.

There was not long, Famy knew that. How many minutes before the Indian returned to work? Famy went up to the counter and collected two more coffees. He set the cups down and inclined his head to the Sikh. He had no feeling about the clear, ice-water knowledge that he would kill this man. McCoy would have done it better, but McCoy had made the sacrifice, and he must fulfil his trust.

The man stood up. "I must return to work. It has—"

140

Famy interrupted. "You will show me the lavatory first?"

"I will. It is difficult to find if one is new."

They walked together down the corridor, around two corners, and they came to the door. "It is here." The Indian smiled, would have walked away, but Famy spoke quickly, at the same time moving inside the door. "I would like to see you again. Where could we meet?" And Mohan Singh followed him, answering, but Famy was not listening, was taking in the layout. There was a man in one cubicle. He would surely be gone in a moment.

At the washbasin, the water running loud, Famy said over his shoulder, "Wait a minute." When in the mirror he saw the man move out of the door, he swept the water from his hands and spun to face the Indian. His forearm, swung from far back, hit the man's Adam's apple. A gurgling, choking moment of protest. Surprise in the eyes before the collapse.

Famy pulled him, limp now and unprotesting, into the farthest cubicle. Not dead yet, but had to be killed, silenced. He worked the shape so that the head faced inward and he had room to close the door. ENGAGED, the catch would say to any who came.

He raised the Indian's head, took the turban from it, placed it carefully on the door hook. Particular not to disarrange it, aware that he would not know how to rebind it. Then unzipped the overalls and pulled them off. Neither overalls nor turban must be defiled if they were to serve his purpose. And now he was ready. A fearful clarity, in slow, stopped motion. Lifted the head again and with all the force in his shoulders slammed it down, once, twice, three times, on the hard white rim of the bowl. Crude, irreversible damage was what he sought. And achieved.

He left the body, kneeling with the head deep in the bowl, having wiped the blood from his hands on the Indian's undershirt. In the breast pocket of the overalls he found the plastic-coated identity card, read the name of the man he had executed in the cause of Palestine. Three minutes later, wearing the overalls, he climbed up over the divider into the next cubicle and hurried across to the washbasins. He scrubbed his hands in liquid soap, checked in the mirror that the turban was straight, and picked up his bag from where he had left it under the basins.

141

Out in the corridor, Famy glanced at his watch. The first El Al jet should land soon. Then about an hour for refuelling. He had far to go, each step more hazardous than the last. He had taken the irrevocable step. Had killed for the first time with his own strength, his own will.

The turban felt strange on his head, a constricting mark of an identity that he could not fully take over. The baggy overalls were right, masking the rifle, its barrel now pinioned downward in the belt at the front of his trousers. One piece of advice he had been given: secrete a barrelled weapon in the very front of your body. The hands always search at the sides. The grenades would have been harder to dispose of on his person had the Indian not carried a small lunch box in the deep pocket of his trousers. The V 40s wrapped well in the greaseproof paper that the nameless wife had packaged around her man's food.

Famy walked boldly towards the security checkpoint between the two giant structures that formed Terminal Three—Departures to right, Arrivals to left—and straight ahead the pendulum bar, with its red-and-white message, large and decisive: STOP. Beyond was the inner realm that he had to join, loaders and mechanics and airline personnel, passengers excluded. A security man operated the bar from a glass-cased booth at the side.

There were several soldiers beside the barrier itself, relaxed, confident of their firepower. A single man was the risk. They had his picture in their minds, the description of his clothes. An Indian in British Airways livery in no way fitted the requirement for vigilance. They looked in the bag, but cursorily, and laughed when he asked in a voice, high-pitched by nerves, but which they took to be the flavour of his homeland, whether he should remove his turban. As they waved him through he shouted, "Good luck."

Their smiles turned to sneers. A thousand against one. So who needed luck?

They had told him back at the camp that the El Al would always come to rest at a place removed from the other aircraft. Gate 7 area, they had said. The soldiers to his front and an armoured car, awaiting an arrival, confirmed the information. He praised their thoroughness. This was where Sokarev would come. As he crossed beyond Gate 6 area, clogged with its quota of Jumbo 747s, more of the reception group came into his view. Police, soldiers, dogs, more armoured cars. Mounted machine guns silhouetted against the sky. Firing power, hitting power, killing power. All there for Abdel-El-Famy. Men did not see another day break when they were struck by this force and velocity. The M1, pressed against his groin, was unequal to the weapons now arrayed in front of him. So easy in the dry heat of the camp to talk of war and to wave the farewells to the men who went without hope of return. But what war is this? In a foreign, alien, hateful world. A war with only one victory, consummated only with the death of Sokarev. And if towards that victory Famy dies, erased without trace, if the big rifles take him . . . not important. Forgotten. As if he had never been. But in the camp, would they not care there? Only from success can the martyrdom come. As in a dream he walked. Why, knowing the forfeit, did we strive so willingly to be remembered? Why, when we know we will be dust, do we seek so hard to be recalled in our friends' minds and in their voices? Famy did not know. Yearned only to be mourned. But for him to be remembered with tears, Sokarev must die. Only then would they weep for him.

"Where the hell do you think you're going?" Strident, breaking in through his fantasies. "Look where you're bloody going."

Famy was rigid. Discovery, disaster. The forklift was five feet away from him, directly in his path. "I'm sorry," he stuttered.

"Not half you won't be sorry, not if this lot runs over you."

"I was watching the soldiers." Famy was recovering. "It will be a big show, all the security things, when the Israeli comes."

"Not here it won't. They won't put him on here. They're not fools. Load up here, taxi onto 28L, across to the VIP suite, lift him on, and up, up and away."

"I didn't know there was a VIP area there." Fishing, Famy.

"The new one. The one the old girl uses when she's off to Balmoral, or where they put Kissinger down, right beside Cargo."

"I'm sorry I was in your way." Famy smiled and turned to walk towards a British Airways plane near Gate 6.

A fleet of trucks hovered under the fuselage belly. He could get a lift from one of them. Say he was urgently required at Cargo.

CHAPTER ELEVEN

Jimmy was aroused from a fleeting moment of sleep by the sound of Jones's voice. Elkin, Jones and the security attaché were examining a sheaf of typewritten sheets.

Jones acknowledged him. Not with warmth, just recognition. Accepts he needs me today, tomorrow'll be ditching time. Quick handshake it'll be, then don't show your face till the next bit of filth needs scooping off the carpet. "Why didn't you wake me up?"

"It's all arranged, Jimmy," Jones said.

Means he thinks it's a piece of cake from now on, all sewn up and can't go wrong. "What's my part in this show?"

"You travel with him to the airport. Hold his hand all the way, into his seat belt. Last thing before they shut up shop, you vamoose down the ramp. Very simple."

"Where's he going from?"

"South side, the VIP area."

"What news of Famy . . . ?"

Jones was not pleased at being spoken to with such lack of deference in front of foreigners. "No word. But the airport's sealed. Troops, police, armour—no need for you to be worried."

"It's not me that's worried. Not my job that hangs on knowing where the little runt is."

THOUSANDS of men work at the Heathrow Cargo Terminal. The presence of an alien in their midst would not be noticed. Famy squatted on his bag in the sunshine in front of a big British Airways shed. He spoke to no one, nor received a word of inquiry. Troops surrounded the white wooden fence that shielded the VIP lounge from his sight. He had to blink in the heat haze to hold his concentration on the gleaming El Al jet near Gate 7. He could make out the armoured cars, and occasionally the figures of the soldiers around them would press into focus. The rifle worried against his body. It would continue to hurt for many minutes before the plane would be ready to take Sokarev on board. He felt a curious calm now. The desire to fantasize was conquered. Awaiting the inevitability of the rendezvous.

SOKAREV was past complaining as they led him out through the kitchens of the hotel. Five men shared the back of the van with him. The security attaché, Jones, Elkin, the Special Branch convoy coordinator and Jimmy. They all ignored him. As if I am in some way culpable, to blame for what has happened, thought Sokarev. He was tired, and he recognized that they, too, were tired; it was in their faces, their clothes, the way they snapped at each other. The equation had often been proved for him in the work at Dimona; tired men operate at reduced efficiency, and that frightened him. He felt a shortness of breath and searched for air, loosening his collar and slipping off his suit jacket. All the ventilation slats in the van were closed. He would have liked one open, but did not feel the authority to ask for it. Instead, he sat and suffered, till he felt a shiver in his limbs, a feeling of cold and sickness. There was nobody to tell.

In the yard of Hammersmith police station he was transferred to a car. There were escorts front and back, but nothing for a casual observer to recognize. Sokarev felt a tug at his sleeve.

"Don't take too much notice of those characters," Jimmy said. "They're all as scared as you are."

FAMY'S whole being was riveted to the movement of the big jet. Three hundred and fifty tons of it, making its solemn progress along the runway, accompanied by two Saracen armoured cars. He could see the small cockpit windows, high above the ground, where the El Al pilot and his crew were sitting. All of them able to see him, but not capable of recognizing their enemy. . . .

The plane was waved inside the cordon of soldiers. More armoured cars were awaiting it, policemen beginning to scurry. The soldiers faced out of their arc, stern-eyed now, keyed, expectant. The nearest was barely twenty feet from Famy. Corporal. Two black V stripes on his tunic arm; self-loading rifle. Famy saw his finger on the lip of the trigger guard, a second's movement and the gun was armed, deadly. And his position, the square of concrete on which he stood, made him Famy's opponent. As inconsequential as that, where a man placed his feet. That decided whether he would kill or be killed.

145

Beyond the cordon of soldiers the company commander saw a line of civilian trucks and cars and lorries held back a quarter of a mile from the plane. Have to wait till the show was over. No non-involved persons inside his line, perfect field of fire around three sixty degrees. Just about perfect, anyway. Only the corner hangar of British Airways cargo complex jutting in and breaking the geometry of his protective circle. Saw the loaders, sitting and watching. Shouldn't have been there, but the corporal dominated them. No need to make a scene, have them shifted. Saw the turban, creased and clean. It stood out in the light, the sun playing on it.

He turned towards the VIP suite and waited for the convoy.

THE CARS CAME fast down the inner perimeter road, motorcycles in front, and all oncoming traffic blocked far ahead.

Jimmy said, "Just about there now, sir. The car goes right up to the steps and you're to be straight onto them. Don't stop. Don't hesitate. Inside, don't look out of the windows, just get into the seat. They're not going to hang about, you'll be straight off."

Sokarev did not reply. Jimmy could see the nerves on his aging face, lips clamped together, breathing coming in irregular sucked heaves. Poor bugger, may have to carry him on.

The convoy swept past the VIP lounge to the fence. The cars S-patterned through the gap in the fencing and raced towards the jet. Amid the protest of the tyres, Jones found himself reflecting at the very vulgarity of it all. No dignity in the moment. Just a game for grownups. But only Sokarev has to play on the field. The plane was huge now, in its silver closeness. And the steps were there, in position, waiting.

THE STIFFENING of the soldiers telegraphed the arrival to Famy. His right hand ferreted down inside the overalls for the safety mechanism of the M1. Already cocked, a bullet nestled in the firing chamber. A hundred yards to the steps. Take him twelve, thirteen seconds. Over everything was a devastating simplicity. When the cars come into sight, start running. Fast, but weaving, and the shot when the man was at the base of the steps. Bank on chaos. However much they have prepared for you, they will never

146

quite have expected the presence, that was what the men had told him in the camp. Confusion, they said, is your greatest weapon.

Three cars snouting around the corner. Famy was on his feet, pulling the zip fastener down the length of his chest. The corporal was barely aware of the action that produced the rifle, before the bullet hit him low in the stomach, throwing him back from the path of Famy's sprint.

As if in slow motion, the doors of the car were opening, men in their suits jumping out. Unaware! The insane exhilaration of the achievement of surprise. Run, weave and duck, maintain the rhythm, give no one the clear sight. When do the bullets come? How long? The bundle in grey, half out of the car, helped by the darker suits, reluctant, impeding them. The first bullet spat at Famy's feet. Idiots, firing low. Halfway there. Sokarev in sight, his head clear. More bullets now, edging closer. And the ranging blast, wide but creeping, of the big machine gun. Sokarev near the steps, wrestling with the men around him. The moment to shoot.

In full stride Famy flung himself, arching forward onto the tarmac. His knees and elbows took the impact. The gun was at his eye, down the V sight, down the needle sight. Eyes smarting, the pain from the fall. The man in grey still struggling. He fired. Knew with that deadening instinct that he was wide, knew it as he heard the empty clatter of the discarded shell case. A moment of silence, breathtaking, then again the machine gun.

No more to see of Sokarev. Everything still in front of him, no man standing. Gone, all of them, at a stroke. At the steps no target.

Four in a burst they teach the soldiers to fire when they feed the belt into the machine gun. One in the right foot, two in the calf, fourth in his hip. Now it was as if a man with a pickaxe was striking him. Not aiming at a rock face but at the delicacy of his flesh. But there was nothing in his hands, only the flat oil-smeared concrete for his fingers to grasp at. The rifle was far to the front, pitched clear beyond reach, beyond his chances of hope and salvation.

In the distance came the shout of command to the soldiers, and to his ears the words echoed and had a strange quality.

"Stop firing."

BETWEEN them Jones and Elkin carried Sokarev up the steps to the plane, the strength he'd summoned to resist now absent.

Jimmy rose from his knees, where he had taken cover in front of the scientist between the steps and the car, and began to walk towards Famy. All the time in the world, the end of the stampede. Around him, soldiers were lifting themselves from firing positions, uncertain what to do. Uneasy in the sudden silence. So many of them, and only this one in contention.

He saw the eyes of the prone man still locked on his M1, tantalizing, out of range. Jimmy swung his foot and kicked it into the middle distance.

"Good try, boy," he said, a private remark. Famy watched him, face unmarked. "Good try. McCoy told us you'd be here. We didn't think you'd get this far. One shot you got off, way off target. Should have been an aimed shot, boy. Never works, all the running around, not with a popgun like that, anyway."

He saw Famy's mouth moving, but there was no sound.

"That's what they gave you, the M1? Not very suitable. Would have liked something with a bit more guts, right, boy?"

Famy nodded agreement. As far around as his eyes could see, the men were now advancing on him. Jimmy put his hand in his pocket, and when it emerged, the PPK was there. He saw Famy try to squirm away, but he was pinioned by the damage to his legs and his hip.

"Don't make it difficult, boy. You knew what it was all about when you came on the joyride. Did well, considering."

Jimmy fired into the centre of the pale brown forehead. Even with a moving target he was usually accurate.

The noise of the shot was drowned by the fan jets of the 747.

FROM beside the car, Jones had watched it. He'd seen the pistol in Jimmy's hand, hadn't looked after that, unable to face the inevitable. The plane was turning, its power rising in ear-blasting crescendo.

"Bloody good job, the way it should be every time," said the Special Branch man, whose eyes had never wavered from Jimmy. Jones bit on his lip, unable to speak his mind, out of step with the mood.

148

Jimmy walking towards him now, a grin of satisfaction wreathing the mouth. Cat with the cream. Well, they'd had their money's worth out of Jimmy boy this time, thought Jones. Earned his retainer, hadn't he? Knifing through his mind the continuous thought. It was what they'd asked for, those politicians with their directives from on high, and they'd been gratified.

JUST BEFORE THE moment of lift-off, Sokarev whispered, straining to Elkin's ear, that he felt sick.

"Don't worry," Elkin said. "It's finished now. We are going home. There is no more to fear." He noted the pallor of the scientist, the perspiration on his head, the way he struggled to reach up to direct the cold-air nozzles towards his face. When they were airborne it would be easier. He told himself that, and settled into the comfort of his seat.

CHAPTER TWELVE

At first the pains were slight, and concentrated in the centre of his chest. Nausea was uppermost. As Elkin slept beside him, Sokarev was able to worm a path over his legs to the lavatory. His retching was painful and hard. By the time the plane was over France the pain was intense and spreading, and still Elkin was insensible. When at last a stewardess noticed Sokarev's distress, he was doubled in his seat. Over the speaker the chief steward called for a doctor.

Elkin stood in the aisle, unable to offer aid to the man he had been ordered to protect, praying there was a doctor. A young man in a T-shirt came through from tourist class and reached low over the heaving form of Sokarev, now stretched across two seats. When he stood up he spoke with concern. "He is subject to severe coronary attack. Has he been under some strain?"

"He is David Sokarev."

"I don't know the name. I've not been in Israel for some weeks."

"He is the one the Arabs were trying to kill. The reason for all the troops at Heathrow. He has been under severe strain."

"He needs morphine," said the doctor. "And I do not carry it with me."

149

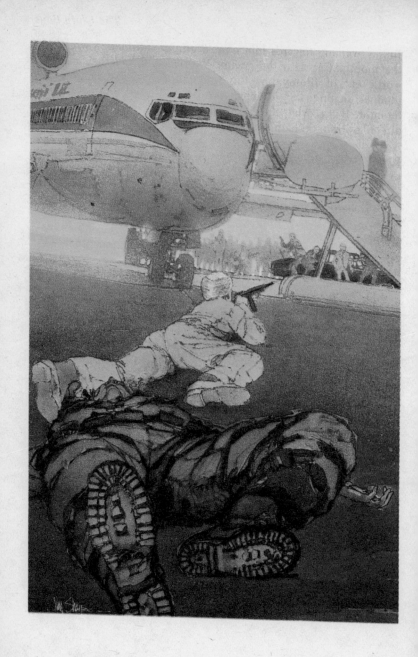

"Call the captain," Elkin said. "Get him here."

The pilot, mid-forties, shirt sleeves, grey hair, a decision maker. "We go for Ben Gurion airport. Beirut is out, obviously. The plane is too big for Cyprus. Athens would save only minutes and the facilities at home are superior. We have less than an hour. The necessary people will be waiting."

The doctor bent once again over Sokarev. "He is overweight, an old man. Not fit. Not equipped to take such turmoil. The bastards always hit when they aren't expected."

Elkin could not reason why he spoke. There was no need, but he replied. "We expected an attack. He did, too."

"And you took him. Knowingly. At his age, in his condition."

"A decision had been taken."

"There is no wound on him. Remember that. If he dies, you and your people will have to know who killed him."

There was darkness around the jet as it whispered its way, ten miles every minute, towards Israel.

"THE PRIME MINISTER is calling, sir." With resignation the Director General of the Security Service raised the phone. As he had predicted to himself, the Prime Minister was furious. Voice raised.

"It was turned into a clear fiasco by your man."

"In what way, sir?" Don't give an inch. No apology, don't make it easy for the inquiry. They'd be taping this.

"In what way? Because of what your fellow did on the tarmac. Right out there, with half the world looking on."

"Please explain, sir." Let the heat cool, then counterattack.

"Don't play the fool with me. Your man executed—only word for it—this Palestinian right out there, in public."

"Your instruction was quite clear, sir. You did not expect the Arab to survive our contact with him." Get that on tape.

"I didn't expect him killed like that, not like—"

"He had live grenades on him. His hands were moving."

"You're justifying your man?"

"His target was still armed and dangerous. My operative made a quick and correct decision. More lives could have been lost."

"It makes our position fearfully difficult." Always the same with

151

these damned politicians. Can't take it on the chin. "It could have very grave repercussions."

"Our man would have felt that the actual danger confronting him was of paramount importance when compared with possible diplomatic repercussions."

Abruptly and without further comment the Prime Minister rang off. The Director General dialled Jones's extension.

LONG INTO THE EVENING Jones sat at his desk. Helen had left, red-eyed, aware of the conversation he had had with Jimmy.

Damn, effing waste, a man like that getting the chop. Awkward bastard, couldn't deny that, and bloody-minded when he wanted to be, but not just now. Had gone with his own dignity, hadn't made a fuss, just accepted it and disappeared to the basement to check his gun in. Typical of the way the department exists. DG couldn't do it himself, had to get a minion to do the dirty work. Told him what the PM wanted, and he'd done it. Jimmy on the scrap heap and the best man they had.

Didn't any of the stupid bastards understand the new warfare? No rules governed this combat. Have to fight the McCoys and Famys with their own kind. He'd never see Jimmy again. Wouldn't be the way of the department for him to have further contact with a man he'd fired. Went back a long way, lot of years, late nights, talk and togetherness. Now all screwed up because of a little swine from a place called Palestine that doesn't exist.

THE IRISHMAN lay frighteningly still on the crisp white bed-clothes. The words were slow in coming, spoken faintly to the detective who sat watch. "Did he make it?"

"He tried and he didn't make it. Shot a soldier, fired on the Israeli. Missed. He's dead now, they shot him on the tarmac." From the bed there was a deep, heaved sigh, then only regular, drug-controlled breathing. McCoy said nothing more.

Through the haze of images there was a certain hard-won precision. Of how the news would spread from Cullyhanna to Cross-maglen, of what the men would say as they nestled in the bracken

152

and waited with their Armalites. And he felt against the clamminess of his arms the white tiles of the cell walls that would be his. There would be bars and heavy doors, and he would slowly rot away, and pray each night for the mercy of sleep.

THERE WAS much noise in the pub, and the swill of beer before closing would soon be under way. There was talk of the day's affairs, but not the usual, not of inflation, not of sport. Attention was gripped by the events at the airport. The picture by the agency man with his telephoto lens had made the final editions of the London papers. The figure on the ground and the man above him with the gun were recognizable enough. Art department had helped with the gun. Justified the headline: EXECUTION.

Jimmy sat in the far corner, solitary at a table, now on his fifth double. He was slumped low with his head close to the glass, watching the stillness of the amber liquid. No bitterness. Just a sense of regret. Ending of an institution.

The barman rang the ship's bell. "Last orders, gentlemen."

Jimmy was on his feet, thrusting forward his glass with the rest of the throng, the BBC news rising above the shouting and demanding. Heard the words, "Sokarev. Heart attack."

"Shut up," Jimmy yelled. "Shut your faces." And a score of faces were turned on him, saw the power of his eyes, of his shoulders.

"An hour after Professor Sokarev had been admitted to intensive care in a Tel Aviv hospital, it was announced that efforts to save his life had failed. The professor, aged fifty-three, was one of his country's principal nuclear scientists. In London, Scotland Yard still has no information on the security man who shot dead an Arab terrorist after the unsuccessful attempt on Professor Sokarev's life at Heathrow this afternoon. But our political editor reports that government ministers are demanding disciplinary action against . . ."

His deep, raucous, baying laughter shook the bar. Laughed till it hurt in his guts, till the pain came to his chest. Cheated us all, Dr. Sokarev, sir. Denied the satisfaction to Famy and McCoy. Ruined our side's triumph. And you, Jimmy boy. He screwed you,

153

too. After all that heartache, all the pain. Screwed everyone. The whole lot of us. Both sides.

Slowly, Jimmy made his way out of the pub, and hiccups were intermingled with his laughter.

FAILURE had been a familiar bedfellow. So many missions launched with high expectation, and rarely the wounding blow that they sought. The leader of the General Command had been brought the transcript of the World Service news from London and had read of the death of Famy, the survival of Sokarev, the flight of the El Al jet from Heathrow. It had been a good plan, he had sent good men, and it had been insufficient.

He walked into the sands seeking solitude and absence from young men about to depart on a new mission. It was not until the stars had risen that he made his way back to the camp and went to sit with the four who were eating together with their friends, perhaps for the last time. He hid depression behind humour and made no mention of the news from London. When the time came for them to leave he walked with them to the jeep and hugged them deep in his bear arms and kissed each on both cheeks. Afterward, in his tent, he lay on the canvas bed and was reading their operational plan when the old man pulled aside the tent flap.

"Israeli radio says Sokarev is dead. Died in Tel Aviv. . . ."

"From what? The reports made no mention of any injury."

"He suffered a heart seizure on the plane."

"So it was not by our hand?" The momentary excitement extinguished.

"But he is dead. We sought to kill him, and . . ."

"Listen, old man. His death is unimportant if it was not at our hand. We had to show we had the power to strike successfully at him. Instead we showed we were not capable. That is no victory. The mission is over and completed. Sleep well, old man."

When the light had gone and the tent flap had been folded back into place, the leader turned towards the canvas side close to his face. And before he slept he thought of the lights of the jeep and the bright furnace eyes of the men he would not see again.

Gerald Seymour

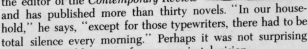

Gerald Seymour grew up to the sound of the typewriter—*two* typewriters, in fact. His father, William Seymour, was a Fellow of the Royal Society of Literature, à past chairman of the Poetry Society, and the author of numerous novels, poems and essays. His mother, Rosalind Wade, is currently the editor of the *Contemporary Review* and has published more than thirty novels. "In our household," he says, "except for those typewriters, there had to be total silence every morning." Perhaps it was not surprising that he rejected literature for a career in television.

There he immediately began to make a name for himself as a news reporter from the toughest corners of the world: Cyprus, Indonesia, Vietnam, Aden, Northern Ireland. In 1970 he was in Jordan when the Palestinian commando movement, PFLP, hijacked three jet airliners to a desert airstrip outside Amman. The film that he, and ITN colleagues, made of the day the planes were blown up in the desert won a special commendation at the Cannes TV festival.

He was in Munich when the Black September gang attacked the Israeli Olympic team, and then moved to the airport in time for the final shootout. Later the same year he was the only foreign journalist allowed a full length interview with the three Arab survivors of the attack.

It was dangerous, often unpleasant work, but it was also the perfect background for the novelist to come. For in 1974 his family heritage finally caught up with Gerald Seymour. He took time off to write *Harry's Game*, the best—and most authentic—of the novels on the Northern Ireland troubles. Now, with *The Glory Boys*, he has broadened his range. He has also used the background material he could never use on television—the inside stories of those London "sieges", of the army at Heathrow, of the Government departments responsible for valued visitors.

Now Seymour has moved with his family to stay in Rome, not simply as a novelist, but still a reporter for ITN. The two careers will still go hand in hand.

a condensation of the book by
ROBERT LACEY

TITLE PAGE ILLUSTRATION BY KEITH RICHENS
PUBLISHED BY HUTCHINSON, LONDON

MAJESTY

ELIZABETH II
AND THE HOUSE OF WINDSOR

This is the story of the private life of the most famous family in the world.

Robert Lacey's story centres on the present head of that family, our Queen: a woman whose relations have had their share of tragedies, sudden deaths, unhappy love affairs and marriages; a woman surrounded by children, horses, dogs; with private friends as well as public servants.

It is from her viewpoint that we are shown people we have read about, yet never really known before: her indulgent grandparents, the unbending George V and stately Queen Mary; her charming but unstable Uncle David, the Duke of Windsor; her shy father, George VI, and her mother, full of warmth and fun; her witty but unhappy sister; her husband, impatient, searching for a role to match his abilities.

Robert Lacey has been supported as no other royal biographer before, not only by the Palace but also by the family's friends, and he has produced a personal story to match all the pomp of Jubilee. He has sought and found the inner majesty of the woman who is Queen.

Grandpapa England

Early in 1926 Britain's picture magazines started publishing photographs of His Royal Highness Prince Albert, Duke of York, together with his wife Elizabeth, the Duchess. No reason was given for the young couple's sudden topicality. The Duchess of York, noted for smiling much more than any other lady in the royal family, had not been appearing in public recently, but the pictures betrayed no hint of why this might be. Her husband was the shy, rather earnest second son of George V, who had reigned since 1910 as King Emperor over the United Kingdom of Great Britain and Northern Ireland and Britain's possessions beyond the seas.

Then, on Thursday 22 April 1926, everything became clear. "Her Royal Highness the Duchess of York gave birth to a daughter," it was announced, "at 2.40 yesterday morning. . . . Her Royal Highness and the infant Princess are making very satisfactory progress." The medical bulletin on the mother and her new baby was reticent: "a certain line of treatment was successfully adopted." The future Queen Elizabeth II had, in fact, come into the world feet first by Caesarean section.

The newspapers were dutifully delighted, but there was no reason why the birth of a daughter to the Duke and Duchess of York should have any special significance. She was not in the direct line of succession. Quite apart from the fact that her father ranked below his elder brother Edward, Prince of Wales, in royal precedence, it was likely that the Yorks would have more children

159

in the future, and among them could be a son. It seemed far-fetched in 1926 to link this new baby Princess with the throne. Her most likely chance of becoming a queen in the future was as the wife of some foreign king—though since the Great War, of course, there were not so many of those about.

Still, it was welcome new blood in the royal family. On the afternoon of Wednesday 21 April, King George and his wife Queen Mary motored up from Windsor to inspect their grand-daughter. The Duchess of York had had her accouchement at the imposing Mayfair home of her parents, the Earl and Countess of Strathmore, and that afternoon there was a crowd of well-wishers waiting outside when the royal car arrived. Queen Mary thought the child was "enchanting".

"You don't know what a tremendous joy it is to Elizabeth and me to have our little girl," Prince Albert wrote to the Queen a few days later. "We always wanted a child to make our happiness complete, & now that it has at last happened, it seems so wonderful & strange. I am so proud of Elizabeth at this moment after all that she has gone through during the last few days. . . . I do hope that you & Papa are as delighted as we are, to have a grand-daughter. . . . May I say I hope you won't spoil her when she gets a bit older."

The new baby was christened in the private chapel at Buckingham Palace by Dr. Cosmo Lang, then Archbishop of York, with the names Elizabeth Alexandra Mary. "I hope you will approve of these names," Prince Albert had written to his father, " & I am sure there will be no muddle over two Elizabeths in the family. We are so anxious for her first name to be Elizabeth as it is such a nice name & there has been no one of that name in your family for such a long time."

The King replied, "I like it & think it is a pretty name." He noticed, however, that the names paid no tribute to her great-great-grandmother Victoria, who had ordained that the names of all children close to the succession should perpetuate the memory either of her beloved Albert or herself. "I hardly think that necessary," decided the King. After all the child was not in the direct line of succession to the throne.

THE EARLY YEARS of the future Queen Elizabeth II have been chronicled in some detail by her family, friends and by one governess. But more important than the nursery progressions which she moved through no faster or slower than any other child, was the context in which she was brought up. It shaped her decisively. The very special flavour of her childhood derived from her parents, her grandparents, and the particular ideals they stood for. It was by them that Elizabeth's own character—still more strongly her own style of monarchy—was determined.

Her family was dominated by her grandfather, King George V. Kings are taken seriously by most people but by no one more than their own royal family. George V was head of his family business, providing his relations with a living, but he also provided them with a meaning to life as they knew it, and the fact that the object of their fealty was such an ordinary man was the secret of the whole majestic mystery.

"Born in the ranks of the working class," said Keir Hardie on the accession of George V, "the new king's most likely fate would have been that of a street corner loafer." This was an unfair description of the King, whose industry and sense of duty buzzed inside him like a dynamo, but it was a realistic assessment of his intellectual attainments. As his official biographer felt compelled to admit, King George V was distinguished "by no exercise of social gifts, by no personal magnetism, by no intellectual powers. He was neither a wit nor a brilliant raconteur, neither well read nor well educated, and he made no great contribution to enlightened social converse. He lacked intellectual curiosity and only late in life acquired some measure of artistic taste." He was, in other words, like most of his subjects.

George V was the first British monarch to exemplify the majesty of the ordinary man. His grandmother Victoria had had ambitions to exert political influence in the tradition of Elizabeth I, his father Edward VII to sway the destiny of nations. George V was more humble. He simply personified all that his people felt most comfortable with and in so doing he found a new job for modern kings and queens to do—representation.

With his spare, upright frame, kindly eyes, cherry-red cheeks

161

and a grizzled beard and moustache reminiscent of the Sealyham terriers he loved so much, George V provided Princess Elizabeth with the very archetype of a grandfather. And to his peoples he was the model of a national patriarch. Always immaculately dressed, with a white gardenia in the buttonhole of his frock coat, the whole trim of the man embodied tradition and continuity. (He was, for example, proud of using the same collar stud for fifty years.) His presence in public exuded duty, dignity, courage, honesty, common sense and hard work—all the virtues that the British believed they possessed in abundance.

Furthermore, as the embodiment of the nation, patriotism for the King was a personal thing. The eldest of his six children, Edward, summed up his father's creed as belief "in God, in the invincibility of the Royal Navy, and the essential rightness of whatever was British".

The royal routine started early. The King liked to spend several hours with the state papers and then would walk into the breakfast room at Buckingham Palace as Big Ben struck nine o'clock. He was seldom without a pet dog and Charlotte, a grey-pink parrot who travelled with him almost everywhere, poking into the jam, butter, or boiled eggs on the breakfast table as the fancy took her. After breakfast she would accompany the King as he inspected the barometer and surveyed the heavens with the weather eye of a sailor—which he was proud, in his youth, to have been. Wet or fine, winter or summer, the ritual never varied.

After breakfast he would telephone his sister, Princess Victoria. "Hello, you old fool," she would greet her brother. "Beg pardon, Your Royal Highness," the Buckingham Palace operator had to interject on one occasion. "His Majesty is not yet on the line."

Family things mattered greatly to the King, and he preserved throughout his life his childhood affection for his younger sister. When she died in 1935, he was so overcome he felt unable to preside over the opening of Parliament, and from the day of her death—very close to his own—his handwriting became shaky and uneven.

His handwriting was in any case slow and laboured, like a

162

schoolboy's. And his spelling was erratic. "His planned education," stated his official biographer, "ended just where and when it should seriously have begun. He was (until he had painfully taken his own education in hand late in life) below the educational and perhaps intellectual standards of the ordinary public-school educated country squire." In fact, after private tuition he had gone to naval academy, then started regular service as a midshipman at the age of fourteen. He had little command of foreign languages. Sent to Heidelberg in 1892 to pick up the local tongue, he described German as "this rotten language which I find very difficult."

The House of Hanover which took over the succession to the British throne in 1714 has, with few exceptions, convincingly proved itself the least cultivated dynasty to rule over any major nation in modern history, and King George V kept up its traditions enthusiastically. His favourite spectacle both in terms of music and drama was *Rose Marie* and he went to see it several times with Queen Mary. He was in no way representative of his nation's intelligentsia—and this worried him no more than his failure to represent the rose growers or the racing car enthusiasts. Britain's greatest royal patron of the arts, Charles I, was, after all, far from being her most successful king.

It was, in fact, as a country squire that King George V was most happy. On 31 December 1888, he had shot for the first time one hundred pheasants at one stand, and he never looked back. Beside his bed he always kept a double-barrelled shotgun, so that he could exercise and strengthen his arm, and never in his life was he happier than when he could walk round the woods, bracken clearings and salt meadows of Sandringham, his Norfolk estate.

After dinner he liked best of all to retire to his stamp albums. But he might instead play a game of cards. He had played whist when he was young, but as auction bridge became fashionable, he found himself defeated by the complexities of bidding. He found his level in poker, playing for mild stakes.

He used to play with friends he had made during his days in the navy, a small close-knit group of associates whose identity meant little to the outside world, partly through the discretion

163

which is the basis of personal friendship with British royalty, partly through the fact that they were men as ordinary as he was.

His piety was simple. Every year the children of the local school at Sandringham were sent up to the big house to collect their prizes from their squire and Sovereign. They would be shown into the King's little study, where he sat surrounded by his red dispatch boxes, with a little dog on the carpet and Charlotte on her stand. He would give each of them a Bible and then tell them how his grandmother ("she was Queen Victoria, you know") gave him a Bible once and advised him to read a chapter every day. "Now *you* can do as you like," he would say. "But if you make that a rule of your life, and stick to it, I don't think you'll regret it when you come to my age." He was pleased to see his grand-daughter Elizabeth brought up in that same tradition.

Behind his bluff exterior, however, he was highly strung. Less governable impulses would burst out in fits of rage, while in moments of sentiment he would break down and cry. Yet he could not talk openly to those who were closest to him. This repression lent a painful tension to his relationships with his children—as Lady Airlie had discovered when she became lady-in-waiting to the future Queen Mary: "The children were expected to keep within their own domain, except when they had a legitimate excuse for leaving it. . . . I never saw them run along the corridors; they walked sedately, generally shepherded by nurses or tutors. . . . King George was fond of his sons, but his manner to them alternated between an awkward jocularity of the kind which makes a sensitive child squirm from self consciousness, and a severity bordering on harshness." King George V got on admirably with his sons once they were married, and he was a model grandfather—particularly to Princess Elizabeth for whom he felt a special affection. But his relationship with his sons as little boys was withered by the consciousness of duty—his ever-present awareness that he was raising future guardians of the throne.

The problem was that royal personages could not be just people, nor even just guardians of an institution, but had to act in some respects as institutions themselves. The King had been

George V riding in Windsor Great Park in 1923 with his four sons: the Prince of Wales, the Duke of York, the Duke of Gloucester and behind him the Duke of Kent.

The christening of Princess Elizabeth in 1926. The baby with her parents and grandparents. Back row: George V, the Duke of York, the Earl of Strathmore. Front row: Queen Mary, the Duchess of York, the Countess of Strathmore.

coached in his monarchical role by the constitutional historian, J. R. Tanner of St. John's College, Cambridge, and he had summarized in a school notebook certain precepts of constitutional monarchy. "The existence of the Crown," he wrote, "serves to *disguise* change & therefore to deprive it of the evil consequences of revolution." He ruled through the disappearance of five emperors, eight kings and eighteen minor dynasties, and on his death Sir Arthur Bryant had no doubt about the reason for his survival. "He and the Queen represented the secret convictions of every decent British man and woman at a time when the intellectual leaders of the nation were preaching the gospel of disintegration and many of its social leaders were making bad manners and loose living a social fashion."

He did not initiate change, but he knew how to yield to it with grace. He bravely put on a red tie to show his goodwill when he became the first British Sovereign to be served by a socialist prime minister in 1924, and restricted his really determined attempts to alter government policy to humanitarian rather than political issues. Presiding over the rites of national life in Britain in the 1920s and early 1930s, King George V set standards for millions, and within his own family, he determined still more powerfully the principles by which the future Queen Elizabeth II was brought up. Both through her parents and by his own influence, he shaped her decisively for the first ten years of her life, and if he could have seen what she has made of it since, there is every reason to believe he would heartily have approved. Princess Elizabeth was to refer to him always as "Grandpapa England" and this was what he was to millions of others as well. He was at the same time their servant and their god.

Grandmothers' Footsteps

Princess Elizabeth spent the first months of her life in Bruton Street in the West End of London. Today it is a street of banks, offices and showrooms. In 1926 it was quieter. Just up the road was Berkeley Square where nightingales still sang, and it was along its paths that the new baby was perambulated every day.

Her nurse was Mrs. Knight, a tall bright-eyed lady who had nursed the Princess's mother, the infant Lady Elizabeth Bowes-Lyon, in the early years of the century. She was an old-fashioned nanny whose life was her work, scarcely ever taking a holiday or even a day off. Mrs. Knight's Christian name was Clara, but most of her charges could only manage "Alla"—and this remained the name by which Princess Elizabeth knew her.

In August 1926, the Duke and Duchess of York went up to Scotland to stay at Glamis Castle as they had liked to do every summer since their marriage. This castle in the Glen of Strathmore, from which the Bowes-Lyons took their title, was where Princess Elizabeth would spend all the summers of her childhood and it was to shape her as significantly as the more obvious influence of her royal grandparents. If her father's family moulded her formal public identity, her mother's gave her the warmth and the gaiety with which she has brought up her own children.

It was Princess Elizabeth's grandmother, the Countess of Strathmore, who set the tone at Glamis. She was a large, stocky presence with a square jaw and bright eyes, the great flywheel maintaining the momentum and balance of the household. Princess Elizabeth's grandfather, the Earl of Strathmore, left most of the entertaining to his wife. He prided himself on being something of an estate manager and spent a lot of time chopping wood.

After dinner at Glamis, Lady Strathmore would sit down at the piano and everyone would gather round to sing. There would be parlour games too, for it was fun rather than sophistication which made invitations to the Glamis houseparties so sought after.

The Strathmores were a pious family. Prayers were said every day in the little chapel at Glamis, where the women would wear white caps made of thick crochet lace, which were provided in the bedrooms. Upright, open and straightforward, the family lived by a simple upper-class code which made them at once fun-loving, considerate, unaffected—and totally self-confident.

They had been by no means over-awed when in the autumn of 1920 Prince Albert started driving over from Balmoral to pay

167

court to their youngest daughter (and ninth child) Elizabeth, who was then barely twenty. It opened the prospect of an honourable connection for the family, of course, but the Bowes-Lyons were not short on connections. Lady Strathmore made quite sure her daughter was not seduced by the tinsel that might have attracted another mother, and she was not surprised when Lady Elizabeth turned down Prince Albert's first proposal of marriage. "I do hope he will find a nice wife who will make him happy," wrote Lady Strathmore to a friend. "I like him so much and he is a man who will be made or marred by his wife."

Her assessment was correct. His marriage was indeed to be the making of Prince Albert, Duke of York. But he had no intention of taking to wife anyone but Lady Strathmore's youngest daughter.

Prince Bertie, as he was known to his family and friends, did not have an imposing appearance, and his speech was punctuated with a stutter that could bring him to a standstill when he was nervous. But he was, at the same time, a man of extraordinary tenacity, and it was this that eventually won him Lady Elizabeth. But she took a lot of courting.

Adopting her mother's standards, Lady Elizabeth knew what she really wanted, and that was absolute purity. At the end of an evening at Glamis the guests would queue for their candles and process up to bed, but there was none of the fun and games that characterized candle-time at raffish Edwardian houseparties—or, indeed, the fast set with which Prince Bertie's elder brother, the Prince of Wales, took up after the Great War. He had already established the first of his series of *affaires* with married women which, comparatively discreet in the 1920s, were to become more and more flagrant. But Prince Bertie had a different outlook. He clung to the fierce morality of his parents and Lady Elizabeth shared his views. "Her circle wasn't more moral in a 'pious' way," remembers one of her companions in the early 1920s. "It just never occurred to us that unmarried people should go to bed together. With the Prince of Wales we knew it was always married ladies. But Prince Bertie's circle were all 'gals', nice 'gals', and Prince Bertie would never have suggested that he might go to bed with anyone. Holding hands in a boat, *that* was courting."

King George V himself did not think much of his son's chances. "You'll be a lucky fellow," he said, "if she accepts you." But in January 1923 a brief telegram to Sandringham—*"All right, Bertie"*—told the King and Queen that their quiet son had been rewarded for his tenacity.

"Bertie is supremely happy," Queen Mary wrote on the night of 20 January 1923 after Lady Elizabeth had been with her parents to stay at Sandringham. Nor could the King resist the charm of his future daughter-in-law. She was always an unpunctual person but when she arrived late at the royal dinner table, she was invariably forgiven. "You are not late, my dear," King George V would say, despite his passion for time-keeping, "we must have sat down two minutes too early."

GLAMIS, therefore, held many memories for the parents of Princess Elizabeth in 1926. Now their baby would be wheeled out in her pram amid the clipped yews of Lady Strathmore's Dutch garden to the sound of water splashing around a little stone cupid in a blue tiled pool. It was her grandmother and her nurse who saw most of her. Her father and mother were busy making ready for a six-month tour of Australia and New Zealand.

The decision to send them was King George V's. He felt it was time that his shy second son was exposed to more rigorous public life. But it was a cruel fate for a young married couple enchanted with their new baby to be sent so far away from her for so long. And it proved to be only the opening scene in a childhood whose predominant theme would be the inculcation of the virtues of duty, self-sacrifice and industry. If these were at the expense of the personal impulses which non-royal personages accept as being the essence of personality, then this had to be accepted as part of the price of privileged birth.

In 1926 Princess Elizabeth's father was paying out his own particular price for his privileges, for the chronic speech impediment which had plagued him for much of his life posed a special threat to his father's plans for him. The tour involved a series of speeches and Prince Bertie had not until then been able to speak in public without being handicapped by his stammer.

What was so galling was that he spoke in private quite fluently and it was only the tension of a public occasion which made it so painfully difficult for him to get his words out. By 1926 he had already been to a series of specialists and gone through the contortions they prescribed to cure him, but to no avail. This failure, in fact, made the stammering worse. Until the age of six or seven he had spoken as fluently as any other little boy. But then he had been compelled by his tutors to write with his right hand, although the left hand came more naturally to him, and it was at this time that he started to stammer. His brothers and sister were allowed to make fun of him, ragging him without mercy after the style set by his father's quarterdeck chaff, and he withdrew still more tightly into himself, only for his parents to interpret his silence as naughtiness, his shyness as moods.

Another affliction was the system of splints in which the Prince was required to spend certain hours of the day. Like his father he suffered from knock-knees, and elaborate braces were devised to correct this fault. "I am sitting in an armchair with my legs in the new splints and on a chair," the nine-year-old Prince wrote bravely to his mother in 1904. "I have got an invalid table, which is splendid for reading but rather awkward for writing at present. I expect I shall get used to it."

But the Prince was putting on a brave face. At times the pain of the splints made him weep so bitterly that his manservant, Finch, whose duty it was to fix them on every evening, would relent and allow him to sleep without them—until the Prince's father got to hear of it. He summoned Finch to the library, stood up and drew his trousers tight to display the curvature of his legs. "If that boy grows up to look like this," he thundered, "it will be your fault."

After an undistinguished period at the Dartmouth Royal Naval College, Prince Albert emerged from adolescence diffident and painfully aware of his shortcomings in the eyes of his father. It was scarcely surprising that his tensions worked themselves out in his speech, and though his loving young wife had done much to help him, he was still in 1926 bedevilled by his past.

Lionel Logue, the speech therapist, who first met the Prince on

19 October 1926, had grasped the psychological importance of instilling his patients with the confidence that they really could defeat their affliction and his success with Prince Albert was startling and rapid. The Prince went almost daily to Logue's consulting room in Harley Street, his wife usually accompanying him to learn the details of the breathing exercises she could help him with while they were away. "I have noticed a great improvement in my talking," he wrote to his father, " & also in making speeches which I did this week. I am sure I'm going to get quite all right in time, but twenty-four years of talking in the wrong way cannot be cured in a month."

For the Christmas of 1926 the royal family went as usual to Sandringham for the holidays. It was Queen Victoria who had instituted the calendar of peregrinations which took the royal family at Christmas to East Anglia, to Windsor for Easter and then to Balmoral in Scotland for August. King George V followed this routine devotedly.

The family's New Year celebrations in 1927 did not last as long as usual, for the Yorks had to be dispatched on their tour of the Antipodes. The Duke and Duchess sailed from Portsmouth in the battle-cruiser *Renown* on 6 January 1927. King George V and Queen Mary had said their farewells at Victoria Station and there the Duchess had to say goodbye to her daughter for six months. "I felt very much leaving on Thursday," she wrote later to Queen Mary, "and the baby was so sweet playing with the buttons on Bertie's uniform that it quite broke me up."

THE ARRANGEMENT was that the care of the Princess should be shared between her two sets of grandparents. So she was sent first to the Bowes-Lyon home in Hertfordshire, and then in February to the Palace. "Our sweet little grandchild, Elizabeth, arrived here yesterday," wrote George V in his diary, "and came to see us after tea."

It was now that the Princess first came into close contact with her grandmother, Queen Mary, whose influence on her life, work and personality was to be second only to that of her parents. Queen Mary was a shy woman, but she set a social example even

171

more formidable than that of her husband, and moulded her own family, including her grandchildren, in a definite fashion.

Enjoyment for enjoyment's sake was low down on Queen Mary's list of priorities. She had been an uneasy daughter-in-law to the jovial Edward VII, whose Sandringham houseparties had featured apple-pie beds, bicycle pumps filled with water and sticky peardrops slipped surreptitiously into guests' pockets—and the feeling was reciprocated. She was never much liked by the Edwardian smart set who used to giggle at the fringe of artificial hair she wore on her forehead like a thick sponge.

When her husband came to the throne as George V in 1910, however, the new Queen Mary had the last laugh, wrapping the Court—and upper-class life which took its tone from Buckingham Palace—in a respectability that still wreathed it securely when little Princess Elizabeth was born.

Not that Queen Mary was totally hidebound. She exerted her influence as Queen in favour of extending birth control among the labouring classes—"Fancy telling them to go off and use self-control," she would snort. But her sentiments were nonetheless practical rather than progressive, and she worked hard to nurture them in her grandchildren, particularly Princess Elizabeth, taking them to museums and art galleries and lecturing them on the heritage and treasury the royal family possessed. Her preferred paintings were usually of her own relatives, and her tastes were not so much artistic as those of the "connoisseur"—furniture, decorations, knick-knacks—her appetites acquisitive rather than creative. Her fancy inclined towards the oriental—miniature elephants in agate or a row of little Buddhas whose nodding heads she would set wobbling in sequence as she walked past them.

Indeed, it sometimes seemed to her children that she regarded them as additional, and rather more tiresome items in her collections. Instinctively disinclined to reveal what was on her mind, she had proved a remote mother, not so much unkind as inattentive. It was the normal thing for women of her station to hire nannies for their children, but in Queen Mary's case it took three years of systematic ill-treatment of her two eldest sons before she discovered what kind of woman she had hired—and only then

Above: *Princess Elizabeth driving with her royal grandparents from Crathie Church to Balmoral in Jubilee Year, 1935.*

Left: *The Duke and Duchess of York in London in 1929.*
Below: *The baby Princess Elizabeth with George V and her nanny "Alla" at a Balmoral fête in 1927.*

because the nanny had a nervous breakdown. "She remained tragically inhibited with her children," wrote her closest friend Lady Airlie. "She loved them and was proud of them but . . . they were strangers to her emotionally."

Lady Airlie discovered that this lack of communication centred fundamentally on the shyness that existed between King George V and his wife. Both found it difficult to talk to each other about deep matters—and even about some trivial ones. The couple had separate bedrooms and they scarcely ever ate alone together: when they did not have official guests, they would eat in the company of an equerry and a lady-in-waiting.

Queen Elizabeth II has not, today, maintained all these habits of her grandmother. But she is afflicted by a similar blend of shyness and severity and has cultivated the same devastating reaction as Queen Mary to observations by which she is not amused —totally ignoring the remark while looking its perpetrator full in the face. Many of her deepest instincts reflect a kinship and closeness to her grandmother that extended throughout her youth, for when Queen Mary died at the age of eighty-five Elizabeth had already been on the throne for more than a year.

ON 27 June 1927 the baby Princess was reunited with her parents whose Australian tour had been a success. Elizabeth was taken out onto the Palace's centre balcony to be held up under an umbrella beside Queen Mary as the crowds cheered ecstatically. It was her first experience of this fierce radiation of public affection and curiosity, and it was a sight that was to mark all the fête days of her life—a great grey sea of humanity surveyed from a balcony as it surged against the railings below.

"Lilibet"

On 21 November 1928 King George V fell seriously ill. Bronchial pneumonia was diagnosed. Bulletins referred to "a decline in the strength of the heart", and his doctors agreed it was only the King's will to live that kept him alive through a succession of operations and relapses. As the crisis passed, the royal doctors decided that the King must be sent to the South Coast to recuperate in the sea air. A secluded mansion near Bognor was hired for his convalescence, and in the corner of the garden a sandpit was dug, for the King's favourite grandchild was an important component of his recovery programme. Princess Elizabeth arrived with her nurse in March 1929. She was nearly three.

"G delighted to see her," wrote Queen Mary in her diary. "I played . . . in the garden making sandpies! The Archbishop of Canterbury came to see us & was so kind & sympathetic." As King George V recovered, he was able to smoke his first cigarette for months and to appear in public on the sea front with his granddaughter. There was great cheering. The King nodded his head in a fatherly fashion and the little Princess waved brightly.

The Yorks were now installed at 145 Piccadilly, across Green Park from Buckingham Palace, and the young Princess would wave across the park from the front windows at 145 Piccadilly soon after her breakfast every morning and her grandfather would look out from the palace at the same time and wave back. He called her "Lilibet", which was her own early attempt at her name. The nickname stuck. She was Lilibet to her family from then onwards.

Her nursery at 145 Piccadilly—where the London Intercontinental Hotel now stands—was up at the top of the house, stocked with dark polished grown-up furniture complete with a glass-fronted display case for delicate toys. The night nursery in which she slept was unplumbed, with a large jug and basin holding water to wash her hands. On the landing outside the Princess took to collecting toy horses on wheels which she could ride around the house. Every evening she would change their saddles and harness before she went to bed.

Her toys were a problem. There were simply too many of them, and it was impossible to stop more arriving with almost every post. On their unexpectedly triumphant tour of Australia and New Zealand her parents had been presented with no less than three tons of toys for her. It was one of several things that made her

175

mother's ambition to raise her like any other little girl unrealistic. Indeed when it was let slip that the Princess's nursery clothes and trimmings were in yellow, pink and blue fell out of favour overnight, and *Time* magazine even put the Princess on their cover for setting a major fashion trend when she was only three.

For Christmas 1929 the Princess was given a pony of her own and could soon ride it well—to her grandfather's approval. "The English people like riding," he said. He had had himself photographed with his four sons, the Prince of Wales and the Dukes of York, Gloucester and Kent, riding side by side in Windsor Great Park. The picture justified his confidence in his subjects' respect for equitation. It proved one of the most popular published during his reign.

But the four young men photographed on their horses were not George V's only children. He and Queen Mary also produced a daughter, Princess Mary (the Princess Royal) and a fifth son, Prince John, who was something of a mystery outside the family. He was a friendly, outgoing boy, much loved by his family, who treasured his naïve little sayings in later years. But he was subject to epileptic attacks and died when he was only thirteen.

IN April 1930, for Princess Elizabeth's fourth birthday, Queen Mary gave her a set of building blocks made from fifty different woods from various corners of the Empire, fun thus being tempered by that blend of the instructive and the imperialistic that her grandmother loved so well.

Then, on 21 August 1930 her mother gave birth to another daughter in a labour that proved surprisingly straightforward after the complications of her Caesarean four years earlier. The one problem was that her parents had been hoping so keenly for a son that they had not seriously considered any girls' names, and it was September before a choice was made.

"Bertie & I have decided now to call our little daughter Margaret Rose," wrote the Duchess to her mother-in-law. "I hope you like it. I think that it is very pretty together."

The most tangible immediate consequence of the birth for Princess Elizabeth was that Alla had now inevitably to concentrate

176

her attentions upon the new baby, and Princess Elizabeth moved closer to the under-nurse, Margaret MacDonald, developing what has, over the years, become one of the closest friendships of her life. Miss MacDonald is today, after nearly half a century of personal service, dresser to the Queen of England, with a suite of her own in Buckingham Palace. She chooses the Queen's clothes and travels with her everywhere. Elizabeth II acknowledges her as one of her most trusted confidantes. She calls her Bobo.

Born in 1904, the daughter of a gardener who later became a coachman and then a railway worker, Bobo has maintained the forthrightness of her origins. She is prepared, as no other of the Queen's servants is, to tell her mistress when she has made a poor showing on television or has not spoken her best. Unsentimental and severe, she has come to provide a unique sounding board, the closest contact Queen Elizabeth can have with the world she looks out at through limousine windows.

By the early 1930s life was taking on a pleasantly settled character for the Duke and Duchess of York and their two little daughters. With their servants and guaranteed income, they were free to enjoy the happiness of young family life in comfort and security, largely cushioned against the impact of the Depression. There were some royal economies. The King gave up his shooting at Windsor, the Prince of Wales presented £50,000 to the Exchequer, while Prince Bertie's gesture was to sell the stable of hunters he had built up. But when in 1931 King George V offered the Yorks the Royal Lodge in Windsor Great Park as a country home, the general economic stringency did not prevent them starting an ambitious programme of building and renovation. They added brand-new wings to either flank of the Lodge, and designed two fine bedrooms for themselves on the ground floor. The Duchess's room was carpeted in her favourite colour, grey-blue, her large double bed having blue silk covers with lemon pleatings; the Duke's more austere room had the character of a sailor's cabin—a hard-looking bed, a simple dressing table and just one bookcase, with only a few personal knick-knacks all laid out as if awaiting the arrival of the inspecting officer.

We know about the decorative features of the royal bedrooms—

177

not usually a subject of public description—because it was about this time, just before the sixth birthday of Princess Elizabeth, that "Crawfie" entered the Princess's life. Miss Marion Crawford came down to Windsor in the spring of 1932 for a month's trial as governess, and stayed for seventeen years. She is today a taboo subject in royal circles, for her great betrayal in subsequently publishing the details of her life with the little Princesses can never be forgiven. Discretion is the quality the royal family prize above all in their friends and servants, since it is the price of any kind of private life, and Crawfie betrayed that trust. But until she left the royal service in the late 1940s and started writing her books and articles, she was cherished as a lively, sympathetic and imaginative friend—and also as an excellent teacher.

She came to the attention of the Duke and Duchess up in Dunfermline, when she was walking several dozen miles a week between her pupils scattered among the hills in the aristocratic mansions there. Prince Bertie, in particular, admired her energy, and both felt that her carefree, spirited style, very much in the mould of progressive nursery teaching at that time, was what their daughters needed. So in September 1932 the governess took over full-time responsibility for the daytime activities of Princess Elizabeth and she found that she was given a surprisingly free hand. "No one ever had employers who interfered so little," she later wrote. "I had often the feeling that the Duke and Duchess, most happy in their own married life, were not over concerned with the higher education of their daughters. They wanted most for them a really happy childhood, with lots of pleasant memories stored up against the days that might come."

Princess Elizabeth could read already. She had been taught by her mother. But now she was six, it was felt she could stand a properly organized school curriculum, and so Miss Crawford drew up a six-day timetable, the mornings filled with half-hour lessons, the afternoons devoted to less academic accomplishments— singing, drawing, music or dancing. Miss Crawford sent a draft version of the curriculum to Queen Mary and was told the Queen considered too little time had been allocated to history and Bible reading. Also, she thought, detailed knowledge of the physical

178

geography of the Dominions and India would be most valuable.

Throughout the early 1930s, a cosy routine was established in the domestic life of the Yorks and their daughters. Home in London was the centre of things. There were very few special parties or treats outside. The Princesses' one annual visit to the pantomime was a highlight much anticipated and long remembered. The Horse Show at Olympia and the Royal Military Tournament at Earls Court were other rare spectacles, together with occasional private film shows when the family gathered at Sandringham or Windsor.

The Duke of York carried out a thorough public programme, concentrating particularly on matters of industrial relations, while his wife also worked through a full schedule of engagements, but the base for their work was at home. So despite the protective screen of governess, nannies and maids, the little Princesses saw quite a lot of their parents—certainly much more than most other children whose parents were in London society.

After a morning of lessons there would be a break for games in the garden. Lunch was taken with the Duke and Duchess whenever they were at home, and after one of the afternoon activities prescribed on Miss Crawford's curriculum, there would be tea, very occasionally with guests of the girls' own age, much more often with the Prince of Wales, who was always popping in. He used to stay for the games that the girls played after tea—snap, happy families, racing demon or rummy. Then there was the highspot of the day, bathtime. When both girls had been undressed and were splashing about, the Duke and Duchess would go upstairs and join in the fun, Alla rather desperately pleading for the children not to be made too excited. "Then," Crawfie remembers, "arm in arm, the young parents would go downstairs, heated and dishevelled and frequently rather damp. . . ."

On Friday afternoons they all piled into the car and drove down to Royal Lodge at Windsor. There would still be work to do, a morning spent going over the previous week's lessons with Miss Crawford, but there was riding or games in the garden with the Duke and Duchess in the afternoon. It was a sheltered, secure existence which few of Princess Elizabeth's contemporaries knew.

Still, it was not over-endowed with the comforts taken for granted today. Life in many royal residences was still carried on by oil lamp, with chamber pots, water-filled jugs and basins, and smelly oil stoves, while even the ostensible stability of royal family life was not as surely based as it appeared to the outside world to be.

The Prince of Wales

During the early childhood of Princess Elizabeth, Edward, Prince of Wales—David to his family—appeared to be blazing a new trail for twentieth-century monarchy to follow. A series of hysterically successful foreign tours had made him a glittering international celebrity. He had fought to get sent to the trenches in the Great War. He had been the first member of the royal family to speak on the radio, the first to be photographed smoking a cigarette. He was a foil to the staid image of his father and mother, and seemed to herald a more open, democratic approach to monarchy in the future. When he saw Australian soldiers being refused service in the Carlton Grill, he went over to shake hands with them and they were shown to a table. He spoke with a twang which some people called cockney and others Long Island, he had taps put on his shoes by Fred Astaire, and at Oxford he had sung *The Red Flag* to his own banjo accompaniment.

The Prince of Wales was Princess Elizabeth's favourite uncle and he shared that side of her childhood indulgent uncles make their own. At the wedding of Queen Mary's niece, Lady Mary Cambridge, in 1931, he was seen to catch the little girl's eye with a secret wink and to win her broad monkey grin in reply. Her parents did not altogether approve. But the Prince rather liked being mischievous with other people's children. He would send his car to wait outside the school where Angie, the daughter of his first mistress, Mrs. Dudley Ward, had special classes in languages and dancing. Angie would play truant, jump in the royal car and go off to tea at St. James's Palace with her mother's great friend— whom she and her sister called "Little Prince".

The Prince of Wales's association with Freda Dudley Ward, the wife of a Liberal MP, went back to the spring of 1918 when they had met during an air raid, and it lasted sixteen years. It is a measure of the discretion surrounding the royal family in those years between the two world wars that although the affair was common knowledge in London society there were at the time very few published references to their friendship.

The Prince would telephone her every morning—her servants described this amongst themselves as "the baker's call"—and they usually saw each other some time during the day. He loved being part of a family for which, ultimately, he held no responsibility, playing with Mrs. Dudley Ward's daughters as a surrogate father, and even being unfaithful to her with passing affairs. Their relationship was played out in the semi-public ambiance of the Mayfair nightclubs around which society gravitated at that period. They would sit together at the Prince's regular table or, if they were involved at the time with other partners, in different parts of the smoke-filled room, dancing on the crowded little floor among the likes of Lady Cunard and Miss Tallulah Bankhead.

This was the other side to the bourgeois respectability in which the future Elizabeth II was being raised—the direction in which royalty throughout history has traditionally been tempted. The contradiction which the Prince represented was a raw nerve for all the family. For King George V and Queen Mary it was even more than a personal matter. There was a danger in growing careless of the gap between public image and private reality. Being royal in their eyes extended far beyond putting on a charming act in public. They had lived through the fall of several dynasties which had been adept at doing that—though no one saw the scenario for the Princes of Wales in such cataclysmic terms in the days of Mrs. Dudley Ward.

Then came Mrs. Wallis Simpson. The Prince had first met the Simpsons in 1930, but it was not until January 1934 that he began to go round regularly to their little flat in Bryanston Square. Ernest Simpson—a New Yorker whose father was English and who had crossed the Atlantic to work in the London office of his father's firm—would often find he had so much to do that he had to leave his wife alone to entertain their royal visitor. David saw less and less of his family—and they were not the only ones cut off.

Frances Donaldson recorded, on the basis of conversations with Mrs. Dudley Ward, that in May 1934 Mrs. Dudley Ward's elder daughter was seriously ill. For several weeks her mother thought of little else. Only when her daughter was out of danger did she begin to consider the fact that, for the first time in nearly seventeen years, although the Prince of Wales was in England, weeks had gone by without his visiting or telephoning her. She put a call through to St. James's Palace. The voice on the switchboard at the other end was that of a friend. For years these two had spoken to each other every day. Now when the telephonist heard her voice, she immediately replied in tones of the greatest distress, "I have something so terrible to tell you," she said, "that I don't know how to say it." And when pressed to continue she said sorrowfully: "I have orders not to put you through."

Mrs. Dudley Ward was never to see the Prince again. By the autumn of 1934 the split between the Prince and his former mistress was common knowledge, and within a few months the Prince had mounted an all-out assault upon the sensibilities of London society, testing its unshockability to the utmost.

Suddenly in the diaries of the period come references thick and fast to the Prince of Wales and Mrs. Simpson, the Prince thrusting his new friend to the forefront of attention at nightclubs, parties and weekends in the country. "Several of my fellow guests asked me what I thought of her," recorded Marie Belloc Lowndes. "I said what had struck me most were her perfect clothes and that I had been surprised, considering that she dressed so simply, to see that she wore such a mass of 'dressmaker's' jewels. At that they all screamed with laughter, explaining that all the jewels were real, that the Prince of Wales had given her £50,000 worth . . . following it up with £60,000 worth a week later. . . ."

Now began the bitterness over Wallis Simpson which divided the British royal family well into the reign of Queen Elizabeth II. One thing that worried them—and hurt King George V and Queen Mary especially—was that many of the jewels in which

182

Mrs. Simpson paraded were royal heirlooms. The King's mother, Queen Alexandra, had personally bequeathed them to the Prince of Wales to be worn by his future wife—for it had naturally been assumed that his wife would need such gems as a future Queen of England.

Until this point his family had accepted David's philandering. But as the Prince of Wales started ostentatiously parading his relationship with Wallis Simpson in the autumn of 1934 feelings began to harden. Her personality was abrasive and in some way exclusive, and the hold it gave her upon the enigmatic soul of the Prince of Wales drove a wedge into the family. They resented her where previous mistresses—Lady Furness, for example, also American and "fast"—had been welcomed. Even the friends who got to know and like the couple very much saw the relationship in essentially the same personal terms as his family did—domination on Mrs. Simpson's part and slavishness on the part of the Prince of Wales. "Wallis tore her nail and said 'Oh!' and forgot about it," remembered Lady Diana Cooper, "but he needs must disappear and arrive back in two minutes, panting, with two little emery-boards for her to file the offending nail."

Then again, there was the strange dulling of the Prince's appetite for his work. It was not deliberate sabotage on Mrs. Simpson's part, for she revelled in his position as a prince. It was almost a change in his person. The Prince may have discovered, as he was later to suggest, a new sense of values in his love for Wallis, or he was, perhaps, just tired of doing the same things the same way for so long. But certainly it was in 1934 and 1935 that people began to notice boredom or even irritation on his face as he carried out his public engagements. David's outgoing charm and gaiety were darkening. He had always been prone to moods and a touchy defensiveness, but now this side of him became more prominent. He saw less and less of his parents, brothers and sister, and when he did he made little effort to communicate with them.

Suddenly there came a much needed diversion for everyone. November 1934 saw the blossoming of Prince George's (later the Duke of Kent and youngest of the royal brothers) whirlwind romance with Princess Marina of the deposed Greek royal house.

The youngest Prince had been a lively attractive boy, immature, but in some ways more polished and educated than his elder brothers. Also he had a sense of fun which meant that, alone among them, he was seldom intimidated by their father. He could laugh his way out of confrontations where his elder brothers faltered, and he had the knack of doing this without offence. As he grew up, he gravitated more and more towards the Prince of Wales. Both enjoyed company, conversation, fun. Princess Elizabeth's father, Prince Bertie, was shy; the third Prince, Henry, Duke of Gloucester, stolid. But the Duke of Kent was the archetype of the rich young man-about-town.

Still in the grip of the Depression, Great Britain had had little to rejoice about for years, and the marriage of the dashing thirty-two-year-old Prince to the fine-featured, aristocratic Princess Marina provided a welcome occasion to indulge in a little happiness.

The charm of the wedding was enhanced by the presence of Princess Elizabeth, now eight and a half, as leading bridesmaid. The object of particular cheers from the vast crowds along the processional route, she signed the register as a witness along with all the grown-ups. Princess Margaret, now four, sat by herself on a little stool just in front of her mother's chair, and when she wriggled or showed too much bare leg her elder sister would correct her.

A few nights before the wedding the King and Queen held a ball in Buckingham Palace and into the guest list the Prince of Wales inserted the names of Mr. and Mrs. Ernest Simpson. George V ran a line through their names without hesitation, provoking the only exchange on this subject that we know of between father and son. It is suggested that it was only on the King being assured that Mrs. Simpson was not his son's mistress that an invitation was sent. We do not know whether, at this stage of their relationship, the Prince of Wales was lying or not.

At the ball Mrs. Simpson was presented to King George V and Queen Mary for the first and last time. "David led me over to where they were standing and introduced me," she wrote in her memoirs. "It was the briefest of encounters—a few words of

184

A happy family group at Royal Lodge, Windsor.

The Girl Guide Princesses send a message by carrier pigeon to mark the birthday of Lord Baden-Powell, founder of the Boy Scouts and Girl Guides.

The Princesses with their governess, Marion Crawford.

perfunctory greeting, an exchange of meaningless pleasantries, and we moved away."

It was now 1935 and the twenty-fifth anniversary of King George V's accession. One school of opinion thought it inappropriate at a time of national economic stringency for too much fuss to be made of this Silver Jubilee. But Queen Mary was adamant that a fuss was just what the people needed to take their minds off their troubles, and a huge upsurge of national affection totally vindicated her confidence. "I had no idea they felt like that about me," said King George V. "I'm beginning to think they must really like me for myself."

Later that year there were still more royal festivities when both Princess Elizabeth and Princess Margaret Rose were bridesmaids at the wedding of Prince Henry, the quiet, straightforward Duke of Gloucester to Lady Alice Montagu-Douglas-Scott. The death, shortly before the wedding, of Lady Alice's father caused the ceremony to be a quiet occasion, held in the Chapel Royal at Buckingham Palace.

Now all the old King's sons were married off bar one. But the omens for that most important marriage of all did not look promising, and in June 1935 arose another of the problems that were to trouble the new reign that was so imminent. The Prince of Wales had long nursed an admiration for the Fascist dictators, and he used the occasion of a British Legion rally in the Albert Hall to endorse a proposal "to stretch forth the hand of friendship to the Germans". German and American newspapers took it as an overt political gesture of British friendship towards Hitler, though they were wrong, as so often at that time, in treating an utterance by a member of the royal family as some sort of kite flown by the British Government. King George V felt impelled to reprove his son. Being a future king involved suppressing personal political opinions, and in that sense David must accept that he could never be totally free and individual—so long at least as he also wished to remain royal.

The seeds of abdication lay within the frustration which this involved for the future King Edward VIII. But in July 1935 the family was more worried by immediate concerns—like Mrs.

Simpson being invited to dinner at the German Embassy. Taken in conjunction with the Prince of Wales's growing indifference to his ceremonial duties and his impatience with normal conventions of all sorts, it all added up to an ominous picture. King George V was certainly worried. Although he could not bring himself to discuss Mrs. Simpson with his son personally, he spent long hours in the last September of his life at Balmoral in 1935, talking over his son's behaviour with the Archbishop of Canterbury. "After I am gone," he said, "the boy will ruin himself in twelve months."

Crisis of Monarchy

"It is this personal link between me and my people which I value more than I can say," declared King George V when he broadcast live to the people of Britain and his Empire on Christmas Day 1935. "It binds us together in all our common joys and sorrows." The royal family all gathered at Sandringham for Christmas as usual, but it was a quieter, somehow sadder occasion than usual. There was a vagueness about the King. Pains in his chest made it impossible for him to walk with his old naval erectness and towards the end of mealtimes his head nodded on his chest. He was now just seventy and had been suffering for months from a renewal of his old bronchial trouble.

Early in the new year the little Princesses were playing in the thin snow that had fallen on the lawn at Sandringham when Queen Mary came out to talk to them. She told them that their grandfather was very very ill indeed, and after lunch she took Elizabeth in to say goodbye to him. The little girl was then nine and a half, old enough to understand these things, it was thought, but Margaret, just five, was considered too young. The King was sitting in his bedroom wrapped in the old Tibetan dressing gown given to him on his visit to India in the early months of his reign. He was sinking fast.

The last entry in his diary, on 17 January, was almost illegible. "A little snow & wind. Dawson [his doctor] arrived this evening. I saw him & feel rotten." The next word is only half formed and it was Queen Mary who, with her customary neatness, rounded off the final page in the final volume of the journal that George V had kept virtually every day of his adult life. "My dearest husband, King Geo. V was much distressed at the bad handwriting & begged me to write his diary for him the next day. He passed away on 20 January at 5 minutes before midnight. MARY R. . . ."

When Lord Dawson had framed the famous final medical bulletin on George V—"The King's life is moving peacefully towards its close"—the BBC cancelled its programmes and dance music stopped in West End restaurants. The little Princesses had been sent back to Windsor a few days before their grandfather died.

"Don't let all this depress them more than is absolutely necessary, Crawfie," wrote the Duchess of York in a note. "They are so young."

After resting in the little church at Sandringham, watched over by his gamekeepers and estate servants, King George V's body was brought by train to London. Laid on a gun carriage it was dragged through the streets past silent crowds to the Houses of Parliament where it would lie in state.

Princess Elizabeth was taken to see the coffin, while the dead King's four sons were standing vigil round the bier. "Uncle David was there," her governess reports her saying on her return, "and he never moved at all . . . not even an eyelid."

"The Vigil of the Princes" was an imaginative sacrament devised by the new King with his flair for moving gestures. But in private things were going less happily. The death of King George V had taken everyone by surprise and no one more than his eldest son. Split between a powerful woman and the powerful demands of his family who refused to acknowledge that Mrs. Simpson could have any role in this agonizing crisis of his life, and faced with the myriad practical requirements of making decisions, weighty and trivial, in the exercise of his new responsibility, Edward all but went to pieces. Friends close to him in the last months of his father's life had found themselves talking about the possibility of the Prince of Wales renouncing his right to the succession and the panic that gripped Edward in the early weeks of his reign could well have reflected the realization that this way of escape was now closed to him.

It is easy for reminiscence about the early months of King Edward VIII's reign to be coloured by what happened before the year was out, but evidence of a general unease seems overwhelming. "And now," Harold Nicolson recorded J. H. Thomas, the Labour politician, saying to him, "'ere we 'ave this obstinate little man with 'is Mrs. Simpson. Hit won't do, 'Arold. I tell you that straight."

It was significant how much public attention now began to focus upon the little Princess Elizabeth. When the *Sphere* described "the youngest royal mourner" at the obsequies for George V "dressed simply in a black beret and coat" the journal reminded its readers how she "stands next in succession to the throne after her father." According to the Countess of Airlie, George V had said just a few months before his death, "I pray to God that my eldest son will never marry and that nothing will come between Bertie and Lilibet and the throne", and it was certainly from the accession of King Edward VIII at the beginning of 1936 rather than from his abdication at the end of the year that Princess Elizabeth began generally to be seen as a future Queen of England in her own right.

In response to the growing public interest in the little girl, journalists were invited inside 145 Piccadilly. Her menagerie of pets was stated to include several corgis and Shetland collies, two fawns, fifteen blue budgerigars and some ponies.

There was a great deal more trivial gossip, but the royal family, including King Edward VIII, were happy to see it published in British newspapers in preference to the topic that was occupying gossip columnists in Europe and North America to an increasing extent. It was only the informal convention in the British press that the royal family's private life was not a reporting matter that prevented most of Britain from knowing something that was an open secret in London society.

It has often been said that the reason why the English establishment never took to Mrs. Simpson was because she was American. This was not altogether true, for unashamedly

189

American ladies like Nancy Astor and Emerald Cunard were totally accepted by society at that time. The more basic problem was that she had no idea of how to behave in the circle to which she aspired. Her brassy repartee jarred on ladies of high birth. She would run her finger along the top of the mantelpiece and call for the housekeeper if she found dust. King Edward VIII had never come across such domesticity before and he found it entrancing. But in a royal household such bourgeois habits were absolutely fatal.

Princess Elizabeth's mother found her especially grating and made little secret of it, and that was true of Queen Mary, the Duchess of Kent, and the rest of the royal family as well. Her effect upon the King, they felt, was getting worse. He was becoming more and more remote, more and more evasive on the few occasions when he could be cornered.

"It was impossible not to notice the change in Uncle David," wrote Crawfie describing a visit by the King and Mrs. Simpson to Royal Lodge. "He had been so youthful and gay. Now he looked distraught, and seemed not to be listening to what was said to him. He made plans with the children and then forgot them."

The reason for his anxiety was simple. It was dawning on King Edward VIII that nothing else would satisfy him but to marry Mrs. Simpson. And all the issues this raised with his family and with his government were coming to assume understandably horrifying proportions.

Serious trouble was already developing, in fact, over the King's official fulfilment of his constitutional responsibilities and this is the real reason why his reign has been considered by his successors as such a stain on the monarchy. It was not directly a matter involving Mrs. Simpson but something rather more worrying.

King Edward VIII had started his reign in a flurry of activity, energetically reading through all the official papers sent him by the government, and often scribbling comments of his own in the margin. After a few months, however, his comments became rarer and rarer. Alarm began to be felt in the Cabinet Office when highly confidential documents began to return obviously unread, occasionally marked with the rings of wet glass bottoms and, worst of all, after extraordinarily long delays. Discreet inquiries were instituted, and it was discovered that red boxes containing crucial Cabinet discussions were going down to his Windsor home of Fort Belvedere to be left unguarded there while an unsupervised cosmopolitan selection of guests came and went.

The problem was more serious than laziness. The King made no secret of his disagreement with his government over the conduct of British foreign policy. He did not see Hitler and Mussolini as threats to British security. The very reverse indeed. When German troops reoccupied the Rhineland in March 1936, breaking the Locarno pact, he made it clear to the Germans that he was opposed to British intervention. Then over the question of Italy's invasion of Abyssinia he was reported in a secret Italian dispatch to Berlin as assuring Mussolini's ambassador that the League of Nations, which was trying to enforce economic sanctions against Italy and to which the British government had pledged its support, could "be considered dead", and that "for peace in Europe it was absolutely essential that two great nations, Germany and Italy, should be afforded full satisfaction by granting them, with full realization of their needs, the necessary colonial markets". This attitude was one reason for the German decision to send von Ribbentrop to London as ambassador in 1936. In his memoirs he explains his feeling that he could be more use at the Court of St. James's than actually directing foreign policy in Berlin, because Hitler's main intention at this time was to neutralize Britain, if possible with an Anglo-German alliance. Some thought it unlikely that such an alliance could be concluded, but "because of Edward VIII, it seemed that a final attempt should be made".

The Prime Minister, Stanley Baldwin, decided to restrict the documents available to the King and all sensitively confidential memoranda were discreetly withheld from the boxes sent down to Fort Belvedere. The selection of documents was restricted principally to papers requiring the royal signature, and this was totally unconstitutional. It was the King's right to see everything. But so lacking in thoroughness was King Edward VIII's scrutiny that he did not realize what was going on.

In 1936, however, Princess Elizabeth was totally unaware of all this, not only because of her age but also because her parents made sure that she should be so. They themselves naturally could not remain so detached. The new King was causing turmoil in the royal way of life they had become accustomed to. He decided that his father's beloved Sandringham was an extravagance, and he asked his brother Bertie to undertake a survey to see how its running expenses could most effectively be reduced, while he himself cut down the beer money for the servants at Buckingham Palace—an undiplomatic gesture when many of them were often employed loading cases of champagne or furniture or lavish quantities of silver plate into official vehicles directed to Mrs. Simpson's grand new flat in Regent's Park.

In the summer of 1936, the King decided to go abroad in the chartered yacht *Nahlin* which through late August and early September meandered down the Dalmatian coast in a blaze of world publicity. From the moment of his arrival in Dubrovnik to the cries of *"Zivila Ljubav"* (the Yugoslav equivalent of *"vive l'amour"*) from 20,000 peasants dressed in national costume, to his appearance stark naked in a Viennese bath house on his way home overland, the King of England was the unvarying centre of attention of newspapers in every part of the globe—every part, that is, except Great Britain and those corners of her Dominions still desperately endeavouring to pretend that Mrs. Simpson—still at this stage a married woman—did not exist, or if she did, that she was no more than a friend, or if she wasn't, that she represented no more than a passing affair of purely private significance.

The unreality of the *Nahlin* cruise beggared description. The King had believed it would be possible for him to undertake it in complete anonymity by pretending not to be the King of England but calling himself the Duke of Lancaster. And when his foreign minister, Anthony Eden, pointed out that significance would inevitably be read into his visits to countries in such a politically contentious area, he pooh-poohed the idea. When he heard that there was a good golf course at Istanbul, he informed the British Ambassador, Sir Percy Loraine, that he would like a couple of days playing there, but that he did not want any official notice taken of the visit. When the ambassador pointed out that Kemal Ataturk, the Turkish dictator, would be mortally offended if the King of England sneaked in and out of his country for the sake of a game of golf, the King was furious. Loraine responded by threatening to resign and Anthony Eden backed him up. With bad grace the King gave in, making his visit official and his golfing appetites did, in fact, pay rich dividends, for Ataturk was deeply honoured by this visit, and his gratitude stood Britain in good stead in future years.

After this involuntary foreign policy coup the King returned to England in September 1936. He decided to hold a houseparty at Balmoral for Mrs. Simpson and some of her American friends, and since the Duke and Duchess of York were staying with their two daughters nearby, the King hoped that they would play a prominent part in the Balmoral entertainments. But the Duchess of York had other ideas. She went over to Balmoral on her husband's insistence, but she made little attempt to hide the resentment she felt at being received by Mrs. Simpson, effectively acting as hostess and by now even sleeping in the bedroom formerly used by Queen Mary. For Princess Elizabeth's mother the whole thing had gone too far. Months previously the King had been invited to open some new hospital buildings in Aberdeen, the closest major city to Balmoral. But he had refused on the grounds that he would still be in mourning for his father—although he had celebrated Ascot that June without bothering about it. The inconsistency of his excuse was underlined by the fact that he instructed his brother to take his place at the engagement, and then on the very day that his brother was performing the ceremony, a royal limousine was seen driving to the station to pick up Mrs. Simpson and her friends from the London train—with the car being driven by the King of England in person.

But by now far more serious issues were involved. In October 1936 Mrs. Simpson formally filed for divorce from her husband, on the grounds of *his* adultery, Ernest Simpson falling in with the prevailing custom that it was the honourable thing for the man to provide the evidence. When that divorce went through she would be in a position freely to marry King Edward VIII.

193

The King's Private Secretary, Alexander Hardinge, felt that the time had come to pay a visit to 145 Piccadilly. The situation was now so grave, he warned Princess Elizabeth's father, that it could quite possibly end in the abdication of his elder brother.

The problem of Mrs. Simpson must now inevitably come into the open, and even if it could be resolved in some way, it left a far deeper issue unresolved, for Edward VIII was engendering a crisis in the British system of representative monarchy that went far beyond whether or not the woman he appeared eager to marry would make a suitable Queen. Flouting the wishes of his elected government, pursuing personal enthusiasms with no regard for the reaction of the nation, the man evidently wanted to be more than a representative sovereign. He wanted to be himself. And that, on his terms, simply was not possible.

"Something Must be Done"

The year 1936 was that in which the Civil War started in Spain. Abyssinia was over-run by Mussolini. Hitler marched into the Rhineland, and the Japanese concluded with the European dictators the Rome-Berlin-Tokyo Axis. But all this counted for little in Britain, engrossed more and more as 1936 moved onwards by the spreading rumours about Edward VIII and then by the final convulsion which ended in his abdication on 11 December.

The date set for the hearing of Mrs. Simpson's divorce petition was 27 October 1936. Her husband did not contest it, and she was granted a decree *nisi*. As the law then stood, this was a conditional decree which would not become a final divorce until 27 April the following year. The King could therefore marry her before the Coronation scheduled for May—except of course that he was head of a Church that totally disapproved of the remarriage of divorced persons.

On the evening of 16 November King Edward went to dinner with Queen Mary and spoke openly to her for the first time about his love for Mrs. Simpson. He was surprised by his mother's

194

sympathy for his personal predicament—until he told her that he was prepared to abdicate if Mrs. Simpson could not be Queen. "To my mother," Edward wrote later, "the Monarchy was something sacred and the Sovereign a personage apart. The word 'duty' fell between us." What did duty mean? In Edward's eyes his duty lay to the woman he loved. His only doubt, he was to say, was not whether Wallis Simpson was acceptable, but whether *he* was worthy of her.

When the King then told his brothers next morning that he was prepared to abdicate if it were the price of marrying Wallis, their reaction was similar to their mother's. The idea of duty and sacrifice which David had in his head was totally alien to everything they lived by. The Duke of York, literally dumbfounded by what it meant for his own life and that of his daughter Elizabeth, could not say anything at all. And the Duke of Kent was consumed with anger. "He is besotted on the woman," he said. "One can't get a word of sense out of him."

Queen Mary was to set down her interpretation of duty in a letter to her son in July 1938. "You ask me in your letter of the 23rd of June to write to you frankly about my true feelings with regard to you and the present position and this I will do now. You will remember how miserable I was when you informed me of your intended marriage and abdication and how I implored you not to do so for our sake and for the sake of the country. You did not seem able to take in any point of view but your own. . . . I do not think you have ever realized the shock, which the attitude you took up caused your family and the whole Nation. It seemed inconceivable to those who had made such sacrifices during the war that you, as their king, refused a lesser sacrifice. . . . My feelings for you as your Mother remain the same, and our being parted and the cause of it grieve me beyond words. After all, all my life I have put my Country before everything else, and I simply cannot change now."

Stanley Baldwin put the nub of the matter more gently. "I pointed out to him that the position of the king's wife was different from the position of any other citizen in the country; it was part of the price which the king has to pay. His wife becomes queen; the queen becomes the queen of the country; and, therefore, in the choice of a queen, the voice of the people must be heard." If the humblest junior officer representing Britain in an Embassy abroad had to have his would-be wife vetted to make sure that she, in her own way, was a representative of whom the government and the people of Great Britain could approve, how much more should the country's supreme—and highest paid—representative of all take account of the opinion of others.

On 18 November 1936 King Edward VIII went to South Wales to inspect the miseries of unemployment there, the famous trip that provoked his still remembered exclamation, "Something must be done!" He toured the labour exchange queues, the slag heaps, the derelict shops for which no one had any money, and when he proclaimed his distress with the famous words that outlived his reign and his exile, he crystallized one of the more enduring myths of recent British history—that he was the people's King who really cared, the representative monarch who went beyond representation to action. The legend has been held up to the discredit of the more reticent style of the brother and niece who succeeded him, and it has even been suggested that the attitude of Baldwin's government during the abdication crisis was inspired by a wish to destroy this fearless crusader for the working man.

But this King who, not content with saying "Something must be done", also promised "You may be sure that all I can do for you I will", knew even as he uttered his cry that he had already told his Prime Minister, his mother, and his brothers of his intention to abdicate the throne. Small wonder that when newsreels next year showed the ex-King celebrating his marriage in the comfort of a French château, the miners of South Wales declined to rise for the National Anthem.

On 3 December the press finally broke silence. And the tone of most comment on the prospect of Queen Wallis presiding over Britain, the Dominions and the Empire, shocked Edward profoundly. It showed him that the rest of the royal family and the Prime Minister were not so out of touch as Edward had been presuming. "They don't want me," said the King sadly as he looked at the press.

Opposition from the Dominions was even fiercer. Imperfect though Edward's appreciation of constitutional monarchy was, he could see there was no future for him as King when feelings were so bitter. He could, perhaps, count on a quarter of the country for solid support, but, for a representational monarch when emotions ran so high, even three-quarters were not enough. In a matter of days, the crisis was over. Rather than divide his nation, King Edward decided to leave it, and told Baldwin so on Saturday 5 December.

At 145 Piccadilly it was impossible to hide from the children that something very exciting and rather frightening was happening. On the day the story broke Edward had gone down to Fort Belvedere and never returned to Buckingham Palace as King, so it was inevitably to 145 Piccadilly over the park that officials went. The Princesses watched the grave dignitaries who stalked across the hall below them and could scarcely miss the noise of the growing crowds outside. There were shouts of "Long live King Albert", for that, it was assumed, was the title that the Duke of York would be taking when he succeeded his brother.

The strain on Prince Albert at this time was intense. "I went to see Queen Mary," the Prince wrote in his journal, "& when I told her what had happened I broke down and sobbed like a child." Furthermore, throughout the crucial days of the abdication crisis the Duchess of York was in bed with influenza. Miss Crawford was summoned to see her when the news, still not public, reached 145 Piccadilly. "The bedroom door opened. Queen Mary came out of the Duchess's room. She who was always so upright, so alert, looked suddenly old and tired.

"The Duchess was lying in bed, propped up among pillows. She held her hand out to me.

"'I'm afraid there are going to be great changes in our lives, Crawfie,' she said. '. . . We must take what is coming to us, and make the best of it.'"

Friday 11 December 1936, was the day when Princess Elizabeth formally became heir to the throne, for her father became King the moment Parliament ratified the instrument of abdication which Edward had signed the previous day.

Lady Cynthia Asquith had been invited to 145 Piccadilly that day, and she found the little Princesses fully aware, in their own terms, of what was going on. Princess Elizabeth saw a letter on the hall table addressed to "Her Majesty the Queen". "That's *Mummy* now, isn't it?" she said.

Princess Margaret, just learning to write, was troubled by practical concerns. "I had only just learned how to spell York— Y O R K and now I am not to use it any more. I am to sign myself Margaret all alone."

Next day came the public proclamation of their father's new title. "Lilibet and Margaret had run as usual to give their father a final hug as he went off," remembered Crawfie, "looking very grave, dressed as an Admiral of the Fleet. . . . When he returned, both little girls swept him a beautiful curtsey. I think perhaps nothing that had occurred had brought the change in his condition to him as clearly as this did. He stood for a moment touched and taken aback. Then he stooped and kissed them both warmly."

The new Queen was just recovering from her flu. "I can hardly now believe," she wrote to the Archbishop of Canterbury, "that we have been called to this tremendous task and (I am writing to you quite intimately) the curious thing is that we aren't afraid. I feel that God has enabled us to face the situation calmly."

Two days previously in the House of Commons Stanley Baldwin, in his memorable speech which made public for the first time the details and course of the abdication crisis, had described the responsibility that faced the new King and Queen. "The Crown in this country through the centuries has been deprived of many of its prerogatives, but today, while that is true, it stands for more than it ever has done in its history. The importance of its integrity is, beyond all question, far greater than it has ever been . . . the guarantee in this country, so long as it exists in that integrity, against many evils."

Integrity was the key word. Edward VIII had played many parts as Prince and King—and had played most of them, on the whole, very attractively. But the actor had got the better of the whole man, and he had come to think it possible to separate his public mask from his private life. It was his tragedy that the unreined exercise of individual inclination, which was the *raison d'être* of traditional executive monarchs, had become the most dangerous variety of original sin in an age which felt entitled to reject kings who loved without its consent.

Coronation

Abdication was Britain's vote for monarchy, but monarchy of a certain style, as Prince Albert, Duke of York, acknowledged by picking out George, the last of his four Christian names, to be his title as King. "What will endear him to his people," declared Stanley Baldwin, "is that more than any of his brothers he resembles in character and mind his father"—and this could already be seen to be true of Princess Elizabeth.

She was a conscientious person. If ever she felt ill she would struggle against being sent to bed. She would insist, "I must not take the easy way out." Every night before she dropped off to sleep she would jump out of bed several times to make sure that her clothes were arranged properly and that she had set her shoes quite straight. She kept detailed accounts of the shilling a week pocket money she received, saving from it to buy materials for the Christmas presents that she manufactured herself, and only occasionally would she venture to let the world wonder whether she might, beneath it all, not be just like any other little girl of ten. When a preacher leaving Glamis Castle promised to send her a book, she said thank you, but asked if it could be "Not about God. I know everything about Him."

George VI was the Boy Scout of British monarchs. "If the worst happens & I have to take over," he had written shortly before the abdication crisis, "you can be assured that I will do my best to clear up the inevitable mess, if the whole fabric does not crumble under the shock and strain of it all." And from the moment of his accession George VI dedicated himself totally to what he saw as his principal responsibility: "to make amends for what has happened."

In the personal crisis that came as a hangover from the great public events of the abdication, George VI was sustained by the strength of his wife and her loyal and unquestioning affection. The King seemed to grow in stature almost visibly through the first critical months of his reign, and he was helped by spending his Christmas holiday at Sandringham, which he loved. When he went to church there on his first Christmas Day as King, over 6,000 well-wishers were waiting outside to cheer him, for Britain as a whole seemed to share his wish to bury the past. It was notable how little mention the press made of the king in exile and the woman for whom he had given up everything. It was not through any deliberate censorship, more because people just wanted to forget.

On 17 February 1937 Princess Elizabeth moved into Buckingham Palace with her family to live "above the shop" and, apart from a short break after her marriage, she has lived there ever since.

The Palace had been bought in 1762 by George III from the Dukes of Buckingham who had used it as their London residence. The original Buckingham House, however, is now out of sight of the general public. The Hanoverians built two wings out from it, and then across the front of them, enclosing a huge quadrangle, the modern and recognized façade onto the Mall.

It was a draughty museum of a place with high ceilings, huge staircases and corridors so interminable that a postman had to trudge around them delivering internal messages. Most of its furnishings and fitments dated from Victoria's time. Electric light had only been installed shortly before King George VI and his family moved in, and even that in a rudimentary fashion. Rooms might well be illuminated by a single bulb that could only be switched on from a point some way down the passage outside, and the ancient skirting boards and floor cavities housed thriving colonies of mice. A "vermin man" was employed full time. Inside this rambling community the royal family were not so much heads of the household as the most prestigious occupants of a block of flats. They had their own separate apartment in one wing at the back overlooking the gardens.

The gardens, from the point of view of the Princesses, provided the principal consolation for the move away from the cosiness of 145 Piccadilly. There was a hill, and also a lake big enough for boating. On one of the lawns stood the summerhouse where King George V had worked in his declining years, with his writing table, pencils and ink pot still there, and now it became the headquarters of the Buckingham Palace packs of Guides and Brownies—thirty-four little girls drawn from the children of Court officials and Palace employees to provide some broadening of the Princesses' sequestered existence.

Contact with everyday life is an experience royalty finds the more valuable for being so elusive. As a child at 145 Piccadilly the glimpsed reality of buses had seemed mysterious and fascinating, and the move to Buckingham Palace in 1937 intensified the difficulty for Elizabeth of achieving what had always been her parents' ambition for both their daughters, to raise them as ordinary little girls.

The new King and Queen tried hard. After their accession their visits to the Bowes-Lyons at Glamis became the more important to them. Here George VI liked to drive the car himself, with a collection of nine nephews and nieces giggling in the back, to one of the secluded beaches on the east coast of Scotland. All the cousins were companions the Princesses could play with naturally, rushing round the corridors and gardens of Glamis, and they provided the basis for the small group of people who have become the personal friends of Queen Elizabeth II today.

Princess Elizabeth's relationship with her younger sister was another aspect of her childhood that was altered by the events of 1936. Until then, comparatively remote from the succession, they had been equal, apart from the four-year gap between them. But as the prospect of the King and Queen producing a son receded, Elizabeth's elevation as heir to the throne could not help but aggravate what has proved to be one of the more troubled themes of her life, her sister's anomalous public and family role in which the accident of heredity has cast her.

Aged six in 1936, Princess Margaret was a bright vivacious little girl. She was already demonstrating a gift for music and also for mimicry—which her father encouraged. George VI had a sense of fun rather than a sense of humour, and usually at other people's expense. So his delight at Margaret's cheeky imitations accentuated his natural tendency to spoil his younger daughter. In the glow of parental approval she developed a more extrovert personality than Elizabeth, less conscientious and altogether less well-mannered.

Certain observers have been critical of Elizabeth's precocious solemnity. But while it has set some teeth on edge to hear Crawfie's report of a little girl telling her younger sister before a garden party, "If you see someone with a funny hat, Margaret, you must *not* point at it and laugh," Princess Elizabeth was, in all fairness, only preparing for her future job the best way she knew how. The world considers itself entitled to laugh at royalty, but it does not take kindly to royalty laughing back.

The date previously arranged for Edward VIII's crowning, 12 May 1937, provided an early opportunity for the new King and his family to be presented to the people in majesty, and throughout the spring of 1937 Britain became gripped with monarchical fervour. "The whole of London is full of stands for the coronation," wrote Queen Mary to the Duke of Windsor, as David was now called (she wanted to borrow his diamond-studded Garter Star to wear at his brother's crowning), "too ugly and the poor daffodils are squashed & hidden underneath." The chief exhibit at the Ideal Home Exhibition was a "Coronation" piano, a white baby grand with blue and red keys, while underwear manufacturers offered chemises with crowns, brassières with crowns (in the centre) and corsets decorated with crown, lion and a unicorn shying up from the left hip.

Through March and April 1937 life for the Princesses revolved around the forthcoming event. It was the theme of Miss Crawford's lessons and Queen Mary unearthed a full colour panorama depicting the Coronation of King George IV. In preparation, Princess Elizabeth was brought out to stand by her parents, shake hands and make small talk at some of their public engagements.

The Princesses' robes for the Coronation ceremony were their first long dresses, though underneath they wore the short white

Left: *Edward VIII abdicates in favour of his brother. Mrs. Simpson's picture is prominently displayed on the newsstands.*

Middle: *The Coronation of George VI. The royal family and their attendants on the centre balcony of Buckingham Palace.*

Bottom: *Queen Elizabeth makes a tour of bomb-damaged South London in 1940, and chats with her fellow-Londoners.*

socks of childhood. Margaret had to have a specially built-up seat constructed for her in the carriage in which she would ride to the Abbey with Queen Mary. It had become over the centuries a matter of royal superstition that the widow of a king should not attend his successor's Coronation. But for once in her life Queen Mary was breaking with tradition. She saw good reason after the upsets of the previous December to demonstrate royal solidarity.

The great day itself started early, since the timetables of modern British coronations are arranged to cram as much as possible in before an early lunch break. The King and Queen were woken at three in the morning by the testing of loudspeakers outside the Palace, and the arrival soon after that of troops to line the streets made sleep impossible for everyone. "At 5 o'clock in the morning I was woken by the band of the Royal Marines striking up just outside my window. . . ." wrote Princess Elizabeth in red pencil in a penny exercise book. She entitled this "The Coronation, 12 May, 1937. To Mummy and Papa. In Memory of Their Coronation, From Lilibet By Herself." "I leapt out of bed and so did Bobo. We put on dressing-gowns and shoes and Bobo made me put on an eiderdown as it was so cold and we crouched in the window looking on to a cold, misty morning. There were already some people in the stands and all the time people were coming to them in a stream. . . ."

In his own account George VI wrote, "I could eat no breakfast & had a sinking feeling inside." Yet it seemed to Ramsay MacDonald that both the King and Queen were in states of religious trance at certain points in the ceremony.

Back in the Palace Elizabeth reported that her sister had behaved impeccably. "I only had to nudge her once or twice when she played with the prayer books too loudly." Lunch had been taken from a cold buffet in one of the Canon's rooms at the Abbey and then the family had driven by a roundabout route back to Buckingham Palace through streets packed with cheering crowds. A machine rigged on a roof in Whitehall had recorded that while the King and Queen's coach had drawn cheers registering eighty-three decibels, the one containing the old Queen and her grand-daughters had attracted eighty-five.

Heir Presumptive

Princess Elizabeth was heir presumptive, but she was not heir apparent. The latter title is given only to the first sons of British Sovereigns, because nothing but death can prevent their ultimate inheritance. But Princess Elizabeth, right until the moment of her accession to the throne in February 1952, could only ever be heir presumptive, since she could only succeed *presuming* that no brother were born—and according to Lady Airlie, this was exactly what the Princess wished for. When first told of her position as successor to her father, she began fervently saying her prayers for a new male addition to the family.

Both the King and Queen, however, enjoyed the size of their neat little family as it was, and the King saw in his earnest elder daughter all the qualities needed in the style of monarchy set by his father. The Princess's simplicity and tender-heartedness—her love for animals seemed to fill a gap in an existence low on playmates, and in London she had several budgerigars whom she would talk to, feeding them and cleaning out their cage herself—were perhaps not conventional qualities to cultivate in a future monarch, but both her parents preferred naïvety to sophistication, and George VI himself found the greatest relaxation from the strain of his work in escaping to Royal Lodge for simple weekend pleasures with his wife and daughters. He loved to go out in the grounds on a Saturday afternoon for a wooding expedition. The King, Queen and Princesses would dress in old clothes and take to the woods with an arsenal of billhooks, axes and pruning knives. The King would work like a man possessed, hacking, sawing, pulling out dead wood, heaping up bonfires, while the rest of the family—and even the chauffeur and detective—would stumble through the wood smoke, their eyes watering, and then go home to tea to nurse their blisters.

It was Miss Crawford who felt her charges' artistic tastes should be cultivated, so she brought up from the picture store every week one of the royal masterpieces, a Rubens, perhaps, a Canaletto or a Gainsborough, to sit on an easel in the Palace schoolroom—while

Queen Mary took the children on winter afternoons to the Wallace Collection to perambulate for hours around the baroque masterpieces, though all it can confidently be stated that the future Elizabeth II acquired from these exercises was the ability to keep walking with an expression of great interest on her face when her feet hurt and it was getting towards teatime.

Elizabeth idolized her father, and as she grew up she appeared, both as a dutiful daughter and as his heir, to be modelling herself on his qualities—especially the persistence she saw as he wrestled with the hesitation in his speech. The King had an eager, schoolboy-like way of questioning cabinet ministers and generals. He could not always digest complex points—for his intellectual level was very similar to his father's—but he would note and memorize abstruse facts and figures diligently. "I found him to be well informed on all that was taking place," said President Truman many years later. "I was impressed with the king as a good man."

Truman got the most important point. George VI was not bright, but he had many honourable qualities. He had a simple piety and what his daughter Elizabeth described after his death as "steadfastness". He would listen to the BBC radio programme "Lift up your Hearts" every morning, and might well introduce the topic of the day into his conversation over lunch. "What do you think of the Ten Commandments?" he might suddenly fire at a guest in the middle of soup.

Fun was the hallmark of King George VI's family life. We notice it in all the remarks of casual visitors to the royal homes. Charades, games, sing-songs, these made the framework in which Princesses Elizabeth and Margaret grew up.

But though their childhood was incomparably jollier than that of their father and his brothers, it is not certain that it was more tightly connected with real human experience and emotion. King George VI felt it was his duty to keep some of his gravest worries to himself, that he should shield his womenfolk from his official anxieties and many of his personal ones. His anguish over his brother David and Mrs. Simpson, for example, was not something he liked to discuss. The pain it caused him only

206

betrayed itself occasionally—in unguarded remarks, special difficulty with his speech or, quite commonly, long moody silences. In later years Lord Plunket used to say he could always tell when the ex-King was due to call on one of his London stopovers because of the sudden chill in the atmosphere—though nothing was said—and the way in which George VI's wife would "drive out" of the Palace. It was the dark side of the family life the King worked so hard to keep sunny for his wife and daughters.

In 1937 the Duke of Windsor provided justification enough for his younger brother to feel upset. Deciding to marry Wallis Simpson that year on 3 June, the date of his father's birthday, was a family matter. But the Windsors' visit a few months later to Nazi Germany, where they were fêted by Himmler, Hess, Goebbels, Goering and Hitler himself—the Duke venturing a wobbly raised arm salute—had wider implications. It did not need the Führer's comment, "She would have made a good Queen" to remind people how close the monarchy had come to betraying its principles.

Mention of the Duke of Windsor was the one thing that appeared to disturb the developing composure of George VI—as in later years her ministers were to describe Queen Elizabeth II as only giving way to emotion on the subject of her sister. She was shy like her father, but there was no trace in her of the high-bred nerviness that seemed to come out somewhere in every generation of the family. She was growing up into a placid girl. For her thirteenth birthday in the spring of 1939 she was given the sort of presents considered suitable for a teenager: a box of fine silk stockings from the Queen, a diamond-studded bracelet from the King, a ciné camera and projector sent by Uncle David, and a silver dressing-table set from Queen Mary, each article bearing the Princess's initials. But physically she still had not matured as fast as other girls of her age. As Miss Crawford put it, "At this age, when so many are gawky, she was an enchanting child with the loveliest hair and skin and a long, slim figure." This childlike appearance was emphasized by her style of dress, still, in her early teens, identical with that of her nine-year-old sister: uniform tweed coats, berets, white socks and plain sandals.

She started her holidays that summer—the last summer of peace for six years—with a cruise in the royal yacht *Victoria and Albert* with her parents and sister along the south coast, and on the afternoon of 22 July the yacht sailed up the river Dart to drop anchor off the Dartmouth Royal Naval College. Her father had concluded his education as a boy with an ignominious period there, finishing sixty-first out of sixty-seven in 1912. But he had enjoyed his time as a cadet, and he was looking forward to revisiting his old haunts with his cousin and fellow naval enthusiast, Lord Louis Mountbatten, known to his family as Dickie.

The Mountbatten destiny had been intertwined with that of the Royal House of Windsor since the reign of Queen Victoria. Dickie, like George VI, was one of her great-grandchildren, and his father Prince Louis of Battenberg had been First Sea Lord at the outbreak of the First World War. But though Louis had won this rank on merit after forty-six years of distinguished service with the Royal Navy, he had been born a German, and less than three months after hostilities started in 1914, he had been compelled to resign his office after public outcry at his origins—the same hysteria against all things German that made it unsafe even to be seen exercising your pet Dachshund in public.

The royal family had come under bitter attack, descended as they were from the German houses of Hanover and Saxe-Coburg-Gotha. Graceful camouflage seemed the only solution, so George V, his family and descendants took the name of Windsor, a stout English title fit to stand with Tudors, Stuarts and Plantagenets (Edward III, it was discovered, had actually called himself "Edward of Windsor"), while the Battenbergs resorted to straight translation to emerge English-sounding enough as Mountbatten.

In July 1939 at Dartmouth the two cousins shared the pleasure of re-living their naval training. The King concluded his inspection of the College and grounds by calling for the Punishment Book to read aloud the register of his misdemeanours as a boy. His recital, we are told, provided "hilarious entertainment" for his audience of cadets and instructors.

The Princesses, meanwhile, were sent off to the house of the

208

officer in charge of the College. There they were playing with a clockwork railway laid out all over the nursery floor (according to Miss Crawford) when "a fair-haired boy, rather like a Viking with a sharp face and piercing blue eyes, came in". It was Lord Mountbatten's nephew, Prince Philip of Greece, who had joined the College as a cadet that year.

"He was goodlooking, though rather offhand in his manner," remembered Miss Crawford. "He said, 'How do you do,' to Lilibet and for a while they knelt side by side playing with the trains. He soon got bored with that. We had ginger crackers and lemonade in which he joined, and then he said, 'Let's go to the tennis courts and have some real fun jumping the nets.'"

Elizabeth never took her eyes off him the whole time, recalled the governess with her gift for the telling personal detail. "At the tennis courts I thought he showed off a good deal, but the little girls were much impressed. Lilibet said, 'How good he is, Crawfie! How high he can jump!' He was quite polite to her, but did not pay her any special attention. He spent a lot of time teasing plump little Margaret."

Prince Philip was just eighteen, almost a young man. Princess Elizabeth at thirteen was really still a little girl, as was made obvious when the Prince came on board the royal yacht that evening for dinner with a group of other cadets. She had been put to bed, and it was Miss Crawford who danced the Lambeth Walk and the Palais Glide with the young officers.

Miss Crawford was right when she compared Prince Philip's ash-blond hair and angular features to those of a Viking. He was in essence a Dane, one of the exports to Greece of the most successful exporting dynasty of modern times, the Danish royal house. The Danes took over the Greek throne in 1863 by invitation when the new nation of Greece, after a hard-won struggle to achieve independence of Turkey's four centuries of domination, had tried several other royal families without success. The eighteen-year-old Prince William of Denmark got the job, and Prince Philip was a descendant of his, born on the island of Corfu on 10 June 1921.

Prince Philip was some way down the table of succession to the throne of Greece. He himself had been carried away from Greece in an improvised cot of orange boxes on a British light cruiser in 1922, during a dramatic rescue operation inspired by King George V himself. The baby Prince's father, Prince Andrew, was being held under threat of execution in Athens, one of several scapegoats for the recent defeat of the Greek armies by Turkish troops. Six other of the scapegoats, five Greek ministers and the Commander-in-Chief, were shot in November 1922, and Prince Andrew would almost certainly have met the same fate if it had not been for the arrival of a British agent, who, by means that are still not clear, persuaded the Prince's captors to release him and send him into exile with his family—the beginning for Prince Philip of a nomadic existence which was not to develop real roots until his marriage.

Prince Philip was a waif in more senses than one. Not only did he lack a conventionally stable home, but he lacked conventionally stable parentage as well. By the time he was born his mother and father had been married for eighteen years and, having raised four daughters significantly older than Philip, had exhausted the possibilities that their partnership could offer them. They drifted apart and lived separately for most of his childhood. It was more a matter of mutual apathy and divergent interests than of any cataclysmic rift. Philip's father had worked hard at his career as a soldier, but the humiliation of his banishment bred in him a cynicism and indolence to which he surrendered, and he gravitated to Monte Carlo and the quietly upholstered life of a playboy of modest means, exhibiting a compulsion to keep everyone around him laughing continuously—a habit that his son was to develop. Prince Andrew also passed on to Prince Philip his short-sightedness. Andrew's monocle and pince-nez made an elegant virtue of his necessity for spectacles, but his son has chosen to be more discreet. Prince Philip wears contact lenses (sometimes lost when he used to play polo), and conventional glasses when he drives a car—except when driving in and out of Buckingham Palace at crowded times of day. Then the spectacles vanish and the Prince's passengers have to take their chances with the Palace pillars.

Prince Philip's mother, Princess Alice of Battenberg, gave him his link with the Mountbatten family. She was a daughter of the ill-treated Sea Lord and first of the Mountbattens. Unlike her husband she did not allow the injustices she suffered to wither her own sense of duty. Through the German occupation of Greece during the Second World War she was to stay living in Athens sheltering refugees from the SS, and in 1949 she institutionalized her personal dedication by founding the Christian Sisterhood of Martha and Mary whose grey monastic robe and coif she wore for the rest of her life, the last few years as her daughter-in-law's guest, a quiet presence in Buckingham Palace. She was a withdrawn woman—her isolation intensified in old age by deafness —and when in the 1920s she was bringing up Prince Philip in the absence of her husband, she relied on friends and in particular upon her brothers George and Dickie Mountbatten.

It was her elder brother George who, until his death in 1938, looked after the boy, sending him to Cheam preparatory school. Philip had until then lived among the disintegrating fragments of his parents' marriage in Paris, attending a little academy for diplomats' children and *émigré* sprigs of nobility like himself, and circulating round his European relations against a cosmopolitan backdrop of mansions and palaces where his young cousin, Queen Alexandra of Yugoslavia, remembers "nannies all cheerfully sitting down to tea with bowls of caviar". She also remembers a naughty little boy running into the Baltic with all his clothes on, falling into the mud of a pigsty to annoy his English nanny, and devising a remedy when hateful cauliflower was served for luncheon: "whoosh, we simultaneously upturned our plates on the snowy tablecloth"—all rather different from the childhood approach to life of his distant cousin, Princess Elizabeth.

Uncle George thought some male discipline was called for and, after Cheam, sent Philip first to Salem, a school in Bavaria founded by the legendary Kurt Hahn. When Hahn moved the school to Gordonstoun in Scotland, Philip went with it.

"Often naughty, never nasty," was his headmaster's verdict on the future husband of the Queen of England. "Prince Philip is a born leader, but will need the exacting demands of a great service

211

to do justice to himself. His best is outstanding—his second best is not good enough."

Service in the navy offered the challenge this diagnosis called for, and Philip's Greek nationality was no bar to him serving as a temporary British naval officer. He had only been a few months at Dartmouth when he met Princess Elizabeth, but he had already won the King's Dirk as the best cadet of his term.

When Elizabeth and Philip met each other the Second World War was less than two months away. Philip was soon swept up into active service, and when he remembered his cousin, it was as a shy thirteen-year-old fond of ginger crackers and lemonade. If the advantages of a dynastic alliance there ever crossed his mind—as they certainly crossed the minds of his relatives—he saw it as a decision for his pending tray.

His young cousin Princess Elizabeth, however, saw things differently. Nearly twenty years later, when Sir John Wheeler-Bennett published his official biography of King George VI, a work commissioned and scrutinized word for word by Queen Elizabeth II, his royally approved verdict was emphatic on the subject of Prince Philip of Greece: "This was the man with whom Princess Elizabeth had been in love from their first meeting."

War

In September 1939 the future Queen Elizabeth II could look back on a childhood which, however happy, had been abnormally secluded, and the Second World War which broke out in that month was to prevent any possibility that her life would broaden significantly in adolescence. National security dictated that the heir to the throne be segregated from the population's communal experience of mass warfare; while national morale had made it impolitic for her to be evacuated from Britain and thus to expand in freedom. Instead these crucial six years in her development were very much like the sequestered dozen that had preceded them, with certain additional restrictions: a Palace-bound existence within one safely fortified strong-point; snatched contact

212

with her parents made more tenuous than ever by the twenty-four hour demands on them of the war; and almost monastic confinement with her enduring trio of female intimates—her sister Margaret, her maid Bobo and Miss Crawford.

As the first Christmas of the war drew close, it was considered safe for the family to go to Sandringham—near though it was to one of the coastlines where a German invasion was considered most likely. The pleasures of Christmas were only slightly dimmed by their father's anxiety about his Christmas broadcast. "This is always an ordeal for me," he wrote in his diary, "and I don't begin to enjoy Christmas until after it is over." But the extra effort which this anxiety stimulated paid remarkable dividends that year. He had come across a poem which was part of a collection of verse entitled *The Desert*, published privately in 1908, and he concluded his broadcast with some lines from it: "I said to the man who stood at the Gate of the Year, 'Give me a light that I may tread safely into the unknown.' And he replied: 'Go out into the darkness, and put your hand into the Hand of God. That shall be to you better than light, and safer than a known way.' May that Almighty Hand guide and uphold us all."

King George VI now had to decide what to do with his daughters under the very real threat of invasion which 1940 presented. Nazi paratroopers were expected to be landing in mass or in small snatch squads to kill or carry off individual targets, and the Princesses were obviously vulnerable. One option was to evacuate them to safety in one of the Dominions, probably Canada. Many British parents who could afford to were doing this with government approval. It would have been understood as prudent and honourable for the King and Queen to do the same. But this was not good enough for George VI. The relief from anxiety that evacuation offered to ordinary parents could not be enjoyed by the King and Queen. And so it was decided that the Princesses would stay. "The children won't leave without me; I won't leave without the King; and the King will never leave," was Queen Elizabeth's officially released explanation of the decision, and it was widely applauded.

Windsor seemed the safest place while offering the least

disruption to family life. So in May they moved into the castle and there Princess Elizabeth settled for the rest of her childhood. Today she still regards Windsor, of all her residences, as home.

Officially it was announced that the Princesses were living in "a house somewhere in the country" but in fact they were remarkably close to London itself, and surrounded by the latest technology of warfare. Anti-aircraft guns poked up incongruously around the battlements. The cellars were made bomb-proof, while troops drilled constantly to protect not only the Princesses but also the Crown Jewels that were wrapped in old newspapers and stowed haphazardly in the castle vaults. It was not at all as an old royal palace should be, and Queen Mary pronounced it "so depressing".

The national crisis meanwhile raised a difficult question for King George VI. Increasing criticism of Neville Chamberlain's conduct of the war had led to a vote of no confidence and he was swept from power on 10 May 1940. The King thought his Prime Minister was very hard done by. "It is most unfair on Chamberlain to be treated like this after all his good work," he wrote in his diary. He did not trust the one acceptable alternative, Winston Churchill, a rogue elephant with a record of shifting loyalties, who had taken his brother's side during the abdication crisis. But it was his duty to act as the instrument of political realities, so on 10 May George VI summoned Churchill to Buckingham Palace.

The peril now threatening Britain was shaping daily life for the Princesses down at Windsor. The gunfire and explosions as the British Expeditionary Force was driven into the sea at Dunkirk were frighteningly audible even that far down the Thames, and gunfire rang out regularly from the firing range set out in the Great Park. George VI took his staff there for regular pistol practice for, as Winston Churchill said, hand-to-hand fighting amid the ruins of Whitehall appeared that summer to be a serious possibility. Churchill's plan was for the special corps of troops guarding the royal family to spirit them off into the country in the event of a German invasion, but George VI was reluctant to agree to any such plan. He was only prepared to retreat to become the head of an armed resistance movement.

IT WAS ON 13 September 1940 at the height of the Battle of Britain that in the King's words, "all of a sudden we heard an aircraft making a zooming noise above us, saw 2 bombs falling past the opposite side of the Palace, & then heard 2 resounding crashes as the bombs fell in the quadrangle about 30 yards away."

The plane had flown straight down the Mall. "A magnificent piece of bombing, Ma'am, if you'll pardon my saying so," was the verdict of one of the policemen guarding the palace, to the Queen.

"I am glad we've been bombed," was Queen Elizabeth's reaction. "It makes me feel I can look the East End in the face."

She need not have worried. If there had ever been any doubt about Britain's loyalty to the royal family it was removed in the autumn of 1940 as day after day King George VI and his wife walked round the streets of the shattered city, heartening the people amidst the rubble that had been their homes. "Thank God for a good King!" cried one survivor as he saw the little couple picking their way through the ruins of his neighbourhood. "Thank God for a good people," was the reply of King George.

As the German offensive switched to other cities, the King and Queen went to visit them too. Through the night reports would come in of a blanket of explosives dropped on Coventry, Southampton, or Bristol and next morning the royal couple would set off to inspect the damage. "I feel quite exhausted after seeing & hearing so much sadness, sorrow, heroism and magnificent spirit," wrote his wife to her mother-in-law. "The destruction is so awful, & the people so *wonderful*—they *deserve* a better world."

Another innovation stimulated by the challenge of 1940 was for Princess Elizabeth to make a broadcast. The suggestion came from Derek McCulloch who, as "Uncle Mac", was making programmes for evacuated children. It seemed to him that her example, evacuated to "a house somewhere in the country", possessed representative significance.

The Princess had been rehearsed by her mother to get her breathing and intonation right, and she delivered the prepared text with aplomb. There was no evidence of nervousness or hesitation in her speech, and when she reached the end listeners heard her say, "Come on, Margaret"—at which her ten-year-old sister, who had been silent at her side, piped up, "Good night, children."

Life in Windsor Castle, protected by a crack corps of troops, and seeing their parents several times every week, may not have been strictly comparable to the lot of most other children evacuated during the war. But with all the chandeliers taken down, and the glass display cabinets turned to the walls, Windsor Castle made a dismal setting for Princess Elizabeth's flowering into young womanhood.

It raised the question whether, in later years, she would feel able to trust herself far outside her immediate set. She was already a shy girl, cautious with all but the few she knew very well indeed. How receptive would she prove in the future to ideas coming from outside her circle?

Still, the war confirmed, if there were any doubt of it, her sense of duty, and Princess Elizabeth—her leisure programmed as thoroughly as ever by the adults among whom she lived—developed from a serious child into a serious girl with no discernible break in continuity, and any tendency to rebellion was stifled by the extraordinary circumstances dominating this crucial stage of her development.

At about this time Prince Philip, not yet twenty, was serving on the battleship HMS *Valiant* in the Mediterranean. In March 1941 he found himself manning a searchlight under heavy fire in the battle of Matapan when some Italian warships were cornered off the Greek mainland's most southerly cape. *Valiant* was seriously damaged—and the Prince was mentioned in dispatches: "Thanks to his alertness and appreciation of the situation," wrote his captain, "we were able to sink in five minutes two eight-inch gun Italian cruisers." Whatever future some members of the royal family might be planning for Prince Philip, it did not carry any exemption from genuine danger.

But the Prince did find time between his naval responsibilities to maintain a "cousinly correspondence" with Princess Elizabeth throughout the war, and on the few occasions he came back to Britain on leave, he visited her and was welcomed by her parents.

Princess Elizabeth makes her first broadcast, in 1940, to all British children evacuated from their homes.

George VI introduces his daughter, the heir presumptive, to the routine of government papers.

Second Subaltern Elizabeth Alexandra Mary Windsor, A.T.S.

They liked him and the King enjoyed hearing his first-hand accounts of battle and chewing over naval life in general.

Elizabeth was transparently devoted to him, but her parents saw little danger in this. She was young and he was evidently preoccupied for the moment with the war. They saw him more as a relative than a suitor. The situation between him and the Princess was never formally discussed because, as members of the same family—and profession—everyone involved clearly understood what it was. There could be nothing to discuss until the war was over.

At the age of sixteen Princess Elizabeth was required by law, along with other girls of her age, to register at a labour exchange. She duly did this at Windsor in the spring of 1942, and this provided the first indication that she was developing a mind of her own. Her cousin, Lady Mary Cambridge, was working as a volunteer nurse in the blitzed areas of London, and the Princess felt that she should do the same. The King did not agree, however. He considered his sixteen-year-old daughter too young to leave her governess, and this remained a source of friction between the Princess's developing independence and her father's innate conservatism. When, two years later, he eventually gave way to her arguments, it in fact proved easy to find some representative war work the Princess could do without unjustifiable risk.

In 1942, however, King George VI's family underwent an experience more totally representative of the national ordeal than any gesture the Princess could make. Flying off to tour RAF bases in Iceland on 25 August, the plane carrying Prince George, Duke of Kent, crashed, and the Prince was killed. "I have attended many family funerals in the Chapel," wrote George VI in his diary, "but none . . . of which have moved me in the same way. Everybody there I knew well but I did not dare to look at any of them for fear of breaking down."

Packed off to the country like some treasure from the National Gallery, Queen Mary was meanwhile contributing to the war effort in her own style. She was eating strictly according to the ration book, and had also agreed to the appearance of bourgeois

218

napkin rings at the table to avoid the need for laundering after every meal. Her most frequently expressed grievance at Hitler was that the man spoke such abominable German, and she kept three suitcases packed in the event of a Nazi landing—with a fourth ready to be filled with her diamonds and tiaras.

By Christmas 1943 Princess Elizabeth was approaching her eighteenth birthday. She had been allocated a sitting room of her own at Windsor and a lady-in-waiting to help with her correspondence. An amendment to the Regency Act allowed her to assist with administrative duties if ever her father were ill or abroad. It was getting difficult casually to dismiss the feeling that she still nursed for her cousin Philip as puppy love—while he, with the war obviously drawing to a conclusion, was considering more seriously what he felt about Elizabeth. Their "cousinly correspondence" had become more intense. And from their conversations emerged sufficient commitment for Philip to start discussing with his relatives the possibility of marriage, or at least some formalized courtship. His older cousin, King George of Greece, approached Elizabeth's father.

"We both think she is too young for that now," wrote George VI in March 1944, "as she has never met any young men of her own age. . . . I like Philip. He is intelligent, has a good sense of humour & thinks about things in the right way." But now was not the moment. The King was not ruling out Philip's prospects; it was just that Elizabeth required more experience of the world before any definite decisions were reached.

The King's reaction seemed reasonable, particularly as he did finally capitulate to his elder daughter's persistent campaign to be allowed to "join up". He could hardly refuse in view of his wish for her to see more of the world, and she saw it at Aldershot as a subaltern in the Auxiliary Territorial Service—"No. 230873, Second Subaltern Elizabeth Alexandra Mary Windsor. Age: 18. Eyes: blue. Hair: brown. Height: 5ft 3ins." Every day she was driven over to pursue the ATS course of vehicle maintenance, working in, on and under motor cars and lorries. She learnt how to read a map, drive in convoy and how to strip and service an engine, and when her parents visited her depot to see her taking her final test they found her in greasy overalls with black hands and smudged face looking out from under a car "very grave and determined to get good marks and do the right thing".

She had, however, scarcely completed her training when the war was over. On 8 May 1945 London celebrated the unconditional surrender of Germany signed the previous day, and George VI led his people in thanksgiving.

Winston Churchill declared that King George VI and his family had more closely identified themselves with their people in war than had any of their predecessors, and his verdict was generally endorsed. "We have been overwhelmed by the kind things people have said over our part in the War," wrote the King in his diary. "We have only tried to do our duty during these $5\frac{1}{2}$ years." But the cost of the strain upon his health had been a high one, and he knew that he was not the only member of his family to have suffered. On the evening of VE day itself, after the family had appeared time after time on the balcony of Buckingham Palace to the cheers of the enormous crowds, he detailed a group of young officers to take his daughters quietly out of the Palace to mingle with the throngs of merrymakers revelling in the almost forgotten experience of brightly lit streets and buildings. The Princesses Elizabeth and Margaret were swept along in the mass rejoicing. "Poor darlings," was King George VI's final entry in his diary for VE day, "they have never had any fun yet."

Marriage

The celebrations of VE day were repeated little more than three months later when the dropping of the atomic bomb in August 1945 set the seal on Japan's defeat, and, in the interim, British political and social history turned a decisive corner. Clement Attlee and the Labour Party were voted to power with an enormous majority and embarked upon the reorganization of post-war Britain and her Empire.

King George VI was as upset by the change as he had been in 1940 when Neville Chamberlain was forced to resign, and he did not conceal his feeling that Churchill had been treated with ingratitude by the people he had led to victory. He was conservative in politics as in life and felt ill at ease with the socialism of the aggressive Labour ministers he now had to deal with—"rather difficult to talk to", he confided to his brother, the Duke of Gloucester.

But his first priority in the months immediately after the end of the war was to re-establish for his wife and daughters something of the family life they had known together before the war. In September 1945 they went to Balmoral for a long and secluded holiday, and the King was able to introduce his elder daughter to the pleasures of deerstalking, and this has remained one of her great, if less publicized, enthusiasms. While she and her father were shooting, her mother was fishing. Reared near salmon rivers, Queen Elizabeth loved to pull on waders after dinner at Balmoral and stride thigh-deep into the pools where the salmon were rising in the evening light. She cast her lines with the deftness of a professional and could play fish doggedly for an hour or more before landing huge specimens, actively keeping up this sport well into the 1970s.

The family rejoiced to be in their element again and organized elaborate picnics in an old schoolhouse abandoned up on the moor. The Princesses stored dry heather and firewood there and cooked barbecue meals—with a degree of assistance from the Balmoral chef who would "start things off" with some of the food before he packed it in the hamper. And afterwards everyone took their pots and pans down to the burn to wash them and leave them clean for the next visit to their playhouse. George VI was happier than he had been for a long time. Six years of war had denied him many of the pleasures of being a father to the attractive growing girls, and he was determined to enjoy that to the utmost now. But his ambition ignored the maturity of Princess Elizabeth. She was now nearly twenty, of an age when any girl would be moving away from her inner family circle. And she was in love. No matter how loving and dutiful a daughter she might be, this could not help but inspire her with new priorities.

With the return of Prince Philip from active service imminent,

221

things started to move quickly—and it was Elizabeth who forced the pace. She placed a photo of the Prince prominently on her mantelpiece and when reproved for her lack of discretion, she simply exchanged it for one of Philip in the bushy naval beard he had sprouted, maintaining that that camouflage would fool anyone. It did not, of course. The very reverse, for soon rumours of romance began appearing in the newspapers, and the picture on the mantelpiece was cited as corroborating evidence. The King, meanwhile, had clumps of young Guards officers organized as dance-party companions and as guests at Windsor or Sandringham.

His mother could see exactly what he was playing at. Out of his hearing, Queen Mary would refer to the jolly young men as "The Body Guard". Lady Airlie, when she looked at the way in which King George VI displayed his devotion to his elder daughter, "wondered sometimes whether he was secretly dreading the prospect of an early marriage for her".

But the King's feelings about his daughter were more complicated than that. Philip was anxious to become a British subject since, quite apart from any question of marriage to Princess Elizabeth, he had his naval career to consider, and he could not hold a full commission until he became British. This, however, contained enormous potential for embarrassment. To naturalize a Greek prince as a British subject might be taken as an indication of British support for the Greek royalists in the latest Greek civil war, or, alternatively, as a sign that Britain regarded the royalist cause as lost and was giving Philip some sort of refuge.

When King George raised the question of Philip's naturalization with the government, he was told the question would have to be postponed until the Greek general election and plebiscite on the monarchy had been held in March 1946.

So a question mark hung over the first Sandringham Christmas the family could celebrate together after the war in December 1945. The "Body Guard" worked hard at creating an atmosphere of raucous festivity in which George VI joined heartily, leading congas and old English country dances that went on into the small hours. But Philip was not there. He was still tied up in the formalities of demobilization. And Elizabeth knew that in any case her own future must wait upon political events in Greece.

IN THE SUMMER of 1946 Prince Philip was granted leave from the navy and came up to Balmoral. But though the March plebiscite in Greece had yielded a majority in favour of the monarchy, it was now judged unhelpful to the royalist cause for a member of the family to renounce his nationality so close to the restoration. So the couple were no closer to a decision than they had been a year earlier. Marriage must wait on naturalization. King George and Queen Elizabeth both felt that the imposed political delay had a helpful personal consequence by postponing a precipitate engagement, though they could sense how very much in love the young people were. But when, in the late summer of 1946, Prince Philip of Greece proposed directly to Princess Elizabeth, she ignored her father, mother, King, Queen and governments and accepted him there and then.

Discretion, however, was the watchword, for Princess Elizabeth did not forget herself so much as to broadcast her betrothal to the world. She had done well enough to carry off her coup, and the only possible basis for her father accepting it was absolute secrecy. Quite apart from the King's personal feelings, a public announcement would clash with plans he had laid for the following months. The royal family had long been committed to making a tour of South Africa early in 1947, in gratitude to the Dominion for coming to Britain's aid at the outbreak of war. George VI had been eagerly looking forward to undertaking this sea voyage and extensive tour with his wife and two daughters. He needed a rest. He was already showing signs of the illness that was to bring about his premature death. Princess Elizabeth's twenty-first birthday, furthermore, would occur during this tour, and arrangements were being planned for a ceremony of dedication to mark this coming of age. An engagement, with all the public anticipation of a wedding, did not fit conveniently into this scheme of things at all, and so the young couple were told that public acknowledgement must wait. They might consider themselves engaged, and might be viewed as such by their intimate family, but so far as everyone else was concerned the romance was off.

Now began the most difficult stage of all, for Princess Elizabeth and Philip had to survive for nearly a year in a limbo derived from George VI's unwillingness publicly to acknowledge their engagement. The Prince was stationed down in Wiltshire at a naval shore station, and in the winter of 1946/7 they quite frequently went out in the same parties of young people, but they were never seen to dance or talk with each other more than with anyone else.

The family set off to South Africa on 1 February 1947. It was a good time to get away to the sun. The winter of 1946/7 in Britain was the cruellest within living memory, unceasing frosts and blizzards bitterly accentuating chronic fuel shortages and the general post-war austerity. But the temperament of King George VI was such that the warmth and sunshine of South Africa, which he desperately needed, only made him feel the more guilty for not being at home. In "mental torment" he contacted the Prime Minister to suggest he should return to Britain, and he was only persuaded to continue his tour—which was, in all conscience, arduous enough in its own right—by reflecting that a precipitate return would magnify the extent of the crisis at home.

The tour was the first ever undertaken by the entire royal family together, and Princess Elizabeth's twenty-first birthday was also the first coming-of-age by an heir to the British throne in one of the Dominions. She made a broadcast to mark the occasion, and this had special significance in the year that India was scheduled to gain her independence. The hope was to reinforce the Crown as the common symbol uniting Britain with her territories and ex-territories at a time when so many other formal ties were severed.

The theme of her address was duty—an act of self-dedication through the immediacy of radio to each of her future subjects. "I declare before you all," she said, "that my whole life, whether it be long or short, shall be devoted to your service and the service of our great Imperial Commonwealth to which we all belong. But

I shall not have strength to carry out this resolution unless you join in it with me, as I now invite you to do; I know that your support will be unfailingly given. God bless all of you who are willing to share it."

The measure of her dedication came on her return from South Africa. Philip was now naturalized under his uncle's surname of Mountbatten, but despite Elizabeth's expectations her father adamantly continued to withhold agreement to her public betrothal. "He had always liked Prince Philip and had grown to esteem him highly," explains Sir John Wheeler-Bennett, "but he still found it difficult to believe that his daughter had really fallen in love with the first young man she had ever met, and perhaps he also dreaded losing her from that compact and happy family circle which had been his delight since his early married days in Royal Lodge."

Finally, however, a full two months after her return from South Africa, as Sir John tells it, "there could no longer be any question as to the wishes and affections of both parties, and their pertinacity and patience were rewarded." On 10 July 1947 it was announced from Buckingham Palace: "It is with the greatest pleasure that The King and Queen announce the betrothal of their dearly beloved daughter, The Princess Elizabeth to Lieutenant Philip Mountbatten, RN, son of the late Prince Andrew of Greece and Princess Andrew (Princess Alice of Battenberg), to which union The King has gladly given his consent."

BRITAIN in 1947 was a sombre place—the bitter winter, rationing, the loss of India and Burma, the development of the Cold War, all this created an atmosphere of gloom through which the news of Princess Elizabeth's engagement burst like light from another world. A people starved of joy found sustenance in the joy of the girl they had watched grow up through all the strains of the previous years, and, far from resenting the additional happiness that marriage brought to a young life that was already privileged beyond most people's wildest dreams, they celebrated with her as generously as they knew how.

There were six hundred rooms in Buckingham Palace, as

everyone knew, and an intolerable housing crisis. But a nation with so many young married couples living with their parents did not want the Princess's husband lodging with his in-laws. The House of Commons voted £50,000 for Clarence House to be redecorated for the couple as a first home of their own.

The couple's first appearance together in public was at a garden party at Buckingham Palace in July 1947. Lady Airlie was impressed by the unpretentious way in which Philip carried himself. "I noticed that his uniform was shabby—it had the usual after-the-war look—and I liked him for not having got a new one for the occasion as many men would have done. . . ."

Presents started arriving from all over the world. Miss Julie Aloro of Brooklyn broke open her money box to send a turkey to Princess Elizabeth, "because she lives in England and they have nothing to eat in England". Many women had realized that the worst part of living through post-war reconstruction for a young girl was the scarcity of nylon stockings, and so these were sent to her literally in their hundreds. The catalogue of the public exhibition of the gifts numbered over 1,500 items.

The procession of international royalty to the wedding in November 1947 recaptured the fiestas of Queen Mary's youth. "A week of gaiety such as the court had not seen for years," wrote her lady-in-waiting. "There were parties at St. James's Palace to view the wedding presents, a Royal dinner party for all the foreign Royalties, and an evening party at Buckingham Palace which seemed after the years of austerity like a scene out of a fairy tale."

"Saw many old friends," wrote Queen Mary in her diary. "I stood from 9.30 till 12.15 a.m.!!! Not bad for 80."

Though Philip did not set much store by titles, the King took trouble personally to select the titles that his new son-in-law would carry.

The paradox was that in an age where the geography of noble titles reflected little or no proprietorial interests, local loyalties were liable to get inflamed if the Princess's husband were made baron, earl or duke of some area that suggested favouritism. So George VI made Philip baron, earl *and* duke of localities

226

The future Queen pledges herself to the service of her people in her 21st birthday broadcast, made during the tour of South Africa in 1947.

The new Duke and Duchess of Edinburgh on their wedding day, 20 November 1947.

judiciously sprinkled around the British Isles—Greenwich, Merioneth and Edinburgh respectively.

However, the order of service for the wedding ceremony on 20 November 1947 took no notice of this long string of dignities. They were not announced until the morning of the ceremony itself, and so the bridegroom was billed as plain Lieutenant Philip Mountbatten RN. It is not generally realized that Philip ceased to be a prince in 1947 when he chose to be naturalized. He was not given the title of a Prince of the United Kingdom until February 1957 when his wife bestowed it on him in recognition of his work in the previous ten years.

Another surprise was the Princess's wedding dress. The Palace had been careful to announce that, in common with other brides, the Princess had been granted a small extra allotment of clothing coupons for her trousseau. But the allowance had been supplemented by material bought in the past by her mother and Queen Mary, not to mention the unsolicited gifts of silk, muslin and brocades that poured in from all over the world, so the result was spectacular. "Mr. Norman Hartnell has shown himself no mean poet," declared James Laver, the well known fashion historian. "In a design based on delicate Botticelli curves, he has scattered over the ivory satin garlands of white York roses carried out in raised pearls, entwined with ears of corn minutely embroidered in crystal. By the device of reversed embroidery he has alternated star flowers and orange blossom, now tulle on satin and now satin on tulle, the whole encrusted with pearls and crystals."

George VI felt moved as he escorted his daughter to give her away at the altar. "I was so proud of you & thrilled at having you so close to me on our long walk in Westminster Abbey," he wrote to her later, "but when I handed your hand to the Archbishop I felt that I had lost something very precious."

At the lunch party afterwards in Buckingham Palace little bunches of white heather, sent down from Balmoral, were set beside every plate and the speeches were kept short. As it grew dark, the couple drove out of the central Palace quadrangle. They were showered with paper rose leaves and pursued by laughing guests to the very railings of the Palace, and there the crowds massed outside took over the acclamation. They cheered the bride and groom all the way along their route to Victoria where a train waited to take them on honeymoon.

A few days later Princess Elizabeth received a letter from her father. "I have watched you grow up all these years with pride," wrote the King, "under the skilful direction of Mummy, who as you know, is the most marvellous person in the World in my eyes, & I can, I know, always count on you, & now Philip, to help us in our work. Your leaving us has left a great blank in our lives but do remember that your old home is still yours & do come back to it as much & as often as possible. I can see that you are sublimely happy with Philip which is right but don't forget us is the wish of

Your ever loving & devoted

PAPA."

End of a Reign

Less than a year after Princess Elizabeth's wedding day crowds gathered again against the railings of Buckingham Palace. From early on Sunday, 14 November 1948 spectators had been drawn by the news that Sir William Gilliatt, the gynaecologist, was staying at the Palace. Soon after dusk the Princess was taken to the royal nursery, now transformed into a surgical ward. The Duke of Edinburgh changed into flannels and a sweater and took his friend and equerry, Michael Parker, off for a game of squash.

They had not finished their game when the Duke was told he had become the father of a healthy baby boy. Racing upstairs, he shook the King by the hand and was embraced by the Queen. When she came round from the anaesthetic, Elizabeth was greeted by the sight of a huge bouquet of roses and carnations held by her delighted husband. There was no need for a bulletin to be posted on the palace railings. A Palace official whispered in a policeman's ear, and he passed the news on to the crowds, so when Queen Mary drove up to inspect her first great-grandchild, the celebrations were already well under way.

Twelve temporary typists had to be hired to acknowledge the

229

sackfuls of letters and presents that arrived at Buckingham Palace for the little boy. His mother naturally found him exquisite, especially his hands, "fine, with long fingers—quite unlike mine and certainly unlike his father's," she wrote to a former teacher.

Queen Mary was struck by the likeness between the new baby and the Prince Consort, and she spent an afternoon with Lady Airlie looking through old photo albums of Queen Victoria and her husband trying to pin the similarity down. "I gave the baby a silver gilt cup & cover which George III had given to a godson in 1780," she recorded in her diary, "so that I gave a present from my gt. grandfather to my great grandson 168 years later."

The child was christened Charles Philip Arthur George, and his daily routine was much the same as his mother's had been at that age. The baby's hairbrush, silver rattle and perambulator were the very ones Nurse Knight had used, and two Scottish nurses were hired. Miss Helen Lightbody—given the courtesy title of "Mrs." because she was the senior of the two—had been nurse to the Duke of Gloucester's children. Miss Mabel Anderson—who has remained Miss Anderson to this day—had got the job through an advertisement in a nurses' magazine. Their empire in Clarence House, where the Princess, husband, son and household moved in 1949, was the pale blue nursery whose glass-fronted cabinets displayed toys museum-style—reminiscent of 145 Piccadilly.

SINCE THE ACCESSION of his wife in 1952, the Duke of Edinburgh has carved out an independent and well recognized *persona* for himself. But in the early stages of his marriage the role of royal son-in-law sat uneasily on him. Palace staff at all levels found him difficult to deal with on occasions—prickly, arrogant. A ceremonial existence one footstep behind his wife was the exact opposite of everything life had been preparing him for. But he was, after all, still a serving officer in the navy. He worked for some time at the Admiralty, walking every morning through the park to his desk job in Whitehall "shuffling ships around", and then he was transferred to a Staff Course at the Royal Naval College down the river at Greenwich. He still nursed the ambition to command his own ship, and with George VI little more than fifty years old, he could reasonably count on at least a decade to pursue his naval career before the need to work as Consort became urgent.

Princess Elizabeth's life was organized on similar assumptions: a young family, an existence in which official engagements, though inescapable, would play a secondary role to being a mother and the wife of a full-time naval officer—there was every promise of a long spell closer to everyday existence than anything she had known before.

But the winter of that year brought the first warning signs that this was not to be. King George VI was feeling discomfort from cramps in his legs, and the pains grew worse. By October 1948 his left foot was numb all day and then the trouble shifted to his other foot. The diagnosis was early arteriosclerosis—obstruction to the circulation through the arteries of the legs. The King must cancel his engagements and rest. He should spend as much as half the day in bed.

The treatment brought results, and after an operation in the spring of 1949 George VI appeared fitter, though weak. It seemed safe for the Duke of Edinburgh to take up a posting in the autumn of that year as first-lieutenant on HMS *Chequers*, the leading destroyer of the first Mediterranean destroyer flotilla, and for his wife to join him.

It was the closest Elizabeth was ever to come to everyday existence. When she flew out to Malta in time for Christmas 1949 she found herself, for the first and last time, free of official life and duties. Lord Mountbatten was flag officer commanding the first cruiser squadron in the Mediterranean and he let the couple stay in his house overlooking the harbour. There was swimming, sunbathing, dancing, outings to beaches, markets to haggle in, shops to visit, ordinary cocktail and dinner parties with other young married couples. True, there was always a detective shadowing the Princess from a discreet distance, and she did have the advantage of her faithful Bobo, and Pearce the footman. But she was a naval officer's wife rather than the King's daughter. Now it was that she learnt to stand on the touchline looking interested and chatting with other polo wives while her husband learned the sport that was Uncle Dickie's passion.

By the spring of 1950 Elizabeth was pregnant again. She came back to Clarence House and in July her husband flew home in time for the birth of a daughter. Princess Anne Elizabeth Alice Louise was born on 15 August 1950, the same morning as the Duke of Edinburgh was gazetted lieutenant-commander. He had achieved his long-standing ambition, a ship of his own, and he threw himself into his new command—HMS *Magpie*, a frigate in the Mediterranean fleet—with the single-mindedness he had shown in his wartime responsibilities. He drove his crew hard at everything. In the annual regatta *Magpie* won six out of ten boat events with the Duke rowing stroke, stripped to the waist, in one of the whalers. Once his wife had finished nursing Princess Anne, she came out to join him again.

But the fun ended abruptly. In July 1951 the Duke of Edinburgh left the navy on indefinite leave—which has been extended to the present day. King George VI was ill again.

1951 was the year of the Festival of Britain. Timed deliberately to coincide with the centenary of Prince Albert's Great Exhibition of 1851 in which Britain had shown off her technical and commercial expertise to the world, the Festival was intended to demonstrate, after the war and austerity, that Britain could still make it. The main exhibition site was on the South Bank of the River Thames where the Festival Hall remains today.

When the King had opened the Festival on 3 May he was very obviously tired and ill. "The incessant worries & crises through which we have to live," he wrote to a friend, "[have] got me down properly." The problem was not the strain of events, however. King George VI had cancer.

At first it was only a suspicion at the back of his doctors' minds. It seemed like slow recovery from an attack of flu late in May 1951. But when Clement Price Thomas, a leading chest surgeon specializing in malignant diseases, was called in, the diagnosis became definite.

King George was never told that he had cancer. The results of Mr. Price Thomas's examinations were explained in terms of a bronchial tube blockage necessitating the removal of one lung. Among themselves the doctors were most worried by the danger of the thrombosis which had threatened earlier. There could be a coronary attack at any time during the operation, with a high risk of one in the few days thereafter.

The King's wife, daughters and son-in-law knew what was at stake. Princess Elizabeth and her husband were due to tour Canada and the United States at the beginning of October and it seemed for a time that they might not be able to go. Their departure date was postponed until the doctors could feel confident of the King's health.

But the operation went well. It seemed safe for Princess Elizabeth and her husband to set off on 7 October 1951, though with their luggage went a draft accession declaration, with a message to both Houses of Parliament. For thirty-five days the couple travelled across the North American continent covering nearly 10,000 miles in Canada alone. In America they eclipsed for a few days even the headlines about the hostilities in Korea.

"We've just had a visit from a lovely young lady and her personable husband," wrote President Truman to King George VI. "They went to the hearts of all the citizens of the United States. As one father to another we can be very proud of our daughters. You have the better of me—because you have two!"

When they got home George VI appeared in good health, and he had been able to show himself to photographers for the first time after his illness on 14 November 1951 when he attended his grandson's third birthday party. This is Prince Charles's only memory of his grandfather—a figure sitting beside him on a sofa. The photograph was printed in time for the Princess's return and, framed, it still stands in the Queen's private sitting room.

The newspapers were delighted at the royal recovery and on Sunday 2 December a day of National Thanksgiving was celebrated in churches all over the country. The King felt fitter than he had done for a long time. He celebrated his fifty-sixth birthday quietly with his family at Buckingham Palace and on 21 December travelled down with them to Sandringham. This year he was relieved of the worry of his Christmas broadcast, for examinations of his chest and throat had left him hoarse. He pre-recorded his address in small scraps as his strength allowed and was able to sit back after lunch on Christmas Day to listen to the edited tape with his family. He had been invited to make a private visit to South Africa in the spring to round off his recuperation.

The King and Queen's departure was planned for 10 March 1952, but his close family knew that George VI might not live that long. Whether or not the removal of his lung had definitely checked the cancer, the risk of coronary thrombosis remained. And the doctors made clear to the King himself, without going into all the details, that his expectation of a moderately active life might only extend a few years, or even less.

George VI, however, was unconcerned. It was foolish, he told Lady Cynthia Colville one evening, to confuse illness with operations. On 30 January 1952 he went out to the theatre with his family for the first time since his illness. *South Pacific* was playing to packed houses at Drury Lane and the royal family went to see it both in celebration of the King's recovery and as a final gathering before Princess Elizabeth and the Duke of Edinburgh embarked on an ambitious tour representing the King in East Africa, Australia and New Zealand.

On the morning of 31 January 1952 King George VI waved goodbye to his daughter and son-in-law from the tarmac of London Airport, and then went back up to Sandringham where a party of friends awaited him for some end-of-season shooting.

5 February was a clear crisp late winter day with blue sky and long shadows. The quarry was hare and the King shot cleanly and fast. After dinner that night he retired to his room relaxed and satisfied. He had not entered the hare in his game book, and that page has remained vacant, for in the small hours of 6 February 1952 the heart of George VI stopped beating.

Accession

On 5 and 6 February 1952, Elizabeth and Philip were resting from the round of official receptions with which they had been greeted by Britain's East African possessions. Back in 1947 Kenya's wedding present to the couple had been a hunting lodge on the banks of the Sagana River in the Aberdare Forest game reserve, and this was their first opportunity to enjoy it. Nearby stood the Treetops Hotel, a hut built in the branches of a giant fig tree overlooking a water hole and salt-lick, where artificial "moonlight" encouraged game to come out of the forest.

On the night King George died Elizabeth was in Treetops Hotel, looking down at elephant, rhinoceros, and water-buck, and it was nearly dawn before she finally retired to her room. That morning she went fishing and managed a better catch than her husband. She was in high spirits. Back inside the sitting room of Sagana Lodge after lunch Elizabeth did not see Michael Parker, her husband's equerry, moving stealthily round the lawn to attract the Duke's attention through the wide bay window. The Duke went out to see what the matter was. He returned to tell his wife that her father was dead and that she was now Queen of Great Britain, her Dominions and her possessions beyond the seas. It was 2.45 p.m. local time, 11.45 a.m. in London.

Michael Parker remembers that the Duke "looked as if you'd dropped half the world on him. I never felt so sorry for anyone in all my life." Queen Elizabeth II, however, betrayed absolutely nothing. She had to show herself to her officials and servants as Queen, and her calm public face, like the mourning clothes she had carried with her abroad, was part of her standard emergency equipment.

Her work started at once. While Philip and the staff concentrated on the plans and packing for the 4,000 mile journey back to London, she completed the documentation of the inheritance, declaring the name by which she would be known, since it was by no means a formality that she should carry as monarch the name she had borne as heir. She drafted telegrams of apology to those awaiting the planned next stage of her tour in Australia and New Zealand. She carried through the civilities common to all royal visits. The case of presentation gifts was unpacked as usual, to disgorge signed photographs and small tokens for each member of the game park staff—cigarette lighters, cuff-links, ashtrays, fountain pens. Then in silence the Africans lined the road to the airport beneath the flags and bunting. The

Queen's reflexes never failed her. As she reached the top of the steps to the plane taking her from Kenya, she turned briefly and managed a wave and a smile.

On a cold February afternoon she came down the steps of her aircraft at London Airport, a small, calm figure in black, to find three Prime Ministers, past, present and future, waiting beside her uncle, the Duke of Gloucester. Clement Attlee, Winston Churchill and Anthony Eden bowed their heads in homage to their new Queen.

She was back home in Clarence House at four o'clock, and at 4.30 a limousine drove slowly out of the gates of Marlborough House. Inside was Queen Mary. "Her old Grannie and subject," she said, "must be the first to kiss Her hand."

THE DRABNESS of ration-book London as it said farewell to George VI in February 1952 suited the national mood. Nearly a third of a million mourners queued for hours to shuffle slowly past his body as it lay in state in Westminster Hall, and the entire country observed two minutes' silence as his coffin of Sandringham oak was lowered into the ground at Windsor to the thud of muffled drums.

Elizabeth II was strained and white beneath her veil. All week since her return from Kenya she had been struggling with her emotions. "My heart is too full," she said in her accession declaration, "for me to say more to you today than that I shall always work as my father did," and as she went back to Clarence House the strain proved too much. She broke down and cried in the back of the car. Her husband comforted her.

Her grandmother felt too weak to attend the funeral in person. For Queen Mary it was the fourth monarch and the third of her own sons she had had to mourn. She stayed in Marlborough House with her surviving friend, Lady Airlie. The two old ladies sat together looking out blankly into the grey February weather saying nothing, until eventually the long cortège wound into view between the crowds standing silently in the Mall. Finally, the gun carriage bearing the coffin itself was in front of them. "Here *he* is," whispered Queen Mary, and Lady Airlie, imagining with her mistress, a shy stammering little boy in a sailor suit, found such a lump in her throat she could not speak. But the old Queen was not crying. She was gazing out into the murk, her features as impassive as ever.

Queen Mary realized she would be the next. She made a new will and reorganized the catalogues of what she called "my interesting things" to make sure that her grand-daughter, the new Sovereign, should receive them in proper condition. And she was, above all, most insistent that her own death, if it robbed her of the pleasure of seeing Lilibet crowned, should not spoil the occasion for the Queen herself or for the nation, since mourning for an ex-Queen Consort should never impede the crowning of a full Sovereign. She kept up her style to the end. She would accept occasional invitations to dinner and would arrive with a footman carrying half bottles of hock. He would open one bottle for his mistress's exclusive consumption and would concern himself with her alone throughout the meal. If he were instructed to open the second bottle, the hosts knew that the evening had been a success.

When the end came, on 24 March 1953, her wishes were observed. Her funeral cortège with regiments marching grandly through the traffic-free streets proved something of a rehearsal for the still grander procession to come in less than three months' time. She was buried beside her husband, in the family vault in St. George's Chapel, Windsor, and so, little more than a year after she had stood there mourning her father, Queen Elizabeth II also said farewell to the woman who, after her own parents, had been the most constant influence on her own character.

She now stood on the stage very much alone. But one member, at least, of the vanishing generation, had no doubt she would rise to the role allotted her. "I," declared Winston Churchill, "whose youth was passed in the august, unchallenged and tranquil glare of the Victorian era, may well feel a thrill in invoking once more the prayer and anthem 'God Save the Queen'."

THE CORONATION of Queen Elizabeth II on 2 June 1953 was celebrated by nearly a quarter of the world. The inhabitants of Britain and the Commonwealth numbered nearly 650 million, and by Coronation Day a fair proportion of them seemed to have congregated in London. The hotels and boarding houses were full. All seats in the stands had been reserved as soon as booking opened, and tickets were selling on the black market for £40 or £50 each. Outside the capital, streets and neighbours organized the distribution of the recently available television sets. There were holidays for everyone, mugs, plates, pamphlets and badges presented to schoolchildren, and car radio aerials had little Union Jacks fluttering chirpily on them. In street parties and church services people recaptured the wartime sense of community lost in the years of austerity. The Coronation occupied a single day, but excited anticipation maintained its enthusiasm for a whole year, and it left a warm glow in its aftermath.

It was an opportunity to enjoy the weight of money in the pocket as the Churchill government dismantled the mechanism of Socialist reconstruction. Ration books and utility merchandise had undermined the Festival of Britain as a celebration of national rebirth. Now the first fancy pottery since the war was released from Staffordshire onto the home market, and the government spent heavily on the trappings of the occasion.

On Coronation eve the Mall was packed, twelve deep, with 30,000 people bedding down with stools, spirit stoves, radios, blankets and waterproofs. It rained on them through the night, but as the morning newspapers came on the streets there were unexpected headlines, and loud cheers. Mount Everest had been climbed for the first time in history and the conquest was the work of a British team under Colonel John Hunt. Edmund Hillary, a New Zealand bee-keeper, had been the first to set foot on the summit with the Sherpa, Tenzing Norgay. It was taken as a better omen than the weather, which was to continue drizzling remorselessly much of the day in defiance of the meteorologists, who had selected 2 June as the most consistently sunny day of the calendar.

At eight o'clock the first of the processions began as the Lord Mayor of London was drawn in his coach to the Abbey by six grey horses, attended by his footmen and a guard of pikemen. The "junior" members of the royal family were driven to the Abbey in cars, and then there were more horse-drawn processions: the princes and princesses of the blood royal, the Speaker with the Mace of the House of Commons, the Queen Mother and Princess Margaret, and all the carriage processions of the colonial rulers, prime ministers and heads of state of the Commonwealth.

The first of the heads of state to arrive at the Abbey was Queen Salote of Tonga, with a bright red feather rising high out of her hat. Opposite her in the carriage was a little man in white, the Sultan of Kelantan. "Who can *he* be?" asked one of the beautiful young men attendant on Noel Coward as he watched the procession. Coward scrutinized the frail figure sitting opposite the monumental Polynesian lady. "Her lunch," he said crisply.

Queen Elizabeth II arrived with her husband at eleven o'clock in the state coach. Extravagantly gilded, curlicued and emblazoned with baroque pastoral scenes by Cipriani, the coach had been built in 1761 for George III and was attended by scarlet-and-gold-coated Beefeaters and postillions. "I was glad when they said unto me, We will go into the House of the Lord," rang out the opening anthem and Elizabeth stepped out on her progress down the aisle.

"Sirs, I here present unto you Queen Elizabeth, your undoubted Queen," called out the Archbishop of Canterbury, as he offered her to the four corners of the Abbey.

Then, as Handel's setting of "Zadok the Priest and Nathan the Prophet" carried through the Abbey the text which had been recited at every crowning in England from the Coronation of King Edgar the Peaceful in 973, the Queen's jewellery and robes were lifted off her piece by piece by her Maids of Honour. Her ceremonial train made a rich crimson pile overflowing from the extended arms of the Groom of the Robes, and Elizabeth II stood divested of all her finery, clothed symbolically in a simple sleeveless overdress of plain white linen, ready for her consecration.

"Be thy hands anointed with holy oil, be thy breast anointed with holy oil, be thy head anointed with holy oil," proclaimed the Archbishop, "as Kings, Priests, and Prophets were anointed."

Re-robed and enthroned in King Edward's Chair, Elizabeth

239

received the elaborate tokens of the responsibility with which she was being invested, the Orb—"remember that the whole world is subject to the power and empire of Christ"—the Royal Sceptre with the Cross, ensign of power and justice, the Rod of Mercy, and also the Royal Ring with a sapphire and ruby cross—"the Wedding Ring of England". Then came the moment of crowning itself as the Archbishop raised St. Edward's Crown glittering high in the air. Elizabeth bowed her head and then slowly, solemnly, the crown descended upon her. There had been several suggestions that instead of this extraordinarily large crown of solid gold she should wear the Imperial Crown of State, especially made to be lightweight for the Coronation of Queen Victoria and worn by monarchs ever since for ordinary ceremonial occasions like the State Opening of Parliament. The St. Edward's Crown, however, is the official Crown of England and the one with which the Sovereign is usually crowned. Elizabeth decided she could wear no other.

Until this moment the peers around the centre of the Abbey had been bareheaded. Now they all simultaneously put on their caps and coronets. "God Save the Queen" swept the shouts from all sides and the entire congregation went on shouting as trumpets blared, the Abbey bells rang and guns fired salutes all over London.

Led by the Duke of Edinburgh, who knelt in front of his wife, the senior peers of each degree—dukes, marquesses, earls, viscounts and barons—came forward one by one to do homage while the choir sang. And then, after taking Communion, the Queen went out of the Abbey to meet her people.

Working Queen

Thanks to television and the cinema Elizabeth II was the first British sovereign truly to be crowned, as the rubric requires, "in the sight of all the people", and the world tour which she and the Duke of Edinburgh undertook in the following winter of 1953/4 was her post-Coronation procession on a similar scale. In Jamaica,

Left: *Princess Elizabeth and the Duke of Edinburgh on honeymoon at Broadlands, the home of Lord Mountbatten.*

Middle: *Four generations. Queen Mary with her great-grandson, Prince Charles, at the christening of his sister Anne in October 1950.*

Below left: *Prince Charles's only memory of his grandfather, at his third birthday party.*

Below right: *Princess Margaret with Group Captain Peter Townsend.*

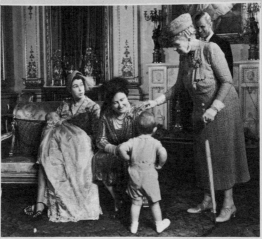

*Anthony Eden, Clement Attlee and Winston Churchill receive
their new Queen as she returns from Africa on 7 February 1952.*

*The Queen, accompanied by her husband,
on her way to Westminster Abbey for her Coronation.*

The crowned Queen enthroned in King Edward's Chair.

The Queen on holiday, riding at Balmoral.

The Queen at work on her papers.

she established what was to become the theme not only of her tour but of her entire reign. "The strongest bonds of all," she said, "are those which are recorded not in documents but in the hearts of the people who share the same beliefs and the same aims."

From the West Indies they sailed through the Panama Canal and on to Fiji and to Tonga where Queen Salote was waiting to greet them with a London taxicab she had ordered during her Coronation visit. By Christmas the royal couple were in New Zealand. "I want to show that the Crown is not merely an abstract symbol of our unity," said Elizabeth II in the first Christmas Day broadcast ever to be made from outside Britain, "but a personal and living bond between you and me."

On 3 February 1954 she reached Australia, where she emphasized that she was visiting her Dominions not as Queen of England, but as their own national Queen. In two months travelling through that country she covered 2,500 miles by rail, 900 by car and 10,000 by plane; she made 102 speeches, listened to 200 more—and had just six and a half days off-duty.

The Queen and her husband visited the Cocos-Keeling Islands, Ceylon, Aden and then travelled on by air to Uganda. Their children, Charles and Anne, were waiting for them off Tobruk in Northern Africa and together the whole family steamed home in the royal yacht *Britannia* for a reception on the Thames in front of the Tower of London. Elizabeth had been away for 173 days.

As the royal yacht approached Britain, her Prime Minister, Winston Churchill, decided it was only proper for him to be on the bridge beside his Sovereign as she sailed up the Thames, so he and his valet travelled down to Southampton to board *Britannia* off the Needles. Elizabeth had a feature film laid on for her Prime Minister's enjoyment. But the refreshment that flowed amply that evening had an adverse effect on Churchill's valet. The man became incapacitated and the Prime Minister was distraught. It was no way for his servant to behave on the royal yacht. So the evening on *Britannia* ended with Churchill surreptitiously undressing the valet and rolling him into his bunk.

Of the new Elizabethans few were more ardent than the Prime Minister, and some close to him wondered whether he was not even a little in love with the new Queen. He had her portrait hung over the head of his bed, and there it remained until the day he died.

But at the very outset of the reign the Prime Minister had had his doubts. He had been prostrated by the death of George VI. Tears poured down his face at the news. "I don't know her," he told his private secretary, Jock Colville. "She's a mere child. I knew the King so well."

"You will find her very much the reverse of being a child," Colville said, and Colville had reason to know. He had served as her private secretary from 1947 until 1949.

Indeed, Churchill soon found himself impressed. "What a *very* attractive and intelligent young woman," he would remark as he returned to Downing Street from his audiences. And with the candour that was his special charm, he would refer to his championing of Edward VIII. "Thank God I was wrong. Thank God I was wrong. We couldn't possibly have got a better King— and now this Queen."

Colville noticed how the Prime Minister's audiences at the Palace were growing longer and longer.

"What did you talk about?" Colville would ask him.

"Oh—racing," Churchill would reply vaguely.

But it was not only racing. In this final stage of his career Churchill, now very close to eighty, was haphazard. He was, for instance, especially lazy over reading his Foreign Office telegrams. One day, during a Middle Eastern crisis, two especially important messages arrived from the British ambassador in Baghdad. Colville put them on the very top of the Prime Minister's pile with a note that they should be read urgently.

But Churchill went off to the Palace without looking at them.

"I was extremely interested," said the Queen, "in that telegram from Baghdad." And went on to list, in her habitual fashion, the four points it suggested to her.

Churchill mumbled, trying to pretend he had read the papers, and came back to Downing Street in a fury. "You should have *made* me read it," he growled at Colville. And thereafter he did read every one of his telegrams before his audience.

Though not intimidated by Churchill as she had been in her first months on the throne, Elizabeth remained perplexed by the almost religious veneration with which he treated her, amused by the frock coat he insisted on wearing whenever he came to the Palace and alarmed by his determination, despite his age and illnesses, to travel all the way to Balmoral to keep up the tradition of the Prime Minister attending the Sovereign there. He would recline serenely in an armchair while the houseparty swirled around him, tottering out to see the children's ponies or to greet the Duke of Edinburgh and the other young guns back from the moors.

By this time the pattern of Elizabeth's working life was settling into the daily routine that it has broadly followed ever since. She would be up soon after eight. A pot of tea would be brought to the royal bedroom by a footman and handed to Bobo to take in. Menservants were never allowed inside. She would read letters from friends, their envelopes specially initialled to distinguish them from other mail. Beside her on the bed would be laid out all the newspapers, and she might turn to the back page of the *Daily Telegraph* to start on the crossword. (Her sister preferred the puzzle in *Country Life*, and indeed won its three guinea prize on more than one occasion.)

Dressed and sitting down to breakfast, she would listen to the BBC news, peppered with the comments of her husband who liked to provide his own running commentary to the world's events. Then, for a quarter of an hour outside the dining-room window, Pipe Major Macdonald of the Argyll and Sutherland Highlanders would march up and down playing his bagpipes. He performed this serenade every morning whenever Elizabeth was at any of her homes, and though Prince Philip had strong feelings of his own about this royal tradition dating back to the days of Queen Victoria, this was one opinion which he kept to himself.

After breakfast the children would come running down from their nursery, just as the little Princesses used to in 145 Piccadilly, to romp with their parents for half an hour. Then Elizabeth would telephone her mother and probably her sister too.

Work would start at 10.00 a.m., usually in her high-ceilinged

247

room at the back of Buckingham Palace, fenced about with palisade of photographs in leather and silver frames—children dogs, horses against bracing, windswept backgrounds. Sh would spend several hours most days there, the desk awash wit papers from battered leather dispatch boxes of the type th Chancellor of the Exchequer holds aloft on Budget Day—the ke cables to the Foreign Office in the last twenty-four hours, order to sign for the Home Secretary—all to be read, initialled, signed.

At least a dozen times a year she would hold an investiture i the grand ballroom of Buckingham Palace, but she has neve treated the honours system with quite the humourlessness of he forbears. When, on one occasion, the regalia got mixed up, an Cecil Day Lewis, the Poet Laureate, received an elaborat jewelled cross with silver chain intended for Lord de L'Isle an Dudley, so leaving nothing for his Lordship, she was vastl amused. Georges V and VI would not have seen the joke.

Elizabeth also initiated a new method of receiving people at th Palace over informal lunches to which would come half a doze guests—at her earliest gatherings the editor of The Times, th Bishop of London, the managing director of Wembley Stadium the headmaster of Eton and the chairman of the National Coa Board. The intention was to give Elizabeth some contact with cross-section of the country, and though some felt that thes selections were too close to the top of the tree, they were al undeniably perched in very different branches. Guests themselve came away with the impression of a friendly, surprisingly informe and amusing young woman. They noted how she and her husban laughed, chatted and even disagreed "like any other couple" (always the great surprise), and noted too the significance of he handbag. Apparently hung on some sort of hook below the table its surfacing was a sign that the proceedings were at an end.

The royal couple's engagement that afternoon might be movin ward by ward through a hospital, strolling through workshops fo the disabled, or inspecting a factory or a regiment at work Always the emphasis would be on meeting people personally, an on being seen at very close quarters by a succession of smal groups rather than to be gazed upon by large crowds.

248

There would be no evident rush, but by the end of an hour and a half they would have been through a lot of different settings and talked to a lot of people. Each visit to each room had been timed in advance, everyone to be presented pre-arranged and checked to make sure cleaners and secretaries would get as much time as bosses, and Elizabeth II would move through them all smiling, shaking hands, asking questions and listening intently to the answers. Just behind her would stride her husband, his conversational sallies more boisterous, the laughter louder. And when the automatic pilot broke down, as sometimes it did, then suddenly the Duke of Edinburgh would be at his wife's shoulder, laughing and joking but firmly taking over the conversation, so that she was free to move on from the temporary obstruction.

Usually home by five, the Queen would kick off her shoes, and into her room a footman would bear a tray of three dishes and several bowls containing separately meat, gravy and dog biscuits. Over the carpet would be spread a white plastic sheet and the bowls placed on it; then, with a silver fork and spoon, Queen Elizabeth II would distribute the ingredients to her corgis, mixing the recipes she knew each of her pets to prefer.

This was the second part of her day set aside for the family— horseplay and games of snap, racing demon and charades, rounded off with lots of splashing in the bath.

On Tuesday evenings she would see her Prime Minister in audience and every day while Parliament was sitting she would also receive an abstract of the day's proceedings there before dinner. At the beginning of her reign, Queen Elizabeth II decided that she would not, in principle, accept invitations to evening dinners. Banquet foods, cigar smoke and making speeches were among her least favourite things, and she was happy to leave them to her husband. But a number of galas and *premières* were inescapable and, with the need to catch up on the boxes, a quiet evening at home, that greatest treat of all, was a rare thing. She might watch a feature film in the Palace cinema, or television— Dudley Moore or in later years *Kojak*. After a day spent shaking hands with people on their best behaviour, television could take her closer to the tastes of her ordinary subjects.

Or she might read a magazine. Her appetite for stories about herself was greater than her press representatives were inclined to suggest—though one exception in the 1950s were those stories emanating from her former governess, Marion Crawford. Crawfie had horrified the royal family soon after she left their service by disclosing the details of her dozen and a half years with *The Little Princesses* in a book of that title, the first and best of a series of variations on a standard theme. It was not that she revealed anything in the slightest shameful. It was the betrayal of confidence that upset them, and one consequence of it was to make a formal oath of secrecy the condition of employment in the royal households. For Crawfie did not only write books. Her weekly outpourings in the columns of *Woman's Own* provided a saccharine commentary that trivialized and distorted the work Elizabeth II was trying to do.

But in 1955 the magazine columns proved the undoing of the ex-governess, for the magazine went to press some time before the events on which Miss Crawford chose to peg her copy. "The bearing and dignity of the Queen at the Trooping of the Colour ceremony at the Horse Guards' Parade last week," she wrote in *Woman's Own* dated 16 June 1955, "caused admiration among the spectators. . . ."

Yet unfortunately the Trooping of the Colour in 1955 was cancelled because of a rail strike, and Royal Ascot was postponed. So Crawfie's sparkling picture of the green turf, white rails and open carriages spanking down the course—"Ascot this year had an enthusiasm about it never seen there before"—created a sensation she did not intend. She concluded her career as a writer more rapidly than that as a governess.

Margaret and Peter

In August 1955 Queen Elizabeth's government found itself involved in a most delicate matter concerning the royal family. I came to its attention then because of an incident that had happened directly after the Coronation service back in 1953.

Elizabeth had just been crowned, and in the annexe at the entrance to Westminster Abbey the guests were steeling themselves for their ride back in the rain to Buckingham Palace. The ceremony had been sapping. Everyone had been up before dawn getting ready, and the day's business was still only half done. Most people were subdued, chatting quietly as they waited for their carriages to arrive. The one exception was the Queen's sister. Princess Margaret was exhilarated. She was laughing and talking, bubbling over with energy; and the man she was so clearly delighted to be with was the Comptroller of her mother's new household at Clarence House, Group Captain Peter Townsend, DSO, DFC. Margaret playfully picked a stray thread off the breast-pocket of his uniform, and then brushed proudly along his row of medals with her white-gloved hand, for she was in love with Peter Townsend, and she did not care who knew it.

It was the sub-plot to the grand Coronation drama. Princess Margaret and Townsend wished to marry. Elizabeth now had to resolve the problem the couple presented—for apart from the fact that the Group Captain did not possess the qualifications of birth hitherto expected of princesses' husbands, and that he was nearly sixteen years Margaret's senior, he had been party to a divorce.

This was the rub. With divorce Elizabeth was faced at the outset of her reign with the dilemma of 1936. Townsend's being the "innocent" party was little help. Her father and grandfather, as Supreme Governors of a Church which set its face more fiercely against divorcees than against almost any other variety of transgressor, had fought an even stronger rearguard action against marital informality than their bishops. The conflict was doubly agonizing, for Elizabeth did not only seek her sister's happiness, she had known and admired Peter Townsend for nearly a decade. An ex-fighter pilot ace, he had come to Buckingham Palace as an equerry in 1944. If events could have turned out as the new Queen would personally have preferred, then Princess Margaret would have been married in the early 1950s to the man she loved, and one of the more troublesome and painful themes of Elizabeth's reign might have been avoided.

Under the Royal Marriages Act of 1772, however, framed after a

Hanoverian marriage scandal, members of the family in line of succession to the throne had to secure the Sovereign's consent if they wished to marry before the age of twenty-five. Over twenty-five they still had to ask permission, but the Sovereign's veto was not absolute.

Since the Royal Marriages Act was a statute like any other, Elizabeth was bound to act upon the advice of her Prime Minister. She put Margaret's request to Winston Churchill. He considered marriage between the Queen's only sister and a divorced royal servant would make a disastrous beginning to the reign. Margaret would be twenty-five in two years' time. Let her ponder her feelings and then, if she still felt the same, the matter could be reconsidered.

Now two years later, in theory Princess Margaret could give notice to the Privy Council of her intention to marry and she would be free, publicly to be betrothed to the man of her choice.

But in practice nothing had changed since 1953. It had not been thought seemly then for a princess to marry a divorcee, and in 1955 the same objections remained. Public controversy was inevitable and there were furthermore powerful voices in the Cabinet who said they would resign rather than be party to advancing the marriage.

The most prominent of these was the Marquess of Salisbury. He knew that Queen Elizabeth the Queen Mother agreed with him, for he was one of the most regular guests at the weekend shooting parties that the dead King's widow had started giving as she recaptured her old *élan*. She remained as affectionate toward Margaret and as friendly towards Townsend as she had ever been, but the fact remained that the Princess's father, George VI, would never have approved the marriage. It was not in the Queen Mother's nature to be stern, least of all towards her children—and hence, perhaps, the need Lord Salisbury felt for sternness on someone's part. As a fervent high Anglican, and as a devout believer in the dignity of the monarchy, he felt he would be compromising his own work and that of his family over four centuries if he did not make a stand. Within the Cabinet few shared Salisbury's fervour, but no one was prepared to put the case against him. Anthony Eden (Churchill had at last retired) conveyed the Cabinet's feelings to the Queen. From the public point of view, the marriage was undesirable. To Elizabeth, however, her sister's feelings mattered just as much, and Elizabeth wanted her sister to be happy. She declined to coerce Margaret. Elizabeth had seen what the striking of moral attitudes had done in 1936, and the ostracism that had followed—and she had no wish to provoke another schism in the family. Margaret should see Townsend openly and spend as long with him as she liked. It was the only humane way the couple could make up their minds. But then on 24 October 1955 *The Times* broke silence in a monumental editorial.

The paper made no criticism of Peter Townsend, describing him as a "gallant officer with nothing to his disadvantage except that his divorced wife is still living". But, whether she liked it or not, Princess Margaret was the sister of the Queen, "in whom her people see their better selves reflected, and since part of their ideal is of family life, the Queen's family has its own part in the reflection. If the marriage which is now being discussed comes to pass, it is inevitable that this reflection becomes distorted. The Princess will be entering into a union which vast numbers of her sister's people, all sincerely anxious for her lifelong happiness, cannot in conscience regard as a marriage."

Even if the *Daily Mirror* retorted next day that *The Times* spoke "for a dusty world and a forgotten· age", and suspected that its editor would have preferred her to marry "one of the witless wonders with whom she had been hobnobbing these past years", *The Times* editorial proved a turning point. The next day, the Chairman of the Methodist Conference felt the time had come to pronounce on his Church's behalf. "Princess Margaret and Group Captain Townsend are popular young people in love with one another," he declared. But even if the Princess were to renounce her income and rights to the throne, to many "her example does not make it easier to uphold the ideal of Christian marriage in a land in which divorce is already too lightly regarded. . . ."

On the evening of Wednesday 26 October 1955 Princess

Margaret and Peter Townsend met for ninety minutes a Clarence House. It could hardly be pretended that pressures had not been exerted on them, but that was in the nature of the situation. And it was because of that situation that Princess Margaret decided she could not, after all, marry Peter Townsend She told her mother straight away and then she told her sister.

Princess Margaret's statement was released publicly on 31 October 1955. "I would like it to be known that I have decided not to marry Group Captain Peter Townsend," she said "I have been aware that, subject to my renouncing my rights of succession, it might have been possible for me to contract a civil marriage. But, mindful of the Church's teaching that Christian marriage is indissoluble, and conscious of my duty to the Commonwealth, I have resolved to put these considerations before any others.

"I have reached this decision entirely alone, and in doing so have been strengthened by the unfailing support and devotion of Group Captain Townsend. I am deeply grateful for the concern of all those who have constantly prayed for my happiness.

Margaret."

The BBC broke into its programmes to broadcast the statement "This is a great act of self-sacrifice," wrote Harold Nicolson in his diary, "and the country will admire and love her for it. I feel rather moved." Most of the editorials of 1 November 1955 bore him out. "All the peoples of the Commonwealth will feel gratitude to her for taking the selfless, royal way which, in their hearts, they expected of her," declared *The Times*.

But the *Daily Mirror* declined to join "in the suffocating chant of 'good show!'" while the *Manchester Guardian* prophesied that "her decision, which has plainly been come to after subtle pressure, will be regarded by great masses of people a unnecessary and perhaps a great waste".

What was the cause in which Princess Margaret had made her sacrifice? The royal family clearly had to stand for certain values in a changing world, but who decided those values was uncertain. Churchmen, politicians and the media had all played some role in 1955, but none of them lay at the root of the social forces which

254

had elevated a love affair into a convulsive national issue. If Queen Elizabeth II had chosen to identify herself with the hostile direction those forces took, she might have appeared to be the moulder of the national moral consensus. But she had dared, less censoriously, to hope that her sister might be able to salvage some personal happiness from the situation—and she had been frustrated in that hope as totally as the Princess.

Criticism

The August 1957 edition of the *National and English Review* was devoted to the subject of the modern monarchy. Contributors included such noted monarchists as Dermot Morrah, and the tone of the articles was almost wholly appreciative. The review's editor and owner, however, a young peer called Altrincham, had decided to contribute some thoughts of his own.

He protested his loyalty, but felt there were criticisms to be made in the Queen's own interest. "The Queen's entourage," he wrote, "are almost without exception the 'tweedy' sort." The Buckingham Palace hierarchy "has lamentably failed to live with the times. While the monarchy has become 'popular' and multi-racial, the court has remained a tight little enclave of English ladies and gentlemen." It was their fault, he felt, that the Queen made such poor speeches. "The personality conveyed by the utterances which are put into her mouth is that of a priggish schoolgirl, captain of the hockey team. . . ."

Indignant reaction was not hard to come by. The *Observer*, for whom Altrincham had written some articles, disowned its former contributor. The *Daily Mail*, however, found to its horror that a majority of sixteen to thirty-four-year-olds agreed with Lord Altrincham, and that all age groups felt that the court circle around Elizabeth should be widened.

Elizabeth II herself has always been well aware of the resentments that her special position and life-style can arouse in the rest of mankind. (One story goes that once, as her car swept past a woman yelling with fury at the royal vehicle that had splattered her with mud in a lane near Sandringham, she said, "I quite agree with you, madam."

"Hmm?" said the Duke. "What did she say, darling?"

"She said 'Bastards!' " replied the Queen.)

At the time of the onslaught from Altrincham she was already taking steps to let some fresh air into the Palace—if slowly. She had introduced her new style of lunch party, and had decided in 1955 to abolish the debutante system whereby she had to sit motionless for hours while hundreds of young women filed reverently past her. In 1957 it was announced that the coming season of royal presentations would be the last.

Another democratization was the decision to rebuild the bombed chapel at Buckingham Palace into a picture gallery open to the public in which the royal art treasures, hitherto reserved for the eyes of monarchs and special guests, could be displayed in regularly changing exhibitions for anyone on payment of a few pence—which, like all the profits from opening Windsor Castle and the grounds of Sandringham and Balmoral to the public, went to charity.

Nor was it really fair to blame the Queen for the bromides put into her mouth not so much by her own advisers as by the government. Prince Philip could deliver salty addresses because he was not the Sovereign. But Elizabeth was and is more circumscribed. Whenever she made a speech the raw material was sent to her private secretaries by the institution concerned and they had to check with the relevant government department if it touched on official policy. So the result was inevitably bland.

Were the criticisms aimed at her "tweedy" advisers justified? Certainly it is difficult not to note how Elizabeth II surrounds herself with advisers of unique urbanity best described, perhaps, by Basil Boothroyd. While he was writing his biography of Prince Philip he was given a room in the Palace to work in, and leaving it one day he accosted Sir Michael Adeane, the principal Private Secretary, walking towards the front of the building. Adeane listened sympathetically to a problem troubling Boothroyd until the writer got the impression, faint as an echo, that he would like to be moving on. It was another minute or two before he said, " do hope you'll forgive me, but I've just heard that my house is on fire. I wouldn't mind, but as it's a part of St. James's Palace. . . ."

The 1950s criticism of Elizabeth's advisers, however, missed the point. She is very much her own mistress, as is evident from the wariness with which her "advisers" proffer advice—so her critics were deceived either by her youth, or by their own respectfulness, in blaming her entourage for what they disliked in her public image. That was how she was, and that was how she wanted her image to be.

Elizabeth's willingness to be more open about herself and her family is a development of her later years. At the beginning of her reign she went to considerable lengths to maintain her privacy. Even quite recently she personally opposed with some vigour the initiative that provided her most successful public relations breakthrough—the television film *Royal Family*. When grudgingly pressed into accepting it by her husband and other members of the family, she remained uneasy with the film crew. It was not so much the camera as the microphone she resented. "I'll sound so silly and trite," she complained. And it was only after months of filming that she relaxed sufficiently for the sequence that subsequently made the film such a success.

Once it was all over she was rather pleased with herself, and in the months following its screening, actually remarked on a change of public attitude she sensed. It derived, she felt, from the film, and this gave her the confidence to embark on more of the informal "meet the people" exercises that have marked her Commonwealth tours, walking through large crowds and talking to ordinary people at random.

Elizabeth's sensitivity over her privacy has been a rebellion against the demands that her job makes on her—and has made on her from an unexpectedly early age. Had her father not died prematurely she should still, in the late 1950s, have been enjoying her own family life. Her reaction has been to retreat into the privacy of her family and tight little circle of friends and, when her quota of public work was done, to guard this jealously as her own domain.

She was most protective over her children. Prince Charles and

257

Princess Anne received significantly less exposure than she an
Margaret had enjoyed as little Princesses, and this was not for lac
of trying on the part of the press. When Charles was sent to h
father's prep school, Cheam, in 1957, there were Fleet Stree
stories about him or the school on sixty-eight of the eighty-eigh
days that made up his first term, and the Queen's Press Secretar
had to warn the editors of the London newspapers that if th
harassment continued Elizabeth would take Charles away an
have him educated privately.

Her day-to-day mothering was a network of small insistence
that her children should grow up as normally as possible: brea
and sandwiches to be finished at tea before the cakes wer
attacked, hems let down, elbows patched, two shillings an
sixpence a week pocket money, and servants instructed to call th
children by their first names when young and not "Your Roya
Highness". Her husband was similarly keen on Charles makin
his own bed and getting to breakfast punctually every mornin
Without these basic disciplines, the Duke would ask, how coul
the boy begin to tackle the life he was in for? When Charles lost
dog lead at Sandringham his mother sent him out next day to fin
it. "Dog leads," she said, "cost money."

Her friends provided a similarly close refuge, a small group ou
of the public eye and anxious to keep out of it. Visiting thei
country houses for weekends, she would normally attend th
parish church on Sunday morning, but her fellow worshippers sav
her presence as a secret to be kept. They did not tip off the loca
press. The English habit of ostentatiously pretending not to loo
creates a certain unease, but for Elizabeth and her hosts it wa
preferable to a battery of cameras at the church door.

The image of Queen Elizabeth II has become inextricabl
connected with horse-racing. Her love of horses had stayed witl
her from childhood, and when she inherited the royal racing
stables on her father's death, the turf became the setting where
she could most easily indulge her passion.

Today Queen Elizabeth II keeps books of racing pedigree:
beside her desk, for the appreciation of bloodstock is one of th
deep satisfactions she derives from racing. It is Queen Mary's

Prince Edward, the youngest of the Queen's four children.

The Prince of Wales, in command of HMS Bronington, with his younger brother, Prince Andrew.

A relaxed group of family and friends at the Badminton Horse Trials.

The Duke of Edinburgh talking to his daughter Princess Anne during a three-day event.

taste for arcane genealogies turned in another direction, and sh
has her grandmother's eye for a well-bred line. It is one are
where it is impossible to say that her success is due to her position
The respect she commands in the racing world has been earned b
hard work, understanding of men, sensitivity to animals and the
consistent success of a real professional.

Cross-country eventing, at which her daughter was to excel, i
another of her interests, and every year she has made an Easte
pilgrimage to the Badminton Horse Trials. It is with her horse
that Elizabeth can be seen most herself, least a Queen. She ca
forget her position sufficiently to leap up and down like any othe
enthusiast, shouting and waving to urge her horse on, and when i
has won you see reborn the delighted grin of childhood photos. O
the racecourse she comes as close as she possibly can to that mos
elusive thrill of all, to be treated just like anyone else—or at leas
as an equal in an open fraternity.

In a life without complete holidays Elizabeth's only relaxatior
is to be taken out of herself, and her love of animals ha
performed this miracle in a way that none of the intellectua
pursuits urged upon her by her critics could accomplish. Nor can a
corgi publish its memoirs. This short irritable beast has become
her cliché, but it is also the talisman of her insistent grasp or
normality. She cares personally for her dogs, feeds them, de-flea
them, shouts crossly at them when they misbehave.

She is an outdoor person, for it has traditionally been one of the
strengths of her family to be frequently in the metropolis bu
never of it. She willingly concedes that she is "county" and
"horsey". If Elizabeth II had not been Queen, she would
certainly have settled in the country, breeding and raising dogs
perhaps, and devoting a lot of her time to worthy local causes—
the Women's Institute, the Red Cross.

Guests she invited to Windsor once she had established her own
style were struck by how unpretentious her way of life was. The
routine was that of a weekend country houseparty. While
Elizabeth worked on her boxes all morning her guests would play
tennis, ride or go shopping in Windsor. There were games of
Scrabble, jigsaws, Agatha Christie novels lying about for those

who wanted to stay in, or records to play. The rack featured prominently albums by Louis Armstrong, Ella Fitzgerald, Lena Horne, Oscar Peterson and the occasional popular classic, Schubert's "Unfinished" or Mahler's "Song of the Earth".

Home from the races in the evening, special after-dinner entertainment would be provided—a film, perhaps. Elizabeth II has always liked Mae West and, in a different idiom, sat through the Beatles' *Yellow Submarine* four times. The whole party might go out to the local repertory theatre to enjoy a drawing-room comedy. But every Ascot week Elizabeth would spend at least one evening showing her guests personally round the library. A librarian would pop out from behind a bookcase, but it would be Elizabeth who opened up all the treasures and explained their detailed attractions on the basis of evident knowledge and long hours there.

In less formal moods the Queen liked most of all to play charades with her guests. Eleanor Roosevelt described playing them at the end of the Second World War when she visited Windsor—to Winston Churchill's unconcealed disgust. But their pedigree went back further. Elizabeth II's taste for parlour pastimes was essentially that of the Edwardian upper classes.

Did all this add up to a reason for the bitter attacks launched upon Elizabeth II and the monarchy at the end of the 1950s? Homespun, unintellectual and not afraid to be thought old-fashioned, she was ill-equipped for the cult of fashion that began to sweep Britain in the late 1950s and the boom time of the 1960s. She could identify nothing solid for her in its enthusiasm for all that was latest and most abstruse, and when the bubble burst in the early 1970s she was seen to have stood all along for values closer to those of her average subjects—who, in the last resort, preferred the commonplace to the craze, the conventional to the eccentric, a day at the races to an evening of atonal music. For Elizabeth II both inherited and cultivated instincts which inspired that most exotic of twentieth-century monarchs, King Farouk, to prophesy that there would, by the end of the century, be only five royal houses left in business—those of Clubs, Diamonds, Hearts, Spades and Windsor.

Family Matters

19 February 1960 saw the birth of Queen Elizabeth II's third child, Andrew. It took outsiders by surprise, but it had long been her settled intention to have a large family—because that was what she personally wanted, and also because it was what she thought good for her children. She had only interrupted the process because of her unexpectedly early accession to the throne.

The 1960s also promised a fresh start for Princess Margaret. Peter Townsend had retreated to the Continent, there to fall in love and marry in 1959 a twenty-year-old Belgian tobacco heiress, Marie-Luce Jamagne—while Princess Margaret had already met a young photographer commissioned to do studies of Prince Charles and Princess Anne, Antony Armstrong-Jones.

On 26 February, a week after the birth of Prince Andrew, the Princess and Armstrong-Jones announced their engagement to be married, and one of their greatest delights was that they had kept their two-year-old friendship a total secret from the press and from almost anyone outside their immediate family.

Though Armstrong-Jones had gone to Eton and Cambridge, his pedigree was scarcely that of a conventional royal suitor. His father was a thrice-married Welsh barrister, while his mother had remarried an Irish peer, the Earl of Rosse, and had had a new family by him. Setting up in London as a photographer, Armstrong-Jones had worked on magazines, portrait commissions and even some fashion designing. He was amiable, polished, talented. But emerging from a cosmopolitan, *demi-monde* of designers, his qualifications for becoming a member of the royal family had to be judged, even in the opinion of the *New Statesman*, "with a leniency which only a few years before would have been unthinkable".

Since the break-up in March 1976 of this sixteen-year marriage, members of the royal family have been given to remarking that Margaret should have married Peter Townsend in the first place, an older, more masterful man. But there is too much hindsight in this. Townsend had not proved *that* masterful. And in 1960,

Antony Armstrong-Jones boasted qualities that won him a closeness with the family and a popularity with the general public that Townsend had never commanded.

Armstrong-Jones had a sense of humour curiously akin to that of Elizabeth herself. They shared the same jokes, the same gift for mimicry. He was also a fairish shot. Elizabeth was delighted he had kindled such a response in her sister. The couple were transparently entranced with each other, lovers and also friends, with their unconventional, semi-intellectual tastes in common. Anyway in 1960, after the trauma of the Townsend affair, it seemed intolerable to consider a waiting period, let alone a veto.

In other circumstances, however, Princess Margaret's choice of partner would have come in for searching appraisal. Her husband (ennobled as Lord Snowdon in 1961) liked in later years to make a distinction: "I am not a member of the royal family; I am married to a member of the royal family." This sidestepped fatally the issue of what marriage into the royal family really entailed.

To start with he tried to accompany his wife on her official engagements. In the early sixties the couple acted as a mini-version of the Queen and Prince Philip, visiting America, giving independence to Jamaica, touring factories in the Midlands. But public life alone did not satisfy the Earl of Snowdon. His commitment to photography remained, and it created a new sort of tension for Elizabeth. It was, of course, in keeping with the times that her brother-in-law should work for a living. It also showed her style that she was the first Sovereign for five hundred years to welcome a commoner as one of her immediate relatives. But the history of the marriage was to demonstrate that other difficulties existed, many of which stemmed from the personality of Princess Margaret herself.

Helping her mother and her sister find satisfying roles had been one of the larger personal challenges of Elizabeth II's reign. In the months following the death of George VI her mother had become disoriented at the loss of the man to whom she had given her whole life. But the sunniness and steel in her make-up helped build a new career. Elizabeth helped her see her usefulness to the new generation of the family as a grandmother and also as a new style of Queen Mother for the community—less intimidating more flexible and fun-loving than Queen Mary.

But Margaret lacked her mother's inner resources. The family had always spoilt her and made allowances for her youth and effervescence, which took the form of a cheeky wit those close to her found irresistible. "Roguish" had been Queen Mary's word for it. "She is so outrageously amusing that one can't help encouraging her." Unfortunately, like her uncle David, she found it difficult to master the tensions of being a modern person in an ancient institution. She preferred to take her tone from her own time, and she reflected the confusion of her age. Her very choice of husband was part of this, someone plucked straight from the glossy world of advertising, couture, interior designing and pop music. In such a *milieu*, Margaret's nose for the day after next was accounted a talent, her restlessness and identification with contemporary modes were welcomed as much as the reserve of the Queen was regretted. Then only the more jaundiced observer suggested that Princess Margaret and her friends were dancing up a cul-de-sac.

The marriage of the Princess to the commoner was the first major ceremonial royal occasion since the Coronation and it was televised around the world. On 6 May 1960 the Mall was blocked solid from end to end, and thousands had slept overnight in the street to secure positions beside the ceremonial route, as they had done thirteen years earlier for the marriage of Princess Elizabeth.

The day broke clear and sunny, a perfect May morning. The last red rose in the sixty-foot-high floral arch spanning the Mall was tucked into place and, between the avenue of white poles bearing the intertwined monograms M and A, the Princess rode to the altar in the glass coach, with Prince Philip beside her. Mrs Armstrong-Jones was cheered all the way back to the Palace, and then along the road through the city to the Tower of London where the royal yacht, *Britannia*, was waiting to take them on their honeymoon.

Eighteen months later a son David Albert Charles, Viscount Linley, was born and, almost four years to their wedding day, a daughter, Sarah Frances Elizabeth. It was part of a flurry of Palace procreation in the early sixties. To the Duke and Duchess of Kent, married in June 1961, were born a son, George, in 1962, a daughter, Helen, in 1964 (a second son, Nicholas, was born in 1970). To Princess Alexandra and Angus Ogilvy, married in 1963, came a son, James, in 1964, and a daughter, Marina, in 1966. To the Queen herself a third son, Edward, in 1964.

These new recruits, of all ages, provided troops for a strategy which Elizabeth had always wished to deploy, the development of her family as a flexible team of individuals who could share her own work at home and abroad.

She was inevitably far less happy, however, about the private development of the Snowdons' marriage. Margaret had proved a possessive wife. Intensely in love with her husband, she smothered him. Her emotional life was keyed to a neurotic pitch. Psychiatric help was called in. Marriage had not resolved but had intensified her problems of identity. She wanted her husband beside her and close behind her, as Elizabeth had Philip. On the one hand she revelled in the irreverent company Snowdon had kept before his marriage. On the other, she insisted on royalty's right to be bowed to, or to decide when she was tired and the party must end. Snowdon, himself highly strung, declined to hide his annoyance at the demands his wife made on him. Annoyance led to unrestrained disagreement—blazing rows even—and, increasingly, to a separate social life. Snowdon had his job which took him abroad on photographic assignments. The scenario for separation was set by the late '60s and European newspapers began running stories of divorce.

As the facts impinged upon the rest of the family, they started to take sides. Snowdon, said some, had not thought hard enough before becoming part of the royal way of life. Margaret, on the other hand, had always been too spoilt. But with time realization grew of a deeper incompatibility that made blame irrelevant. The unconventional qualities, the insistence on being different, that had seemed to harmonize at the time of their engagement, had proved destructive. Neither made allowances, each was cruelly capable of making the other unhappy.

A royal family group photograph, taken to mark
the Silver Wedding of the Queen and Prince Philip, November 1972.

Key: 1. Princess Margaret. 2. Lord Snowdon.
3. The Duke of Kent. 4. The Duchess of Kent. 5. Lord Nicholas Windsor.
6. Prince Michael of Kent. 7. Prince Philip. 8. Prince Charles.
9. Prince Andrew. 10. Angus Ogilvy. 11. James Ogilvy.
12. Princess Alexandra. 13. Marina Ogilvy. 14. Princess Anne.
15. Earl of St. Andrews. 16. Queen Elizabeth II. 17. Queen Elizabeth the
Queen Mother. 18. Lady Sarah Armstrong-Jones. 19. Viscount Linley.
20. Prince Edward. 21. Lady Helen Windsor.

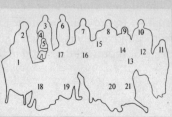

Elizabeth's first reaction was that things would improve. When her sister talked to her of divorce she counselled delay. Her hope was for reconciliation. But the rift widened. The Princess no longer carried out many public engagements with her husband, and when she did the undisguised antipathy of the couple was tangible. The dignitaries involved were embarrassed and the word spread. Invitations were diverted to more distant relatives— Princess Alexandra, or the Duchess of Kent. It became obvious that reconciliation was a very long hope, so Elizabeth, and the couple themselves, had to work out a *modus vivendi.* Should a façade of harmony be patched up, or should the marriage publicly follow the logic of its private separation?

Once faced squarely, divorce was not the unthinkable prospect it would have been in earlier reigns, and the relaxation of the divorce laws meant it could be conducted without specific allegations of misconduct—provided both parties agreed to separate.

Princess Margaret and her husband did agree. The technicalities were straightforward; formal separation and a two-year wait, after which the marriage could be dissolved at any time. But timing was delicate. There were the children. Separation was better postponed until they were old enough to go away to boarding school. Finally the separation was announced on 19 March 1976.

When the public furore died, as it did within a matter of days, it was suddenly appreciated how the crisis had not weakened, but had strengthened the royal family. For Elizabeth's strategy, as she made clear by inviting Snowdon after the separation to family occasions like her own fiftieth birthday party, was to face up to the reality of the broken marriage. It was not a matter for blame or for sweeping under the carpet. It was at once a tragedy and an everyday occurrence with which many other people had to live. She personally was a friend of Snowdon, and was as concerned to help him through the crisis as her sister. Casting either of them into outer darkness would help no one, least of all the children, and it was a poor alternative to providing a public example of the caring support one person can give others in such a situation.

So a threat to the ideals of representative monarchy was turned to its advantage, and it was to the same end that Elizabeth in the early 1970s sought to heal the wound of abdication. Scarring was inevitable, but there was no reason why the bitterness of 1936 should poison the final years of her uncle and his wife.

The enduring enmity of Queen Mary and Queen Elizabeth the Queen Mother—who blamed her husband's premature death on the burdens Edward had passed on to him—made an early change of style impossible. Edward came to George VI's funeral in 1952 alone and was also alone by the deathbed of his mother the following year. But the new Queen worked to settle the feud. Elizabeth went to visit the Duke and Duchess when they came to London for an operation on his eye. She made sure younger members of the family paid calls on the couple when they were in Paris. They were small, personal gestures, but in 1966 Elizabeth extended a public hand. She invited to the unveiling of a commemorative plaque to Queen Mary not only the Duke but also his wife. The couple rode in the official procession and afterwards they were seen to chat with the Queen and even the Queen Mother, putting a brave public face on her daughter's decision.

In May 1972 Elizabeth paid a state visit to France. Knowing her uncle was dying, she went to visit him at his house in the Bois de Bologne. Her husband and Prince Charles went with her and were photographed greeting the Duchess before going up to the sick room.

Eight days later the Duke of Windsor was dead. His body was flown to London and the Duchess followed, to stay in Buckingham Palace as Elizabeth's personal guest. The Duke was buried privately in the royal burial place at Frogmore, near the garden where he and his brother Bertie had played as children, and it was announced that in due course the Duchess would lie beside him, in royal ground at last.

The wheel had come full circle, but it also provided a new starting point in the reign of Queen Elizabeth II. In the 1960s with the Snowdons' marriage going adrift, and the Windsors still taboo, Elizabeth might have seemed seated in a shaky saddle. But time, a certain luck and a great deal of quiet persistence had turned all these problems to her advantage. The emergence of her son, Prince Charles, once written off as an impossibly late developer, the bristly authenticity of her daughter—and even sadnesses like the death of her cousin Prince William of Gloucester in an air crash in 1972, all added to the representative texture of her family. Elizabeth did not contrive this panorama of human experience, but it has been her conscious policy to establish the whole unit, rather than one or two individuals, as the focus of national sentiment, and it is her own personal presence which has been the calm centre holding together the activity all around her.

Elizabeth and Philip

The wit and wisdom of Prince Philip first became a prominent component of Elizabeth II's monarchy in the 1960s. In the early years of the reign Philip had stayed deliberately in his wife's shadow. She was the star of the Coronation and the great world tour; he had played a supporting role, his most important work being to boost her confidence and to act as a back-up in public.

But as she became engrossed by her new family, he struck out more on his own. His function in the mechanism of his wife's monarchy came to be crystallized by the remark he made in October 1961 to one hundred and twenty leading British industrialists: "I think it is about time we pulled our fingers out." Seized on avidly by the media, this became the motto for the Prince's one-man ginger group to stir Britain out of the apathy and indolence into which, it became fashionable to diagnose, she had sunk since the Second World War. It was politically unacceptable for the Prince to air publicly his private opinion of the British working man, so his barbs were aimed at his own commissioned officer class, the executives. His natural verve—of a piece with his sharp-cut, forceful features—made up an appealing image as a national super-manager.

It was his modern interpretation of a role that successive consorts have found it difficult to define satisfactorily. It was Prince Albert, the great-great-grandfather of both Elizabeth and

270

Philip, who had first carved out a solid role for the Queen's husband. It was his inspiration to steer the monarchy away from partisan involvement in politics towards the representative role rounded off by George V, identifying the monarchy with the middle-class ideals of domestic virtue, good works and diligence. He also established the modern principles and mechanism of consultation between government and Crown, right down to the boxes, in whose processing he participated personally. Today the Queen bears the burden of the boxes alone, and when the time comes for her to share it, it will be Prince Charles who is inducted constitutionally into the process. Prince Philip has always felt he can be of more use in other directions.

He takes a cue from Prince Albert, however, in his patronage of science, design and technology. In the quarter of a century since he was appointed 1951's president of the British Association for the Advancement of Science, he has hammered at the themes that seem important to him: that commercial laboratories pursuing profitable ends in secret are starvers of the national good; that the need to maintain humane priorities in science since "we can either set the world free from drudgery, fear, hunger and pestilence, or obliterate life itself"; and that it is important to preserve the world's wildlife—where his special sympathy, it has been suggested, may not be unconnected with the fact that royalty itself can be seen as an endangered species.

He has no hesitation in exploiting his royal position for any cause he judges worthy—as an incentive, when graduates of his Award Scheme for young people are invited to Buckingham Palace, or as a crude exercise in arm-twisting, as when he decided that the National Maritime Museum at Greenwich, of which he was a trustee, was not getting its fair share of funds.

"I see it as my duty as a Trustee to pursue the matter until a satisfactory solution is reached," he wrote to the Chancellor of the Exchequer after a lengthy correspondence. "If this is in the least embarrassing to you or to the Treasury, I am quite prepared to discuss with the Prime Minister my giving up the position of Trustee." The Museum got its funds.

At times his style verges on thuggery. He has cultivated an

271

affable public manner, but when he argues seriously the atmosphere can get ugly. He is a clever man who spends a lot of time thinking problems through to conclusions that harmonize with his own particular vision of the world, and his patience is rapidly exhausted by people who do not share it.

Prince Philip will bully people he thinks will let him, and though his wife is not among them—for she can be tougher than him when she wants to be—he also presides over his home as an old-fashioned *paterfamilias*. Elizabeth gallantly suffered her breakfasts to be dislocated for some time by his sausage-frying activities—a craze with an electric pan—until he was forced to agree that the aroma was still lingering at lunchtime, and that was a rare dislocation of their conventional husband-wife roles. He has the last word on the estates, which he runs, in the car, where she has learnt to draw breath only silently, and in public life as well. His long war with the press, for example, is not a one-man idiosyncrasy. It deliberately represents one dislike that runs right through the royal family at the way in which the media intrude on what they regard as their private lives, and Philip sees the protection of his wife as a pre-eminent responsibility. He was the moving force behind the *Royal Family* film, but that did not stop him getting irritated on occasions with its director. "Don't bring your bloody cameras so close to the Queen," he shouted.

He makes no apologies for what he is, and his wife would be the last person to expect him to. "There is something valuable in people living their own style," he says. "I don't think people mind a little downright rudeness or prejudice. They excuse all that provided the person actually does the stuff they expect them to do."

But it is the eternal problem of representative royalty that their people expect contradictory things of them. They expect their Queen to be more trend-setting and adventurous, but they also want her motherly and comforting. They regret Prince Charles's "stuffy" upbringing and lifestyle, but they would not be happy with him as a long-haired dropout. And the Duke of Edinburgh, who is idolized for being dynamic, virile and opinionated, is also criticized for these very qualities. A Gallup Poll in 1969 showed him as first choice for national dictator, but when he remarked to

272

Alfredo Stroessner of Paraguay that it was "a pleasant change to be in a country that isn't ruled by its people", there was a howl of outrage in Britain.

The provisional assessment of Prince Philip, Duke of Edinburgh, must remain open. He can be difficult, but Elizabeth II does not pity herself as a woman married to a boor. She is in love with her husband, and he with her, and if it is no longer the wild passion of youth, one of its principal components over the years has become mutual respect. They talk—and listen—to each other more than most other people who have been together for thirty years. They are openly affectionate when together, and when apart talk constantly about the other. They are husband and wife but they are also, almost independently, friends, and their friendship is the stronger for their having interests which are not identical. He gets bored by racing and sees no reason to accompany her to every single meeting. She does not share his enthusiasm for sailing or technology or after-dinner speeches.

Prince Philip is seldom happier than at ease among the brandy and cigars of a regiment or club (although like his wife he does not smoke), and happier still to be guest of honour with the chance to get up on his hind legs and speak. With his annual volume of orations running around one hundred and fifty, all written by himself, salted with his own jokes and elaborating the themes dear to him, speech-making can be numbered among his principal hobbies. Both Elizabeth and her husband are pleased with the arrangement whereby he carries out this function, leaving her free to watch television, see friends or get on with the boxes.

It is not as though they do not see each other all day. They are each others' closest colleagues. Their offices are side by side. They almost invariably lunch together, many of their public engagements are carried out *à deux*, and they deliberately exploit the extra roles that their respective genders allow them to play. As a woman, Elizabeth can get involved in areas into which a male sovereign might not enter; as a man, Philip can range and jest in a way queen consorts have not found possible.

It has, paradoxically, given the monarchy greater resilience in an aggressively egalitarian age to be represented by a woman, and

273

a shy one at that. For, as Sovereign, a character so abrasively masculine as Prince Philip might have provoked resentments from which his wife's reign has been largely free. As it is, he has lent tang to a cocktail which might otherwise have been too bland.

They have their quarrels. Voices are raised. "Watch out, a couple of acid drops," a footman will whisper to the chauffeur as they stride out icily silent to their limousine. But the prevailing alchemy is laughter. Those close to them report a lot of that.

Elizabeth herself is made to be an inspiring old Queen. From grave childhood through austere adolescence, she has seemed programmed for wise old age—a latter-day Victoria—and her first twenty-five years on the throne are in many ways only a prelude to her second quarter of a century.

Will she abdicate? The question is put regularly to Buckingham Palace and is invariably denied. But this means little. It is not her policy always to take press secretaries into her confidence.

She can be the more a Sovereign for the fact that her son fulfils on her behalf some of the functions that princes can carry off so well—for abdication would deprive her countries not simply of a wise figurehead, but also exclude Prince Charles from many of the activities which lend him glamour—flying planes and captaining ships—and also remove the special patronage he can give to activities like his community work among young "dropouts".

Queen Victoria made her son a pathetic figure by denying him access to real responsibility, and the way in which Queen Elizabeth II seems likely to avoid this situation is to shift certain burdens onto her son. She could then assuage the guilt of observers unhappy to see her toiling in old age.

In November 1972 Queen Elizabeth II and Prince Philip celebrated their silver wedding. "I think," said Elizabeth at the Guildhall dinner after the service of thanksgiving, "everyone will concede that today, of all occasions, I should begin my speech with 'My husband and I'." There was once, she said, a bishop who was asked what he thought about sin. He said simply that he was against it, and her answer to anyone who asked her the same question of marriage and family life would be equally simple. "I," said Elizabeth II, "am for it."

274

Robert Lacey

Robert Lacey has spent two years engrossed in the activities of a woman who is not his wife. "While he was writing *Majesty*," says Sandi his wife, "I felt I was sharing my house with the Queen."

She might have wondered, what does Robert see in her? When he left a secure job on *The Sunday Times* to write this book, his colleagues certainly thought he was crazy.

Robert didn't write a word for the first year: he just read and read. He put his notes into five green loose-leaf folders, each one representing a decade of the Queen's life. He also gathered a great mileage of words on tape. After a hesitant start, distant members of the royal family gave interviews, and then by recommendation they passed Robert on to others.

Robert Lacey's own first memories of the Queen are painful. He was nine, and had been fooling around during the National Anthem at a Coronation street party in 1953. He got beaten for it by his mother with a garden cane.

At school Robert was a scholar and an athlete, and broke a six-schools record in the steeplechase. He cycled keenly. (He still does.) He got a scholarship to Cambridge, where he read history, and at this time did Voluntary Service Overseas in Togoland, working with missionaries to build two churches in the bush.

One of his Cambridge tutors encouraged Robert to write a biography, and his first, of Elizabeth I's favourite, the Earl of Essex, went straight into the bestseller lists. He has also written a life of Sir Walter Raleigh.

His wife Sandi is a graphic designer, and they live with their son Sasha and daughter Scarlett at Dulwich. Apart from mowing his lawn fanatically, Robert has no serious hobby except his work, and he's already outlining his next book, a spin-off from *Majesty*. He says he honestly cannot think how he's going to spend his high royalties from this book. "A lot will go in taxes. Most of it. I'm going to pay up."

To the end Robert Lacey is undoubtedly a loyal subject of Her Majesty!

Ordinary People

A CONDENSATION OF THE BOOK BY
Judith Guest

ILLUSTRATED BY GEORGE JONES

PUBLISHED BY COLLINS, LONDON

Ordinary people feel joy, love, fear, and sometimes—amongst the laughter and the tears—an agonizing sense of loss. For seventeen-year-old Conrad Jarrett the loss was that of his older brother, Buck. Conrad had looked up to Buck, tried to be like him. Now everywhere, every day—at school, at home—Buck is a presence felt, deeply missed. Conrad's anguish becomes more than he can bear.

This is the story of his desperate act of rebellion and the uncertain days that followed. It is about his compassionate father and his beautiful, talented mother—a family like so many, being brave, enduring, learning together that love, openly shared, is the ultimate triumphant answer.

CHAPTER ONE

To HAVE a reason to get up in the morning, it is necessary to have a guiding principle. A belief of some kind. A rear window sticker, if you like. People in cars on busy freeways call to each other: BE KIND TO ANIMALS—KISS A BEAVER; comfort each other: HONK IF YOU LOVE JESUS; antagonize each other with statements: ROD McKUEN FOR PRESIDENT.

Lying on his back in bed, Conrad gazes around the walls of his room, musing about what has happened to his collection of statements. They had been mounted on cardboard, and fastened with pushpins so as not to deface the walls. Gone now. Probably tossed out with the rest of the junk—all those eight-by-ten color prints of the great baseball teams—junior-high-school mementos. Too bad. It would be comforting to have something to look up to. Instead, the walls are bare. They have been freshly painted. Pale blue. An anxious color. Anxiety is blue; failure, gray. He knows those shades. He told Dr. Crawford they would be back, paralyzing him, shaming him, but his psychiatrist was not impressed. *Lay off. Quit riding yourself. Less pressure, more humor.*

Right, of course. The thing that is missing here is a sense of humor. LIFE IS A GODDAMN SERIOUS BIG DEAL—he should put that on his rear window, if he had a window, which he doesn't, not Conrad Jarrett the seventeen-year-old failure. A book report due

279

Wednesday for his English Lit. class. The book has not been read. A test in U.S. history.

He rolls over, pulling the pillow tight around his head, blocking out the sharp arrows of sun that pierce through the window.

Morning is not a good time for him. Too many details crowd his mind. Brush his teeth first? Wash his face? What pants should he wear? What shirt?

Back in the hospital Dr. Crawford had tried to prepare him for this. "It's all right, Con, to feel anxious. Allow yourself a couple of bad days now and then, will you?"

Sure. How bad? Razor-blade bad? He wanted to ask but he hadn't, because at that point his suitcase was packed and his father was already on the way to pick him up and remarks like that only got you into trouble. And he'd had quite enough of that place. In the last months he had been able to spot the permanent residents every time. That unmistakable shuffling. Mostly old men but some younger ones, too, in the dull maroon bathrobes, sides flapping loosely like the drooped wings of dying birds. Never. It was too damn small a world. Except that you always knew where you were. Mornings you talked, then had occupational therapy— macramé, painting, clay. Afternoons you could nap, go for a walk, work out in the gym. Evenings there were card games, Scrabble, backgammon. Leo told him once, "Stop worrying. You're okay. You can play Scrabble, that means you can concentrate."

Conrad had laughed. "It means you can spell," he said.

His father calls to him from the other end of the house. He thrashes to a sitting position, calling back, "Yeah! I'm up!" and miraculously he *is* up and in the bathroom, washing his face, brushing his teeth. Keep moving, everything will fall into place.

He looks in the mirror. The news isn't good. His face, chalk white, is plagued with a constantly erupting rash. This is not acne, they assured him. What it *was*, they were never able to discover. Typical. He tries to be patient as he waits for his hair to grow out. He had hacked it up badly, cutting it himself in the hospital the week before he left. ("I didn't think they would let you have scissors," his grandmother said to him. "They shouldn't have," he an-

280

swered her, oh so casual, thereby relieving the listeners of shock and embarrassment while exhibiting his sense of humor.)

This house. Too big for three people. Straining, he can barely hear his father and mother synchronizing schedules at the other end of the hall. It doesn't matter. They would not be talking about anything important. They would not be talking, for instance, about him. They are people of good taste. They do not discuss a problem in the presence of the problem. And, besides, there is no problem. There is just phase two. Recovery. A moving forward.

From what? Toward what? He dresses himself (progress!), looking out of the window, studying the lacy line of Russian olives that separates their property from the next-door neighbors'—what's their name? They've lived there for years—damn it, that's the kind of stuff that scares you, not being able to remember names. Cahill. Their name is Cahill. Okay, now relax.

But he cannot relax, because today is a target date. Tuesday, September 30. He has been home one month. *And what are you doing, Jarrett? Asking weird questions like: From what? Toward what?* Questions without answers. Undermining. Worse than acne.

There is a prickly sensation at the back of his throat. He turns away from the window, picking up his books from the desk. Then he puts them down again. Follow routines. First the bed; then line up the towels in the bathroom; then pick up books; then eat breakfast; then go to school. Get the motions right. Motives will follow.

Vaguely he can recall a sense of calm that he had laid claim to on leaving the hospital. There were one or two guiding principles to get him through the day. Some ambitious plans, also, for putting his life in order. But the details have somehow been lost.

RAZOR in hand, Con's father, Calvin Jarrett, stands before the mirror, offering up a brief prayer: *Thanks. Appreciate all you've done so far. Keep up the good work.* Beside him, his wife brushes her hair. Beth's face is soft in the morning, flushed, slightly rounded, younger than her thirty-nine years. Her stomach is flat, almost as if she never had the babies. She pins her hair into a neat coil at the back of her head. Beautiful hair, the color of honey.

"Did you call him?"

"Yeah, he's up," Cal says.

Beth sighs. "I hate to play golf when it's cold. Your hands freeze. Why doesn't anybody know enough to quit when the season's over?"

He kisses her on the neck. "I love you."

"I love you." She looks at him in the mirror. "Will you talk to him this morning, Cal? About the clothes. He has a closetful of decent things and he goes off every day looking like a bum."

"That's the style. Decency is out, chaos is in." As her brows lift, he nods. "Okay, I'll talk to him."

"And about stopping by the Lazenbys' on the way home. Carole called again. It's such a little thing. . . ."

"I don't want to pressure him about that. He'll do it when he wants to. Carole understands."

Beth shrugs. "When people take an interest, it would seem courteous—"

"We all know he's courteous." He turns his attention to his beard. Every morning the same face, the same thoughts. A good time to take stock, though. Calvin Jarrett, forty-one, tax attorney. Orphaned at age eleven. He has thought about that lately, about the Evangelical Home for Orphans and Old People, a red brick building on Detroit's northwest side, where he grew up. Wondering if it still exists. Strange that he has never checked. An odd kind of orphanage: most of the kids had at least one living parent; some even had two. He had moved there when he was four. Occasionally his mother visited him. Periodically she explained why he was not living with her: there was no room for him in the apartment, no money. No one claiming to be his father had ever come to see him; he had no memories of being any man's son. So, if anyone should ask, he can always point out that he had no example to follow.

And what is fatherhood, anyway? Talking to a kid about his clothes. Not applying pressure. Looking for signs. He knows what to look for now: loss of appetite, sleeplessness, poor school performance—all negative, so far. His son eats, sleeps, says he's happy. Another duty: asking silly questions. Are you happy?

He has had a vision, all these months, of boys with their heads next to stereo speakers, their long legs draped over chairs and sofas. Or their arms stretched toward a basketball hoop in the side drive. (He had sunk the posts himself when Conrad was eight, Jordan, nine, just after they bought the house.) Where are all these kids? Joe Lazenby, Phil Truan, Don Genthe, Dick Van Buren—they are all seniors in high school this year. Is eighteen too old to play touch football on the lawn? Basketball? Is it girls? Studies? Since he has been home, Conrad has gone once to the movies. Alone.

Responsibility. That is fatherhood. *Make sure he calls that doctor in Evanston.* Why? Because his own vision, of boys hanging around, isn't coming true? It has only been a month. Stay calm.

Now that Conrad is home from the hospital, the responsibilities seem enormous. Staggering. His job alone, nobody else's. Motherhood is different somehow. *Your mother wants me to tell you, you have a closetful of decent clothes.* He will smile. "Okay. You told me." But then he will ask, "What's wrong with what I've got on?"

Nothing I can see. Only I don't pass up any chances to discharge these fatherly duties. This is the age of perfection, kid.

Strive, strive. Correct all defects. All those trips to the orthodontist. Both boys had inherited Beth's small, determined lower jaw. On them it had required thirty-eight hundred dollars' worth of work. "Hell, what's a little money?" he had raved. "This is the age of the perfect mouth!" But, secretly, he had been proud that he was able to afford such expenses. He had arrived. He was here. Not bad for the kid from the Evangelical Home.

And now? Where is he now?

BETH sets breakfast in front of Cal: eggs, bacon, toast.

Conrad looks up. "Morning."

"Morning. You need a ride today?"

"No. Lazenby's picking me up at twenty after."

Cal treats this as a piece of good news. "Great!" Said too heartily, he sees at once. Conrad frowns.

"I've got to dress," Beth says. "I tee off at nine." She crosses to the doorway. Conrad is reading.

283

"What is it, a quiz?" Cal asks.

"Book report." He holds up the book. *Jude the Obscure*.

"How is it?"

"Obscure."

Cal sips his coffee. "No bacon and eggs this morning?"

He shakes his head. "I only wanted cereal."

Con has lost twenty-five pounds in one year. Another year before his weight will return to normal, Dr. Crawford predicted.

"You ought to keep trying to put weight on," Cal says.

"I am. You don't have to be heavy to swim, though, Dad."

Back to the book, and Cal studies the rectangles on the tile floor. Familiar and orderly. "How's it going?" he asks.

Conrad looks up. "What?"

"School. Swimming. Everything okay?"

"Yeah, fine. Same as yesterday."

"What does that mean?"

A faint smile. "It means you ask me that every day."

"Sorry." Cal smiles, too. "I like things neat."

Conrad laughs, closing the book. "Okay, let's talk."

"So, how come Lazenby's picking you up?" Cal says.

"He's a friend of mine."

"I know that. I just wondered if it meant you'd be riding with him from now on."

"I don't have a formal commitment yet. I'm gonna have my secretary talk to his, though."

"Okay, okay."

Con does a familiar thing then: shoves his hands into his back pockets and rocks back in the chair. A good sign, despite the weary look about the eyes. The eyes bother Cal. He still believes in the picture in his wallet of a boy with longish dark hair, and laugh lines about the mouth and eyes. This gaunt figure that sits across from him still grins, still kids, but the eyes are different.

His old self. That is the image that must be dispelled. Another piece of advice from Dr. Crawford. "Don't expect him to be the same person he was before." But Cal does expect that. As does everyone. Yesterday, Howard, his father-in-law, had called him at the

284

office. "Cal, it shocked me. He looked so . . . tired out. Run-down. And he was so quiet. Just not like his old self at all."

And who was that? The kid who got straight A's all through grade school and junior high? Who rode his two-wheeler sixteen times around the block on his sixth birthday, because somebody bet he couldn't? Who took four firsts swimming in the hundred-meter freestyle last year? No, he is not much like that kid.

He says, "That Dr. Berger. Have you called him yet?"

An immediate reaction. The chair legs come down. "I'm swimming every night until six. Dr. Crawford didn't say I had to call him, Dad."

"I know." He waits while Conrad stares at the table. "I think you ought to. Maybe he could see you on weekends."

"I don't need to see anybody. I feel fine."

"I want you to call him anyway," Cal says. "Call him today."

An obedient boy. Well mannered. Even in the hospital, with his fingernails bitten to the half-moons, the dark circles under his eyes, always his behavior was proper. "Thanks for coming," he would say each time as Cal readied himself to leave.

Growing up is a serious business. He, Cal, would not be young again, not for anything. And not without sponsors: a mother and father, good fortune, God.

CON sits on the porch steps, waiting for Lazenby, shivering in his thin denim jacket. He should go back inside, get a heavier one, but he doesn't want to risk it. Not that she will say anything. But the hurdle has been jumped once today. Enough. He glances at his watch. Almost eight thirty. *Has Lazenby forgotten?* He prays he hasn't; then she would have to drive him. The two of them alone in the car and he not wanting to say the wrong thing. *Move it, Lazenby. Don't make me wait here until she comes out.*

Abruptly he jumps up, walks to the end of the circular drive. Facing the house, he stares up at his bedroom window. In the early morning the room is his enemy; there is danger in just being awake. Now it is a refuge. He imagines himself safely in bed with the covers pulled up. Asleep. Unconscious.

An unpleasant thought nags at him. His father has noticed. Whatever is wrong with him is now visible. That command: "Cal him *today*." Worrying. There is something to worry about, as he has suspected. He did not want his suspicions confirmed. Now he has infected his father, and the gray disease is dangerous to both of them. His grandmother was eager to inform him: "Conrad, if you *knew* the strain that man was under these past months; my hear went out to him, I can't tell you."

Then don't! Con felt like screaming. He wants to belong to this house again, needs to be part of these tall windows, walls half hid den behind thick rhododendron leaves, the cedar hedge in front all elegance and good taste. Good taste is absorbed through the skin, like rays from the sun, in this elegant section of Lake Forest Illinois, a direct quote from a newspaper article. They had laughed when they read it and he laughs now, out loud. See? Haven't los your sense of humor after all; your sense of identity is what ha been misplaced. No. You don't lose what you never had.

Joe Lazenby's red Mustang hurls itself into the driveway, and Conrad climbs in the back seat to sit beside Dick Van Buren. Van Buren moves over to make room. "I damn near killed myself ove this political-sci exam."

"Yeah, I was up until two o'clock, trying to make sense out of th garbage."

"It helps," Lazenby drawls, "if you read the garbage when it' assigned. Instead of inhaling it the night before the exam."

Kevin Stillman sneers. "Get a sense of reality, Lazenby. W swim every goddamn day. When are we supposed to study?"

Lazenby shrugs. "I swim. I study."

"Yeah, you're perfect." Stillman twists around in the front seat "What're you reading, Jarrett? Is that Hardy? Junior English?"

Conrad nods. They are all seniors this year, except him. He ha taken no finals last year.

"You got all junior classes this year?" Stillman asks. "They didn' pass you on anything?"

Van Buren yawns. "They don't pass you on breathing in tha dump if you haven't taken the final."

286

Lazenby says, "Kevin, quit messing around with the dial, get something and leave it."

Stillman continues to mess around with the radio. Conrad feels the slow, rolling pressure of panic building inside himself. The air in the back seat is being sucked out the windows by a huge vacuum. Relentless, it will soon crush the car like an eggshell.

"Hey, there's Pratt," Stillman says.

A small, neat-looking redhead in a blue skirt and tan jacket is hurrying along the street, her books in her arms.

"Nice legs," Stillman says. He sees Con glance out the window. "Hey, look. Jarrett's finally interested in something." Lazenby and Van Buren laugh, and Stillman leers at him. Conrad's skin prickles. He forces a laugh from the back of his throat, turns his attention outside the window. *Forget it. Stillman was never a friend.*

"CONRAD, in *Jude the Obscure*, what's your theory on Jude Fawley?"

"What?"

Miss Mellon smiles at him. "Do you think he was powerless in the grip of circumstances, or could he have helped himself?"

He stalls. "Powerless? I guess he thought he was."

"What's the difference?" Her full attention on him now. It will smother him. Too much interest makes him unable to think.

"The guy was a jerk," somebody says. "All hung up on what was the *moral* thing to do. It didn't make any sense."

"That's too easy, Joel." And he breathes again as her attention shifts. But she corners him after class.

"I don't want you to feel pressured about this report," she says. "Do you want an extension?"

"No." Backing slowly out the door. "I'll get it done."

"You're sure? There's no need to push yourself. . . ."

Wrong. There is a need. To regain his spot on the swim team, to get back into choir; there are no choices at all, just endless motion. And no more mistakes. Like the ones he had made last year, when everything was sliding. He had made a lot of them then. He had brought Miss Mellon some poems. "Why are you writing all this

287

about violence and war, Conrad? This doesn't sound like you."
Now it's as if the whole thing were her fault, and she is trying to
make it up to him. He doesn't know what he wants from people except that he prefers indifference to concern. Easier to handle.

At a meeting before school started, the principal, Mr. Knight
had said, "Maybe we ought to cut down on some of these extras,
Conrad. Maybe drop choir. . . ." But, no, he had not wanted that,
and then Faughnan, the choir director, had told Knight that he
was short on tenors; he needed Conrad.

Choir is the one time of day when he lets down his guard; there
is peace in the strict concentration that Faughnan demands. Faughnan is a perfectionist who cares about nothing but music. His shirt
sleeves rolled up, his tie undone, he drives them. They work every
minute, and there is only one way to prove yourself. You sing, and
sing, and sing. All else is unimportant.

"Nice job, tenors," Faughnan will say once in a while. He allows
himself the smallest thrust of pride on those days. However, today
is not one of those days. They sift down off the stands and he stops
to retrieve his books from the back table. In front of him are two
sopranos, one blonde and one redhead. The redhead's hair hangs
silk-smooth and straight, almost to the middle of her back. No, not
red; more of a peach color. He could touch it if he wanted to.

"Hi, Con." The blonde has turned around.

"Hi." He can't remember her name. His face burns.

"Have you met Jeannine?"

"No."

"Jeannine Pratt, Conrad Jarrett."

"Nice to meet you." She smiles, puts out her hand. He stands
there, stupidly confused. He still cannot remember the blonde's
name, and the redhead, he suddenly remembers, is the girl he saw
from the car, the girl Stillman had kidded him about.

"I think you stand behind me," Jeannine says.

"You sing better than you talk," the blonde says, giggling, and he
remembers. Gail Noonan is her name. Buck took her out once.
"Well," she says, "we'll see you."

They turn away, and he walks blindly out the door behind them.

288

toward history class. He hums a simple melody to relax himself. Even the most insignificant encounter is alive with complication and danger. He wishes himself, for a moment, back in the hospital, where things were predictable.

He yawns at swim practice, and Salan, the coach, catches him. He calls him over afterward.

"Jarrett, you having fun out there?"

"Fun?"

"Yeah. You oughta be, you know." He sits, hands on his thighs. "The point is lost if it's not fun anymore. Right?"

"I guess."

"You guess."

Conrad, sick with fright, waits for the axe to fall. *Doesn't matter, doesn't matter, I didn't really want to swim.*

"You on medication, Jarrett? Tranquilizers?"

"No."

"Did I ask you before if they gave you shock out there?"

"Yeah."

"Yeah, what?"

"Yeah, you asked me before," he says. "Yeah, they did."

Salan clicks his tongue in disapproval. "I'm no doctor, but I don't think I'd let them mess around with my head like that."

Conrad says nothing. *It wasn't exactly an orgy of pleasure for me, you dumb jerk.*

Salan is shaking his head. "Look, I'm not being too rough on you, am I? But I'm wondering if it's gonna be too much for you." He leans back, one arm around an upraised knee. "This is a team effort, Jarrett. I've got room for guys who are willing to work. Thing is, I can't figure you out anymore."

Conrad lets out his breath at last, slowly. "I'll work," he says. "I want to work."

"Okay, then. Better plan to stay after practice. Starting tomorrow. Go take a shower now." His tongue clicks again, this time in dismissal, and Conrad heads for the locker room. He is shivering. *Never hit it off with the guy. He thinks there is only one way to do everything, only one main street.*

IN THE CAR ON THE way home, Kevin Stillman says, "What d'you think, Jarrett? Danoff and Edge look pretty good, huh?"

There is a sudden, electrical silence. Danoff and Edge are sophomores. They have beaten Con in practice every day for two weeks. Lazenby says, "They're not that good, Kev."

"No? They look pretty damn good to me."

Lazenby drops Con off, and he lets himself in with his key. The house is dark. Silent and empty. He goes upstairs to his room. He sets his books down on his desk and stands looking out the window. Idly, he opens the desk drawer, sifting through a pile of papers: old stuff, schedules, letters. Funny she has never cleaned out this drawer. He should do it; maybe sometime he will. His fingers suddenly touch the glossy and slick surface of a photograph. He pulls it out. Along the bottom it reads FIRST PLACE MEDLEY RELAY TEAM. Lazenby. His brother, Buck. Himself in the middle. Arms around each other, grinning at the camera, all confidence. He snaps the drawer closed.

He goes out into the hall just as his mother reaches the top of the stairs. She jumps.

"Sorry," he says.

"I didn't think you were home yet."

"I just got in," he says. "How was your golf game?"

"Fine. Cold." Beth's hair is loose about her face. "Your father called. He'll be late. We're not eating until seven."

"Okay."

She heads toward her room. "I have an awful headache. I'm going to lie down awhile."

"Okay."

She is almost to her door and he calls after her, "I swam pretty well today. Salan wants me to stay later and work out. I might be starting in the fifty."

"Good." The door closes behind her, and he stands a moment in the hall, then goes back into his room. He shuts his door and leans against it, trembling. A dull, roaring sound in his ears as he doubles over, arms crossed and pressed against his waist. His stomach tightens, as if to ward off a blow.

290

CHAPTER TWO

THE restaurant has a heavy Mediterranean decor that Cal finds oppressive. But Beth had called him this morning, asked him to meet her here, her voice full of excitement and good news. And she looks like good news, seated across from him in a sleeveless knit suit the color of straw. And, who'd guess it, we've been married nearly twenty-one years. She is all elegance and self-possession. So beautiful in every detail that men and women both like to look at her.

He met her twenty-two years ago on the tennis courts at the Beverly Racquet Club. Ray's father was a member, and Cal and Ray were working off the tensions of a law exam. She liked to play with men because the competition was better, she had told Ray, approaching him. She had a friend; would they like to play mixed doubles? Ray was all for it, and afterward Ray got the friend, and Beth and Cal were paired off together. They went out to dinner. Cal never had another date with any girl except Beth.

"I was afraid I hadn't made enough of an impression, and you wouldn't see me again," he confessed to her later.

"I was afraid, too," she said. "I thought you might be engaged or married and Lord, what a job it was going to be, getting you away from her!"

Now, in the restaurant, she has pulled an envelope from her purse. "What have you got there?" he asks.

Sheets of slick paper are suddenly before him: Athens, Rome, London, Dubrovnik. "Cal, don't you think London would be fun? Like something out of Dickens. Christmas in London . . ."

"Listen," he says, "I don't think we should plan to go away for Christmas this year."

She looks at him over the rim of her glass. "We go away for Christmas every year."

"I know. But not this year. The timing isn't right."

"What does that mean?"

"You know what it means."

"Yes." She turns her head slightly away from him. "Well. They said it would be better to leave in the middle of December and book a flight back after the first week in January."

"We can't go in the middle of December. He'd have to miss a week of school. And another week in January would be two weeks."

"He could meet us there when school got out. He could fly back by himself. Mother and Dad would—"

"*No!*"

The waiter appears with the menus. After they order, Beth says, "Why don't you ask him if he wants to go?"

"I think," he says, "that was our mistake. Going to Florida last Christmas. If we hadn't done that . . ."

"It wouldn't have made any difference. Dr. Brandt told us—"

"Dr. Brandt told us he was depressed. Dr. Brandt is a G.P. What the hell did he know?" He sets his glass down, rapping it against the table. The sound is loud, making her jump.

"Are you blaming him now?"

"I'm not blaming anyone. It wasn't anyone's fault, I know that."

"You don't believe that," she says. "You just say it."

"I believe it," he says. "I'm not even talking about blame, I'm talking about being available. We were busy every minute in Florida. There wasn't time to talk."

"What was there to say? Do you even think he knew at that point? And if he did know, do you think he would have told us?"

"I don't know."

The waiter brings their lunches. When he leaves, she leans toward Cal. "You know how good it feels to get away. All the wonderful places we've been—Spain, Portugal, Hawaii. I know we have expenses. But I need to go! I need you to go with me."

"I want to go with you," he says. "Maybe in the spring."

She sits back. "No." Her voice is flat. "If we don't go now, we won't go in the spring, either."

"That's silly," he says. "We will. I just think that—this time we might try handling things differently."

"*This time?*"

He is upsetting her, upsetting himself, too.

"Are we going to live like this? With it always hanging over our heads?"

"Nothing is hanging over our heads," he says, as much to himself as to her. "Don't worry. Everything is all right."

She looks at him and gathers the colored sheets of paper into a neat pile. "I don't understand you at all," she says.

HE SITS at his desk, working on some papers. Beth's father, Howard, has just called to talk about the Mercedes dealership opening in Evanston. "Light at the end of the tunnel, Cal. People buying expensive foreign cars again. Hell of a good sign, wouldn't you say?"

Yes, he had agreed with this spot analysis of the U.S. economy, his mind automatically registering the clichés. Where was "out of the woods"? It was missing today.

He gets up to stretch and goes to the window. The offices of Hanley and Jarrett, attorneys-at-law, on the eighth floor of the State National Bank Plaza, overlook southwest Evanston. It is a good location. Years ago, when he and Ray were getting started, their one-room Chicago office was hot and crowded, their cramped apartments hotter and more crowded yet. No more. Now Ray and Nancy live in Glencoe, and he takes the train in from his English Tudor castle. Ray tells Cal he is crazy to drive. But Cal prefers his car. It gives him control over his schedule.

He looks down at the papers again. Remembers other papers. "Severe depressive episodes: high risk of suicide" was the initial diagnosis on the commitment papers he signed last January. A seven-word diagnosis. Is there a seven-word cure? *Is Con cured?*

He reaches into his desk drawer for the Evanston telephone directory to look up the address: Tyrone C. Berger, M.D., 651 Sherman Avenue South. Near the plaza. Con can walk to the office when he's through. They can ride home together. Con had told him last night that he made an appointment. A good boy. Obedient.

Another duty of fatherhood. Checking up, signing commitment papers, authorizing treatments. Protecting yourself from further grief, from any more facts of history that cannot be changed. Like

294

the loss of Jordan—"Buck"—his elder, his lighthearted son, the one who never worried. Two sons, Jordan and Conrad, born fourteen months apart. One now deceased. Another word from the commitment papers. Part of the background information he had to furnish.

Beth was right. He does not believe himself to be innocent. It has to be his fault. But where is the fault? Is it in believing that the people you love are immortal? Untouchable? No, everyone believes that. Only no one knows it's what he believes—until it happens.

The topic of London is not finished, he is sure. Well, why not go? What difference will it make? If she's right and it made no difference, then last year was nobody's fault. That is the truth. That is what makes it all so impossible to understand.

CON goes to a directory on the far wall of the shabby lobby. Eleven names, seven with M.D. after them. The top name is the one he is looking for: T. C. BERGER M.D. 202. He glances at his watch. Four o'clock. Exactly. Well, no backing out now. He is to meet his father at his office at five fifteen. "Don't be late. I've got a meeting tonight." Translated: "Don't let the guy upset you; show up when you're supposed to."

In the narrow hallway, a single light bulb burns. High, old-fashioned doors with glass windows, all dark. Any people in this building? Panic begins to settle in around him.

At the end of the hall is a lighted doorway. The letters, stuck to the glass with adhesive backing, spell out T. C. BERGER M.D. He opens the door and steps inside.

He is in an entry, empty of people, with a chair in it, a floor lamp, a small table strewn with magazines, a green metal wastebasket. Opposite him is an open doorway; an overturned chair blocks it. A scene of total disorder confronts him as he moves toward the other room. Books, magazines, loose papers everywhere, plastic cups, ashtrays, all tossed together in the middle of the floor. In the midst of it a man stands, his back to the doorway. As Conrad approaches, he turns. About him there is the look of a crafty monkey—dark skin, dark crinkly hair, a body that hunches forward—an elongated question mark.

295

"Wait," he says, "don't tell me. Jarrett."

The eyes, a compelling and vivid blue, beam into whatever the touch. They touch Conrad's face now, and the effect is that of bein in an intense blue spotlight.

"You look like somebody Crawford would send me," he say "Somebody who's a match for my daring wit and inquiring mind.

Conrad asks coolly, "Am I seeing you? Or are you seeing me?"

He laughs, delighted. "Let's see the appointment book." He step over to the desk, rummages fiercely, and holds up a noteboo "Tuesday, four o'clock. Conrad Jarrett. Ah. I knew it." He grins.

Eccentricity. A favorite put-on of psychiatrists. Conrad does no trust them. Too many oddballs at the hospital. Only Crawford ha behaved as if he knew what he was doing. He picks up the over turned chair.

"Bring that over here," Berger directs him. "Sit down." He con tinues to prowl around the room, lifting books, retrieving papers stacking up plastic cups. On further examination, he resembles compact, slightly undersized gorilla.

"I think I was ripped off this afternoon," he says. "Somebod was after drugs, I guess. What a neighborhood."

"You going to call somebody?"

"You mean cops?" He shrugs. "What's missing? Maybe nothing Maybe they even left something, who knows?" He moves to th small sink in the corner. "You want some coffee? Listen, do me favor, look on the desk, see if you can find a data sheet—you know name, age, et cetera—fill it out for me, will you? Gotta keep records the state says. Rules." He sighs. "Did you say yes or no?"

"What?"

"Coffee. Yes or no? Sit down, sit down."

"No. Thanks." Obediently he goes to the desk, searches until he comes up with a blank information card. He begins to fill it out Berger drags the other chair over to the desk.

"How long since you left the hospital?"

"A month and a half."

"Feeling depressed?"

"No."

"People nervous? Treat you like you're a dangerous man?"

He shrugs. "Yeah, a little, I guess."

"And are you?"

"I don't know."

Berger grins. "You look sensible enough to me. At least, you looked sensibly disgusted when you walked in here. God, it is disgusting, isn't it? The second time this year. What do you think I oughta do about it?"

Con looks for psychological design in the question. No. Nobody would go to this much trouble just to set up a test for him.

He says, "I guess I'd just clean it up and forget about it."

"Yeah, you're right." The man sits back, watching as Conrad fills out the card. "Sure you don't want any coffee?"

Conrad shakes his head, hands him the card.

He reads it quickly. "Good, neat print. So. What're you doing here? You look like a healthy kid to me."

"What I'm doing here," Conrad says, "is that I had to come."

Berger nods. "Rules." He tosses the card onto the desk. "So, suppose you didn't have to come. What would you be here for?"

"I wouldn't." He shifts awkwardly under the piercing blue gaze.

"How long were you there?"

"Eight months."

"What did you do? OD? Make too much noise in the library?"

"No." Looks steadily at the bookcase in front of him. "I tried to off myself."

Berger picks up the card again, studies it as he blows on his coffee. "What with? Pills? Gillette Super Blue?"

He sees the way to handle this guy. Keep it light. "It was a Platinum-Plus," he says.

The eyes are fixed upon him thoughtfully. "So how does it feel to be home? Everybody glad to see you?"

"Yes. Sure."

"Your friends, everything okay with them?"

"Fine."

"It says here, no sisters, no brothers. Right?"

"Right," he says. *Don't panic. Release is inevitable. Soon.*

Berger leans back, hands behind his head. He could be twenty-five, or forty. "So, what d'you want to work on?" he asks.

"Pardon?"

"It's your money, so to speak. What d'you want to change?"

He thinks then of his father, of the struggle to keep between them a screen of calm and order. "I'd like to be more in control, I guess. So people can quit worrying about me."

"So, who's worrying about you?"

"My father mostly. This is his idea."

"How about your mother? Isn't she worried?"

"No."

"How come?"

"She's— I don't know, she's not a worrier."

"No? What does she do, then?"

"Do?"

"Yeah, what's her general policy toward you? You get along with her all right?"

"Yeah, fine." He is abruptly uncomfortable. An endless grilling process, like it was in the hospital.

"You've got a funny look on your face," Berger says. "What're you thinking?"

"I'm thinking," he says, "if you're a friend of Crawford's, you're probably okay, but I don't like this already. Look, what do you know about me? Have you talked to Crawford?"

"No." The smile is benign. "He told me your name, that's all."

"Okay, I'll tell you some things. I had a brother. Buck. We were sailing on the lake. He drowned."

"When?"

"Summer before last."

"I suppose you and Crawford talked about it," Berger says.

"Every day."

A pigeon lights on the windowsill. It pecks inquiringly at the window for a moment, then flies off.

"Okay," Berger says. "Anything else?"

"No," he says. "Yeah. About friends. I don't have any. I got sort of out of touch before I left."

"Oh?"

He does not respond.

"Well," Berger says. "I'd better tell you. I'm not big on control. I prefer things fluid. But it's your money."

"So to speak."

Berger laughs. "How's Tuesdays and Fridays?"

"Twice a week?"

He shrugs. "Control is a tough nut."

"I've got swim practice every night."

"Hmm. That's a problem. So, how do we solve it?"

A long silence. He is tired and irritated. "I guess I skip practice and come here twice a week," he says.

"Okeydoke."

It is over, and Berger walks him to the door. "The schedule," he says, "is based on patient ratings. A scale of one to ten. The higher I rate, the fewer times you gotta come. Example: You rate me ten, you only have to see me once a week."

Conrad laughs. "That's crazy."

"Hey, I'm the doctor." Berger grins. "You're the patient."

THE first session has been gotten through. And the guy is not bad; at least he is loose. The exchange about the razor blades reminded him of something good about the hospital; nobody hid anything there. People kidded you and it was all right; it even helped to stay the flood of shame and guilt. Remembering that day at lunch when Stan Carmichael rose from his chair pointing his finger in stern accusation. "Profane and unholy boy! Sinner against God and man, father and mother! Fall on your knees! Repent of evil, Conrad Jarrett!" and he had nodded, eating on, while Robbie leaned across the table and asked, "Stan, may I have your gingerbread, buddy?" And Stan broke off his ravings to snarl, "Damn it, Rob, you scrounge off my plate at every meal; it's disgusting!"

So, how do you stay open, when nobody mentions anything, when everybody is careful *not* to mention it? *Ah, Jarrett, what do you want? Want people to say, "Gee, we're glad you didn't die"?* Poor taste, poor taste.

299

He is suddenly aware of the other people on the street, hurrying by. See? No one's accusing. They don't even seem repelled. As a matter of fact, they don't even notice. Still, as they pass him, he carefully averts his gaze.

CHAPTER THREE

IN HIS office, Cal stands at his desk and looks at his calendar. Wednesday, November 5. See Ray about Braddock. Call his broker. Set up a meeting for the nineteenth. Duties, services, advice. A good thing you do not have to know who you are, Cal Jarrett, in order to perform, because today there is a minimum of information available on that subject.

He hates fighting, and last night they had fought—over London.

"I think you're being unreasonable," Beth said, "not even asking him about it. Why won't you admit that you don't want to go?"

"You ask him, then! What am I? The official interpreter here? You see him every day, don't you? Give him the pitch."

"I don't see him any more than you do," she said coolly. "What are you afraid of? It's a question. It requires a yes or a no. You certainly ask him enough other questions: How did he sleep? How does he feel? How did *I* sleep? How do *I* feel?"

"Okay," he said. "How *did* you sleep? How *do* you feel?"

"That's not *it!*" she said. "I don't want you to start asking *me* the questions, I want you to just stop!"

Fair enough. If she knew, though, that it is not only of Conrad but of himself that he is asking questions now, basic, hopeless questions. *Who the hell are you?* as he walks down the street. Who in the world knows who he is all the time? It is not a question to ask a guy over a sandwich. If you must ponder it, then do it alone.

I'm the kind of man who—he has heard this phrase a million times, at parties, in bars. I'm the kind of man who—he tries to apply any familiar terms to himself, but without success.

Arnold Bacon. Now there was a man who knew who he was. In 1967 his obit had been in the *Tribune:* "Nationally known tax attorney dies at seventy-two. . . . Tragic loss to the profession . . ."

He was a senior in high school when he first met Arnold Bacon. Bacon had come up to him at, of all places, a Christmas tea at the Evangelical Home. "Well, young man, what are you planning to do with the rest of your life?" He had laughed politely, but Bacon was serious. "I've looked at your grades," he said. "You're smart. You ever thought about going into law?"

He had thought about being a soldier of fortune. Or a fireman. A professional athlete. Those wistful occupations faded out of the picture after that December afternoon. He was accepted to prelaw at Wayne University; he took a part-time job clerking in Bacon's office; he graduated from Wayne and was accepted into law school at the University of Michigan, backed by Bacon's recommendation.

A lucky accident. Bacon took him on; became his mentor; told him what courses to take, which scholarships to apply for; came to his aid financially. It was almost a father-son relationship. Bacon had no sons. He needed a student, an apprentice.

But Bacon had not approved of law students who married while they were in school. Diffusion of energy, he called it. And so, of course, everything had changed after Beth. Bacon had been Cal's first actual experience with loss.

When he was eleven, he learned the association of that word with death. The director of the Evangelical Home had called him in to tell him of his loss. His mother had passed away. For a short time he became a figure of some importance to his peers. And he was invited to the director's office for cocoa, and sermons on Love and Loss, and How a Christian Deals with Grief. The only difference he perceived was that he no longer had any visitor or presents on his birthday or at Christmas. But he did not at the time understand the meaning of loss. And of grief.

He had grieved over Arnold, though. Not when he died; it was too late then. But when Arnold had turned indifferent after the marriage, *that* was grief. It had undermined him, taken away something that he hadn't even realized he possessed.

I'm the kind of man who—hasn't the least idea what kind of man I am. There. Some definition. He is no closer than he was back in the director's office, listening to the sermons.

So, how does a Christian deal with grief? There is no dealing; he knows that much. There is simply the stubborn, mindless hanging on until it is over. Until you are through it. But something has happened in the process. The old definitions, the neat pigeonholes have disappeared. Or else they no longer apply.

His eyes move again to the calendar. Wednesday, November 5. Of course. At least he knows what is wrong today. Today is Jordan's birthday. Today he would have been nineteen.

KAREN smiles at Con. Deep dimples in her cheeks. He had forgotten that about her, had forgotten how she lowers her head when she is nervous. Nervous now as she sits down across from him in the narrow drugstore booth. It makes him feel protective.

"Hi. How are you?"

"Fine. And you?"

He grins, shrugs his shoulders. "Not bad. Light, scattered paranoia, increasing to moderate during the day." She frowns and looks away. "Hey, I'm only kidding. I'm fine. Really."

She used to wear her hair long and straight. Now it is short, curling softly about her face.

"I like your hair that way."

"Thank you." They look at each other. Slowly sinking in the awkwardness of the moment. He didn't want that to happen. They were good friends at the hospital. They would talk for hours on the stone bench outside the rec-room door.

"It's great to see you," he says.

"Good to see you." Again she ducks her head. "I can't stay too long. Our drama club is doing A Thousand Clowns. We're going wild trying to get it together. I'm secretary this year, that's probably why we're so disorganized—"

He says bluntly, "Well, don't let me hold you up, then."

All that time it took him to get here because it is near her house in Skokie, and she sits there as if she is being held prisoner.

"I'm sorry," Karen says. "I really did want to see you. Only I was sort of afraid. You seemed so down, over the phone."

"I'm not down," he says. "Everything's great. I'm swimming—"

302

"You kids gonna order?" The waiter eyes them sourly.

"I'll have a Coke," Conrad says.

"Just coffee for me." Karen gives the man a smile. Nothing doing. He scribbles off a bill and slaps it down with a grunt.

Conrad shakes his head. "Hostile."

She giggles. "Definitely a low-self-image day." And they relax. She, the seasoned veteran, out six months to his three, asks, "Are you seeing anybody?"

"A doctor? Yeah, are you?"

"I went for a while," she says, "but then I decided it wasn't doing me any good. Really, the only one who can help you is you. Well, you and God." She stops to take a breath. "Anyway, that's what Dad says. It's what they told us in the hospital, too, didn't they? That you have to learn to help yourself." She smiles. "I don't mean that there isn't any value in it, if you need it. I mean, for some people it could be just the right thing. . . ."

To reassure her, he says, "I don't know how long I'll keep it up, either. I only go to get my mind flushed out. After an hour with this guy you're not too sure about him, but you know you're okay."

His visits with Berger have gotten to be something that he looks forward to, a chance to feel better twice a week, even if the feeling doesn't have much carry-over yet. Now he is disgusted with himself for his slandering words.

"Hey," he says. "Remember Crawford, how he was always telling you to go with the things that made you laugh? Yesterday I heard a guy on the radio talking about how to take care of your trees. If you water after five, be sure to water only every other root. 'In other words,' he says, 'the U.S. Department of Agriculture requests that you use alternate roots after five o'clock.'"

"Con, you made that up!" She is laughing at last.

In the hospital, he was the only one who could make her laugh. His heart swells with pleasure. Calmly, so as not to alarm her, he says, "You know, losing a whole year out of your life is turning out to be sort of a disadvantage, don't you think?"

"I don't think about it," she says. "You shouldn't, either. Just keep going, get into things. Try to be less intense."

Well, that's what he was asking for, wasn't it? Then why do the words irritate him so? With an imaginary pencil he writes in the palm of his hand. "Just a minute, 'less intense,' gee, you sure do make it sound simple, Dr. Aldrich."

She frowns. "It isn't simple. But at least I try."

"Don't I act like I'm trying?" He makes a face, teasing her.

"I don't know. I don't really know you, Con."

This hurts. And then she looks at her watch, and this hurts, too. "I'm late. I've got to go."

"So. Go." He spreads his hands palms down on the table.

She hesitates. "Listen, call me again. I'd like to see you."

"Sure." Call me, I'd like to see you. But just not real soon.

She picks up her coat. "The thing is, we should both be careful about who we see. It isn't good for either of us to get down."

"I'm not down!" More calmly he repeats, "I'm not down."

"Well, it's contagious, you know that. We can't risk it."

"Okay." God, he did not come here to drain strength away from her. He would not do that to anyone, least of all her.

She gets to her feet. "I'm sorry. I wish I could stay longer. You will call me?"

"Yeah, sure."

And then she is gone. He pays the bill and sits a while longer. He had thought that he would ask her to a swim meet. How stupid to think that she would go for that. Dull stuff compared to *A Thousand Clowns. Ah, come on, Jarrett. She is a nice girl and she is right. It's a dangerous business. How would you like it if some screwed-up guy kept asking you to make him feel necessary?*

There is a sign over the door: No LOITERING. The waiter keeps glancing over. Con gets to his feet. *Okay, Karen, see you around. Who needs you, anyway? Who the hell needs anybody?*

THIS Saturday, Cal has repaired a broken doorknob, watched Michigan beat Navy on television, played tennis with Al Cahill, his next-door neighbor. A familiar pattern of triviality, the things that move time.

He pours himself a Scotch and water. Another pleasure. This

first drink of a Saturday evening. Later on he may become bored and drink too much. Or else he will enjoy himself, relax, and drink too much. Another familiar pattern. He has noted that lately; when they go out, he drinks too much. Because drinking helps. It deadens the pain. Tonight he will have to take care not to get blitzed.

Waiting for Beth, he wanders into the den. Conrad lounges on the couch in jeans and a blue work shirt, watching television, hands in his pockets, legs stuck out in front of him.

"Your basic teenager," Cal observes.

Conrad eyes the gray slacks, black turtleneck, gray plaid sport coat. "Your basic suburban lawyer."

Cal sits down beside him. "Where were you today? I needed a tennis partner."

"Over in Skokie."

"Oh? Doing what?"

"Seeing somebody I know."

"Anybody I know?"

"No."

Period. "What're you doing tonight?"

"Studying. Got a history midterm on Tuesday."

He hopes Con is not uptight about the tests. Should he tell him not to worry? No, he will think it means he, Cal, is worried. "How's Joe Lazenby?" he asks. "You see much of him?"

"On the way to school. At practice. On the way home."

Not an answer, really, but it is conversation. Cal wants to keep it flowing between him and this mysterious stranger, his son. He asks, "Why don't you see what he's doing tonight?"

"I think I ought to study."

"Can't you study tomorrow?"

"It's a *midterm*, Dad." His eyes have not left the set.

"Okay. It takes time to get back in the swing of it, huh?"

Conrad looks over at him and grins. "You been hanging around with Grandfather again?"

Cal laughs. Con will be eighteen in January, but he looks younger than that, and vulnerable, yet older at the same time. Tired. He has an urge to shield him, but how? There is no way. He says,

"Your mother and I were talking about going to London sometime."

"Not for Christmas?" There is an odd look on his face. Fear?

"No, this Christmas I thought we'd just stay around here. Maybe in the spring."

"Yeah, that'd be fine. Unless—if she wants to go for Christmas, I'll go. I don't want to spoil things."

Beth is in the doorway. "I'm ready, Cal."

"Okay. In a second."

"We're late." She moves down the hallway to get her coat.

He doesn't want to leave yet. He has to get over this feeling of panic every time he leaves Con alone in the house. "We'll be over at the Murrays', did I tell you that?"

"No. Fine."

"The number's in the book. Philip Murray."

"Okay."

And he knows what Conrad is thinking: What would I need to call you for?

In the car, Beth says, "I told you he'd go if you asked him."

"He doesn't want to, though."

She shrugs. "Well, it's too late now, anyway."

She gave up on this, suddenly and simply. He hasn't realized until this minute that it has been several weeks since the subject of London was mentioned. Now he feels at once relief and guilt.

"We'll go in the spring," he says. "I promise."

She doesn't answer.

"Who's going to be there tonight?" Testing. Her tone when she answers will tell him if she is angry.

"Well, the Murrays. It's their house." She slides over next to him. Grateful, he squeezes her hand. "And Mac and Ann Kline. Ed and Marty Genthe. And us."

"Why us? We hardly know the Murrays."

"That's why you have people over, darling. To get to know them better."

He does not want to know Phil Murray any better. He has played golf with him three times. The first time, he was told Phil's reasons

306

for joining the golf club. "I'm an insurance salesman, Cal. A damn good one, too." He had laughed and said that he had all the insurance he needed. "That's what you think." Phil had spent the rest of the round telling jokes about crooked lawyers.

Cal says, "Let's not stay too late."

Beth is looking at herself in the rearview mirror. "How do you know you won't have fun?"

"I can read my mind. It says, 'Stay home, read *The Rise and Fall of the Third Reich,* do something constructive with your life.'"

"Everybody has to eat dinner," she says.

THE Murrays live nearby in a wide, square-pillared house. Sara Murray sweeps them inside and ushers them into the large, elegantly furnished living room, done in shades of champagne and white. As is the hostess. She is a tiny woman in a long, silky gown with a deep neckline. "Ed, make room for Beth."

"Come here, you gorgeous thing," Ed Genthe says, taking Beth's hand and pulling her down beside him on the couch.

"Edward," she says, laughing. "Control yourself!"

Gracious as always, but Cal knows she doesn't like this. She is wearing a white knit pantsuit, a black blouse, her hair tied back from her face with a black silk scarf. She *does* look gorgeous.

"Cal, what would you like?" Phil asks. "Scotch?"

"Yes, please. Just a short one."

Sara passes around a tray of cocktail snacks gracefully arranged in rows: sausages and mushrooms in tiny pastry shells, hot puffs of cheese-flavored dough. "Come on, take lots."

"Cal, you playing in the lawyers' golf invitational next spring?" Mac Kline drifts over to where he is standing, beside the mantel.

"I'm not sure I've posted enough scores to qualify."

Sara jockeys in between Cal and Mac with the tray. She has a frenetic-butterfly manner that grates on his nerves. He glances at his wife, who is not that type at all. She is cool and relaxed at parties. He would prefer talking to her.

"I saw Conrad the other day," Marty Genthe says. "It's nice when someone that age is courteous. Most of Donald's friends can't be

307

bothered even remembering my name. It's just, 'Oh, hi there.'"

Suddenly everyone is listening.

"How is he doing?" Ann Kline asks. "I hear he's swimming."

"He's fine," Beth says. There is something final and forbidding about the answer, but Sara doesn't hear it. They are still newcomers here, and she wants to be polite.

She asks, "Has he been sick?"

"He was sick for a while," Beth says. "He's fine now."

"Another drink, Cal?"

"Yes, sure." He crosses to the bar, the skin on the backs of his hands tightening as if from an electric shock.

HE SITS between Ann Kline and Marty Genthe at the table.

"Sara, what a meal!" Marty says. "It's a tough act to follow."

"Oh, no," she protests, "it's just plain food."

"The cheese sauce is great," Ed says.

After dinner the children are served up. They enter the living room on cue to say their good-nights. The handsome fourteen-year-old daughter supervises her younger brother and sister, while the elder boy stands, shy and solemn, in the background. He reminds Cal of Conrad at that age. So earnest, so polite. Adults and children beam awkwardly at one another until Sara's motherly pride is satisfied and they are dismissed.

"Good-looking children," Cal says.

"Thank you." She gives him a grateful smile.

In knots of two and three they sit in the living room. Beth and Mac are in one corner. Cal sits on the couch between Sara and Marty, feeling pleasantly high. He has an arm around each of them, and has to disengage one from Sara to sip his drink.

"Cal, how are things, really?" Marty asks. A brittle, attractive red-head, she is looking at him. "Going all right?"

"Pretty well," he says. "Only I miss the kids who used to hang around. What's Don doing these days?"

"Oh, the same old things. Girls. Swimming. You know how boys are, they don't tell you anything unless you *bulldoze* it out of them."
She laughs. "To tell you the truth, Donald says Conrad isn't . . .

308

as friendly as he used to be. I suppose he feels a little, I don't know, self-conscious."

"About what?" Sara asks. "I'm sorry, it's none of my business, of course."

"No, it's nothing," Cal says. He is suddenly uncomfortable. The drinks have made him fuzzy. He shouldn't have said that, about the boys not coming around.

"Don says he doesn't come to practice Tuesdays and Fridays."

"No. He sees a doctor in Evanston twice a week."

"You mean he's still having problems?"

"Not exactly. It's somebody to talk to," Cal says lamely. He had not intended the conversation to go this way.

"Cal, we've got to go," Beth calls. "It's late."

"Hey, what d'you mean? Party's just getting off the ground!" Phil protests as they move toward the hall.

Somehow they are into their coats and out the door, and the night is cool and silent all around them. He gets in the car.

"Do you want me to drive?" she asks.

He glances at her, surprised. "Do you think I'm drunk?"

"I don't know, are you?"

So she had heard the conversation. "No," he says. "I promise." Seeking to lead her away from it, he laughs. "The thing you can't forgive about Phil Murray is that he's a crashing bore."

"I want to tell you something," she says. "You drink too much at parties."

"Okay."

"You let her pump you. You let her drag that stuff out of you, and in front of someone who doesn't even know us."

"My sentiments exactly." He nods, hoping to head her off.

"Why did you tell her he was seeing a psychiatrist?"

"Look, some people consider that a status symbol," he says, "right up there with going to Europe."

"I don't. And I thought your blurting it out like that was in the worst possible taste. Not to mention a violation of privacy."

"Whose privacy?" he asks. "Whose privacy did I violate?"

She does not answer.

309

THE LIGHT IS ON IN Conrad's room. He is asleep, lying on his back
A history book lies open on the bed. Cal sets it on the nightstand
Reaching for the lamp, he looks at Conrad. His right arm is out-
stretched. Still biting his nails. So what? Lots of people do it.

He looks at the thin, vertical scar that extends two inches up
the inside of Con's arm. "He meant business," the intern told him in
the ambulance. "Horizontal cuts, the blood clots. It takes a lot
longer. You were damn lucky to catch him."

High achievers, Dr. Crawford told him, set themselves impossible standards. They suffer excessive guilt over failure. He had
groped to understand. "But he's never failed at anything!"

Cal snaps off the light. *Listen,* he prays, *let the exams be easy.
Don't let him feel he is failing.*

Beth is waiting for him. She puts her arms around him, all
tawny, smooth skin, those gray eyes silent and insistent. She leads
tonight, and he follows, everything floating, melting, complete.
Afterward, she slides away from him, and her hair, soft against
his shoulder, smells sweet and fresh, like wood fern. He buries his
face in it. "Let me hold you awhile."

But she is tired. She curls away from him in sleep. He rolls to his
back, hands under his head, staring upward. Other Saturday nights,
lying in bed, waiting for the comforting sound of a car door slamming and whispers of laughter under the windows. And at the beginning of the evenings the jokes, the hassles over clothes. *Hey,
that's my sweater! The hell it is, possession is— Hey, Dad, what's
possession? Possession is gonna get your head broke—now give it
to me!* And sounds of a struggle and laughter.

He is condemned to wakefulness. Without expectation of anything—of a car, of whispers, or laughter. Resigned, he keeps watch
and continues to listen.

CHAPTER FOUR

A SURPRISE quiz in trig. He takes his seat, his stomach pulling nervously. He wills himself not to panic. *I know this stuff. I know it.*

Across the aisle sits Suzanne Mosely. Her brow is furrowed, her

mouth pinched. It makes him ashamed of his own fear. She has al
ways had trouble with math. Mr. Simmons is staring at him. Guiltily
he looks down at his paper. *Stay calm. It will come.*

Halfway through the test his pencil point snaps. He straightens
up. It is not as hard as he thought it would be. He stretches and
goes to get another pencil from Simmons's desk. No pencil sharpen-
ing during a quiz. Returning to his seat, out of the corner of his eye
he can see Suzanne's paper. Cross-outs everywhere. Poor kid. He
knows what that feels like.

There are five minutes left when he hands in his paper. He leaves
the room, stands near the lockers as he waits for the bell. Suzanne
comes out and leans against the wall. God, she's so fat. But pretty

She is staring at him now. Tears are spilling down her cheeks.
Helpless, he watches. "Hey. It's only a stupid test," he says.

She glares at him. "You can say that. You passed it. My dad's going to kill me. God, why am I *so dumb!*"

The bell rings. She turns away from him and he runs to catch
up with her. "Listen, if you want some help—"

She stops in the middle of the hall to stare at him.

"I'll help you. In study hall. Or after school some night."

"Why would you want to do that?" she asks. "No. No, thanks, it's
all right."

A voice cuts across the hall. "Hey, Jarrett!" He looks over. Stillman grins at him. Suzanne has gone on and Conrad stands looking
after her, feeling relieved, and yet oddly hurt.

In the locker room that afternoon, Stillman lies in wait. "Hey,
Jarrett, lemme know about her, will you? I'll let you know about
Pratt, if you let me know about Mosely."

"Mosely?" Van Buren echoes. "*Mosely?*"

Con slams his locker closed and their laughter follows him up
the stairway to the pool. *Jerks. To hell with them forever.*

In bed, Con waits for sleep. He cannot get under until he has reviewed the day, counted up his losses. He must learn more control.
Next time laugh when Stillman needles you.

312

What about the test? Did he pass it? He thinks so. Suddenly he realizes why Simmons had kept an eye on him during the hour. That was the class. Last year. A quiz returned. Across his paper in red: "Incomplete. See me." He had stared at it all through the hour, his eyes slowly filling with tears, and Simmons bending over his desk, asking, "Jarrett, are you sick?" Nodding, stumbling up the aisle, facing the blackboard as Simmons wrote out a hall pass. Out of the classroom, and into the parking lot to find a car that was unlocked. Him on the floor in the back seat, crying, leaning out to be sick in the snow. He had left school that day, walked around uptown, looking in windows at the Christmas displays.

And the next day his homeroom teacher had said, "I got a skip notice on you this morning. What happened?"

"Nothing. I didn't feel like going to class."

The teacher had looked at him. "Okay. Let's forget it. We'll talk about it after the holidays."

The holidays. Christmas in Florida. Lying on the bed at the hotel, staring at a mosquito on the ceiling. The only memory he has of that period. That, and the remorseless blue of ocean.

Brightness surrounds him, but it is night. He walks. The sand is stiff and squeaks under his feet. The moon is above him and to his left. For miles and miles the sand stretches in front of him. The mouth of a tunnel appears, a metal cylinder curving ten feet over his head, the lower rim buried in the sand.

He enters it. Brightly lighted inside. A sharp right turn ahead obscures his view. When he turns the corner, the tunnel continues on, no end in sight, only the dimensions have shrunk. Now he must crawl on his hands and knees. When he raises his head, he sees nothing. Only darkness. He is convulsed with panic and begins to work himself backward. His feet strike the wall of the tunnel. He tries again. Solid wall no matter where he moves. His head is wedged against the ceiling, his chin touching the floor. Oh, God. He is sealed in this metal tomb and the walls press upon him from all sides. He cannot breathe, cannot move. Must. Must. Twisting violently onto his back, he screams.

313

It wakes him. Did he scream out loud? He listens for some sound in the house, for someone pounding toward his room. Nothing. The blood tingles in his veins. His heart is thudding painfully.

He sits up, turns on the light, but slowly. No sudden movements. He feels he will shatter into a million pieces if he is jarred.

"I DON'T hold much stock in dreams," Berger says. "In fact, I don't hold stock. Of any kind."

Con is annoyed. "What the hell kind of psychiatrist are you? They all believe in dreams."

"Do they? Damn, I'm always outa step. Do me a favor, will you? Lie down. On the floor, that's it. I want to try something."

"Boy, you're nuts, you know that?" Still, he obeys, lowering himself to the carpet and stretching out, hands behind his head.

"Change of perspective," Berger says. He likewise lowers himself. "Steadies the blood."

"Steadies the blood," he scoffs. "I lie down all the time at home. It doesn't help. Maybe I need some kind of tranquilizer."

"*Tranquilizer?*"

"Yeah. What d'you think?"

"It is not my impression," Berger says, "that you are in need of a tranquilizer."

"I feel nervous all the time. I can't sleep."

"Maybe you oughta drop a course or two."

"No. I'm behind already."

"Behind what? The great schedule in the sky? The golden grade book? What?"

"Man, you're preaching again. And your ceiling's dirty."

"So, sue me. Listen, kiddo, I lied. I believe in dreams, and I especially believe in yours; they're fascinating as hell. Only I also like to hear about what happens to you when you're awake, okay? Something is making you nervous. Now what is it?"

Con sits up, reaches for his coffee. "Okay, I know what it is. I don't want to swim anymore. I look horrible. He's got two guys who are better than me swimming the fifty, and, anyway, I don't give a damn about those guys, they're a bunch of boring jocks. And

314

I can't *stand* him, he's a—" He breaks off, his stomach in knots.

"Well," Berger says. "Why don't you quit?"

"I can't. I beg him for one more chance. Then I swim for two months and quit again. It'd look so stupid."

"Forget how it looks. How does it feel?"

He shakes his head. "No. That's what happened last year. It's the same damn thing I did last year."

"Forget last year. You think you're the same person you were last year?"

He shrugs, lying down again, staring at the ceiling.

"So, tell me about the coach," Berger says.

He smiles faintly. "He's a jerk. He says to me—this is typical—'Jarrett, I had a friend who was hospitalized for this same thing five years ago. Been in and out of institutions ever since.' Now what the hell am I supposed to say to that?"

"What did you say?"

"I told him I wasn't planning on going back. He says, 'No, I don't suppose you are.'"

"Sometimes," Berger says, "people say stupid things. They feel like they gotta say something, you know?"

"Sometimes people say stupid things because they're stupid."

A clock on the wall ticks away, and it is relaxing to lie here with this placid man beside him. But it is five o'clock, time to go.

"This problem, kiddo," Berger says, "it's real, you know. A good, healthy problem needs a good, healthy solution. Real problems, real solutions, you get it?"

"Sounds like a chapter heading to me."

Berger sighs. "I hope to hell you're writing this stuff down. It'll be a shame if it's lost to future generations."

"I've got it taped up over the back of the john."

LAUGHTER drifts up from the locker room. From the top of the stairs, Con can hear Stillman say, "Lazenby, why are you so nervous about making a commitment, just yes or no!"

"It costs money, that's why. For three bucks I like to know what I'm seeing."

315

"Hell, it's a French sex film, what more do you have to know?"

Con starts down the stairs, rubbing his head with a towel. Lazenby says, "Okay. How about if I ask Jarrett?"

And he stops, loops the towel around his neck, listening.

"You ever think about doing anything without Jarrett?"

"What's that mean?"

"Means what it says. I just wondered."

Genthe says, "Hey, what's with Jarrett, anyway? How come he gets all the extra practice time? Hell, I could look better if I had extra practice time. . . ."

"You couldn't look better if you were a girl," Truan jeers.

He stands outside the open door, smoothing his hand lightly along the polished wood frame, slowly, slowly.

Lazenby says, "I just thought we'd ask him, Kevin."

"You know what happens when you hang around with flakes," Stillman says. "You get flaky."

"Man, d'you mind?" Lazenby says. "He's a friend of mine."

"He's a flake."

"You oughta get off his back, Kevin," Van Buren says. "The guy's got enough problems."

"He sure has."

More laughter. Con turns abruptly, heading back up the stairs. Salan is sitting where he left him, bent over the clipboard. He listens, his mouth a taut line, as Conrad explains.

At last he says, "Jarrett, you gotta be kidding me. I excuse you from practice twice a week so you can see some shrink. I work with you extra time *at your convenience;* now what the hell more am I supposed to be doing for you?"

"Nothing." *Shrink. Hate that word. Coarse, ignorant, just the kind of word you'd expect from a jerk like Salan. Will not get mad. Control is all.*

"A bright kid like you," Salan continues, "with everything going for him. Why do you want to keep messing up your life?"

He says carefully, "I don't think it'll mess up my life if I stop swimming." *Stay calm, stay calm. This is a sensible decision. A real solution to a real problem.*

316

Salan says flatly, "Okay. This is it. I'm not taking you back again. You remember that."

I'll remember. Aloud he says, "No, sir. I won't ask you to, sir."

THE locker room is empty. He dresses, packs his athletic bag slowly. Stalling, but he knows it's no good; Lazenby will wait for him. He doesn't want to ride home with them, but why the hell should he walk? Why should he freeze because they are jerks?

He heads for the car. Truan, Van Buren, and Stillman are in the back seat. He gets in front. Lazenby asks if he is interested in going to the show tonight. He declines. He has to study.

"You oughta lay off studying, Jarrett," Stillman says. "Screws up your mind. Keep all the channels clear for heavy thought."

They laugh. To his ears the sound is forced, false.

"We'll be back by eleven," Lazenby says.

"No. I can't."

"Who says?" Stillman asks. "Your mom?"

He ignores that. The ride seems long. Even though he is the first to be dropped off.

"I'll see you tomorrow," Lazenby says.

"I've got to go early," he says. "I'll get a ride with my dad."

"How early? I can go a little early—"

"No, that's okay. I'll see you there."

Let them find out from Salan that he is finished with them. He gets out and closes the door without looking back.

HIS father stops at the door of his room that night. The ritual stop. "How's it going?"

"Okay. Fine." He returns the ritual answer. He does not want to discuss quitting the team tonight. There will be flak, and he isn't ready for it. He has done it, maybe for the wrong reasons, but it was the right thing to do.

Summers ago in Maine they all climbed Cadillac Mountain, looking in every direction—nothing to see but water, except for the thin strip of land holding the mountain and the park to the state of Maine. They tossed out the adjectives. Majestic. Awesome. And

317

then somebody said excessive, and they all laughed. That was it. Everything seems excessive now and too intense; Karen is right. Learn to relax, don't think so much, just *be*.

Night is fast replacing morning as the worst time for him. The way it used to be in the months after the accident. He wasn't sleeping much. And suddenly he wasn't sleeping at all, his body was tense, his brain seethed from night until morning. He would crawl into bed, praying, and he would lie there and lie there until at last he would hear the warning click as the radio turned itself on and it was morning again. His father would come down the hall to make sure he was awake. *Awake*. And he was never able to tell them. He would get up, get dressed, eat his breakfast, go to school. He was so tired, so tired. He told Crawford once that was why he had done it—he had to get some sleep.

But things are not that bad. Not yet.

CHAPTER FIVE

CAL runs into Carole Lazenby near his office. Her large-boned, square figure looks out of place here, among the snazzy secretaries parading the streets of Evanston at noontime. And because she looks so real, he is absurdly glad to see her, asks her to have lunch.

"Gee, nobody's asked me to lunch in ages!"

She offers to take him to the University Sandwich Shop, where she commands a discount with her student ID.

"What are you taking?" he asks.

She laughs self-consciously. "It's called Search for Identity."

Funny, he would never have picked her out as a woman with identity problems. He tells her so, but she just laughs.

"Looking forty in the face is what scared me, Cal. Maybe if I were your wife, I could handle it better."

"Why?"

She laughs again. "I guess because she doesn't look it."

A pleasant lunch. He has forgotten how easy she is to talk to, how genuine. She asks about Con, and he mentions how he misses seeing Joe around the house.

318

"Yes, they don't spend much time together, do they? Well, you tell Connie I miss him. Tell him to stop over sometime soon. Beth, too. How is she? I only see her at bridge once a month, and we never seem to get a chance to talk."

"She's busy, too," Cal says. "She's chairing the tennis tournament at Onwentsia next spring. She spends a lot of time over there."

"I admire her organization," Carole says. "She's such a perfectionist. And yet she never lets herself get trapped into things she doesn't want to do. Now there's an art."

After lunch he walks Carole to the corner. On the way back to work he thinks, Beth never lets herself get trapped. Not strictly true. He can remember when she felt distinctly trapped. When Jordan was two years old and Con ten months, both of them spreading havoc in that tiny apartment. "Those first five years just passed in a blur!" he has heard her say gaily at parties. But he remembers them, and the scenes: her figure tense with fury as she scrubbed the fingermarks from the walls; she bursting suddenly into tears because of a toy left out of place or a spoonful of food thrown onto the floor. Everything had to be perfect, never mind the impossible hardship it worked on her, on them all, never mind the lack of meaning in such perfection. They learned, all of them, that certain things drove her to the point of madness: dirt tracked in on a freshly scrubbed floor, clothing left out of place. And, he had to admit, he liked a clean house, he liked the order she brought into his life, perfectionist that she was.

And so had he been, after a fashion. No more. Not since the summer before last and an unexpected July storm on Lake Michigan. He had left off being a perfectionist then, when he discovered that not promptly kept appointments, not a clean house, not membership in Onwentsia or the Lawyers' Club, not power or goodness— not *anything*—cleared you through the terrifying office of chance; that it is chance and not perfection that rules the world.

"WOULD you like a drink before dinner, darling?" Beth asks.

"No, thanks." Cal glances at his watch. "Is Con home yet?"

"Not yet."

319

"It's six thirty."

"He's been later the past couple of weeks."

"I've got an idea," he says. "Why don't you come down tomorrow and take a look at that car with me? We can have lunch."

"I can't tomorrow."

"I ought to put the order in, to get delivery before Christmas."

"Then do it," she says. "I'm not good at buying cars, anyway."

"You don't sound terrifically sold on the idea."

"I'm sold. I think it's a nice idea."

"Well, it would give him some independence."

"Fine. I'll leave it up to you."

If it were up to him, he would give him everything—sun and moon, eternal happiness. *Here, will this fix it?* But nothing need fixing, does it? Things do seem better, more relaxed, just since Thanksgiving. No, even before that. Is that illusion or reality? And if all is well, why does he keep looking for signs?

The front door opens. Con comes in.

"Hi. You're late tonight."

"Yeah, a little. Hey, it's snowing." He sits down, and Cal hands him the sport section. "You finished? Thanks."

"How's it going?"

"Great. He gave back the trig quiz today. I got an A."

"Great. Terrific."

"Well," he says, and shrugs, "it was just a quiz."

"That your first A this semester?"

He looks up from the paper. "Yeah. I'm getting back in the swing of things, huh?" He grins.

So truth is in a certain feeling of permanence that presses around the moment. They are ordinary people, after all. For a time they had entered the world of the newspaper statistic, a world where any measure you took to feel better was temporary, at best. But that is over. This is permanent. It must be.

AT FIRST he was afraid that the hours after school would drag, but they do not. He fills them with studying, at school or in town at the library. The old building is dark and comfortable, with it narrow stained-glass windows and soft leather chairs. Or else he walks to the north campus of Lake Forest, where he can sit on a park bench and watch the birds.

This month he has another activity. Christmas shopping. He wanders through the mall admiring the piles of merchandise in the windows—sweaters, shirts, scarves, jewelry. Undaunted, the traditional Christmas scene-stealers—carolers, shepherds, angels, wise men—do battle in the same windows with the tainted goods that surround them. He is not daunted, either. Christmas means gifts, and he puts his money down with the rest, says, "Have a nice Christmas," when he is handed his packages. "You, too," they say.

Before class one morning Lazenby corners him at his locker. "What happened? Salan says you quit."

He nods curtly.

"Why?"

"I felt like it," he says. "It was a bore."

He rummages busily in his locker. Lazenby leans against the wall. "Con, is something the matter?"

"What d'you mean?"

"I don't know." He shrugs his shoulders. Big, blond, sincere type. When he was in the hospital, Lazenby wrote him his only letter, told him the scores of the Cubs and White Sox games; at the bottom of the page, "I miss you, man." He had read it a million times before he finally threw it away.

"Listen, don't worry," Conrad says. "Everything's fine."

"I don't know, man. You've been acting funny lately."

It trips the lever on the thing he meant *not* to say. "Laze, take my advice. You hang around with flakes, you get flaky."

"I knew that was it. Well, why you teed off at me?"

"I'm not!"

"Ah, Connie. I *know* you." He tries a grin. "Look, I'm sorry. I'd be mad, too, but you shouldn't have quit—"

"That's not why! I said it was a bore." He slams his locker closed and walks away. Lazenby falls into step beside him.

"Wait a minute, will ya? I talked to Salan and he says—"

"Well, quit talking to people!" he snaps. "Leave me alone!"

321

The bell rings shrilly. They stare at each other.

"Ah, the hell with you," Lazenby says.

A hollow feeling in his stomach, as if he has been punched. *Never mind. The hell with him, the hell with them all. They were Buck's friends, anyway.* He walks on to class, feeling nothing.

"So, WHAT does your dad say about it?" Berger asks.

He sighs. "I haven't told him yet. He'll just worry."

"So you haven't told anybody? Your mother?"

"My mother? No. Listen, my mother and I do not connect, I told you that before. We don't ride the same bus."

"So, does that bother you?"

"No. Why should it?"

"I don't know. Some people it might bother, that's all."

"My mother is a very private person," he says. "My mother—" He stops. Careful. "People have a right to be the way they are."

"Noble thought," Berger says. "So how's it going? You feeling better since you're not swimming?"

"I guess." He slides down to the end of his spine, his legs stretched in front of him. The clock ticks loudly.

"Come on," Berger prods. "Something's on your mind today."

"Nothing's on my mind. I don't think anything. I don't feel anything." Abruptly he sits up. "I oughta go home."

"Maybe so. What is it that you don't feel? Anger? Sadness?"

A tiny seed opens inside his mind. In the hospital the seed would grow and produce thick, shiny leaves with fibrous veins running through them. More leaves to come. Like tiny, curled-up fists they will hit at him. He wets his lips nervously. "What time is it?"

"Lots of time," Berger says. The eyes are fixed on him, a tender and compelling blue. "Hey. Remember the contract we got? You wanted more control. You see any connection here, between control and this—what'll we call it—lack of feeling?"

He closes his eyes. A jungle in there, inside his head. He opens them quickly. "I didn't say I never feel things. I feel things."

"When?"

He doesn't answer.

"Come on, kiddo, I'm doing all the work here. I thought you told me you didn't like to play games."

"I don't. I'm not. I don't know what you want."

"Then I'll tell you. I want you to leave 'I don't know' out there on the table with the magazines, okay?"

"And if I don't have an answer? You want me to make one up?"

"Yeah, that'd be nice. Make me one up right now, about how you've turned yourself inside out and the overwhelming evidence is that there are no feelings in there nohow."

"I said I have feelings."

Berger sighs. "Now you have 'em, now you don't."

"Why are you hassling me? Why are you trying to get me mad?"

"Are you mad?"

"No!"

Berger sits back in the chair. "Now that," he says, "is a lie. You are mad as hell. So why don't you do something?"

"What?"

"Jeez, I don't know! Tell me to go to hell."

"Go to hell."

Berger laughs. "When's the last time you got really mad?"

He says carefully, "When it comes, there's always too much of it. I don't know how to handle it."

"Sure, I know," Berger says. "It's a closetful of junk. You open the door and everything falls out."

"No," he says. "There's a guy in the closet. I don't even know him, that's the problem."

"Only way you're ever gonna get to know him is to let him out now and then. Along with the boots, and tennis rackets, stale bread, whatever you got stored up there. You go through it, sort it out, throw some of it away. Then you stack up the rest, nice and neat. Next time it won't be such a big deal."

"I don't have the energy," he says.

"Kiddo, you got any idea how much energy it takes to hold the door closed like you do?"

"Sometimes," he says, "when you let yourself feel, all you feel is lousy."

323

Berger nods. "Maybe you gotta feel lousy sometime, in order to feel better. A little advice, kiddo, about feeling. Don't think too much about it. And don't expect it always to tickle."

On another shopping trip after school he nearly walks into someone.

"Oh," she says. "Hi. How're you?"

He mumbles an apology, then looks at her. It is Jeannine.

"What're you doing up here?" she asks. "I thought the swim team practiced until six."

"They do," he says. "I don't swim anymore."

"Oh. Don't you swim as well as you sing?"

"What?"

She laughs. "Just kidding. I'm getting to know your voice now. You're the tenor who stays on pitch."

He takes it as a reprimand. She should not be able to hear him above the others. "I'll sing softer tomorrow."

"No. You know, you ought to be doing the solo in that Russian thing. You have much better tone than Ron."

The voice of authority. He knows about her: that she has applied for a music scholarship to the University of Michigan, that she takes voice lessons. He has stood in the back of the auditorium, listening to her practice, while Faughnan stands next to her, instructing her. She nods her head, goes back and repeats, all the time looking as if she *is* the music itself, and she is small and grave and beautiful.

"You want to have a Coke?" he blurts out suddenly.

She hesitates. "Sure. Fine."

They walk along the street together, and she fills the spaces easily with words, while he, dumbstruck at what he has just done, struggles with the overwhelming problems confronting him: where will he take her, what will they talk about?

Not Pasquesi's. It is always crowded after school, filled with people that he knows, and yet doesn't know anymore.

"There's a place up around the corner," he says.

"Fine. It's nearer to my house. I have to be home by four thirty. My little brother doesn't have a key."

324

She looks up at him. Clear blue eyes. Like Berger's.

Inside the nearly empty coffee shop (it is *not* an in place, obviously), she slips out of her coat. He cannot look directly at her, focuses his eyes slightly to the left of her face.

"Well," she says, "I'm doing all the talking. What kinds of music do *you* like?"

He shrugs. "I don't know. Modern jazz. Folk rock."

"Do you know baroque? Telemann? Ortiz?"

"No. Tell me about them. Telemann and who?"

She blushes. "What a dull conversation. I'm sure there must be things you'd like to talk about."

He laughs, reaching into his back pocket. "Sure. I carry a list around with me. Here. Pick a subject."

She looks up then and smiles at him. "Why is this always so hard? The first time you talk to somebody . . ."

He calculates quickly. The first time. Other times—and the tension within him dissolves. They talk: about movies, about books, about classes, about making friends. . . .

She glances at her watch. "Oh, I've got to go."

He walks her to the railroad tracks, where they talk some more. It is snowing again.

"I told my mother to give him his own key, but he's sort of a scatterbrain. She's afraid he'll lose it. He's eleven. Do you have brothers and sisters?"

"No," he says. "No, I don't."

She makes a face. "You're lucky. Anyway, thanks for the Coke. And thanks for walking me." She runs across the street, turns, and waves. He waves back and heads down Western, his head bent against the snow. He would like to run, only the street is crowded. People would stare at him. He turns his head as he passes the window of a travel agency. He stops, goes back to get a closer look at a travel poster: SKI THE LAURENTIANS!

He narrows his eyes, sees the path again, clear and steep. Buck sweeping around the curve and disappearing. The wind screams in his ears as he blindly follows, staying up nearly to the end, when the smallest of moguls flips him. And Buck bending anxiously over

325

him. *"Hey, buddy, you okay? Talk to me!"* *When he can breathe,* *when he knows that nothing is broken, he wheezes, "I missed the* *goddamn turn!" and Buck sits down beside him, laughing.*

He hangs on now, presses his hand against the window, waiting for the familiar arrow of pain. Only there is none. An oddly pleasant swell of memory, a wave of warmth flooding over him. It is a first.

At peace with himself, he walks home through the falling snow.

CHAPTER SIX

THE Christmas-tree lot has a sign over it: FIRS BY LENNIE. Canned music blares "O Come, All Ye Faithful," and Cal clenches his hands together against the cold, stamping his feet.

"How's this one?" The lot man lifts a tree from its hole.

"No. Not tall enough," Conrad says.

"You want taller? I got taller. Come on, sonny."

The man is built like a lumberjack with a red-and-black checked shirt tucked into mud-colored overalls. They follow him.

"How about this?"

"No," Conrad says. "Too scrawny."

The man gives Cal a faintly patronizing smile, showing him what he thinks of fathers who let their sons run things. He points out a huge blue spruce. "Okay, how's that one?"

"That's terrific," Conrad says. "Hey, that's it."

Cal issues a feeble protest. "Con, it's twelve feet tall!"

"You guys live in a church, or what?"

Cal reaches for his wallet. "Okay, how much?"

"Twenty bucks."

He whistles. "Thought this was a buyer's market."

"Not this year." The lot man is cheerful, forgiving. "Pay at the booth. Me and sonny here'll tie it on your car."

Weightless with joy, he watches while his son assumes the burden of this small decision. At dinner tonight Conrad had told him of his plans for the kind of Christmas they should have this year. "Just greens and pine cones, nothing fancy. Lights, but no ornaments. Popcorn, cranberries, candy canes, how does that sound?"

A few deft strokes and the picture had been painted as easily, as confidently as Con had scanned the menu and ordered: "Hamburger. Onion rings. Chocolate malt. Banana cream pie."

Just last summer they had sat at a lunch counter near the hospital. Con had stared at the menu. Finally he had passed it over to Cal with a weary sigh. "You order, okay? I can't decide."

THE tree fits easily under the cathedral ceiling in the family room, dominating the space before the window. Cal lies on his back giving the screws in the tree stand a final tightening. Conrad holds the trunk. The front door opens, Beth joins them.

"How do you like it?" Cal asks.

"It's lovely," she says.

He feels a sudden rush of love for her, gets to his feet. "How was your meeting?"

"It was interesting," she says. She goes to the bar. "I think I want a drink. How about you?"

"Sure. Here, I'll make them."

"We've got popcorn and cranberries to string," Conrad says to her. "You want to help?"

She looks at him for a long moment. "Of course."

"So what was so interesting?" Cal hands her the glass.

She swirls the Scotch, looking down into it. "Not what happened," she says. "What I heard from Carole Lazenby. But it's not my news, it's Conrad's."

Conrad is looking at her warily.

"It was rather embarrassing," she says, not looking at either of them. "Carole thought I knew. After all, it happened a month ago."

"*What* happened?" he asks.

"Dad," Conrad says, "I quit the swim team."

"Quit? Why?" And then it hits him: the nights he sat waiting for six thirty, the newspaper in front of him, unconcerned. He knew exactly where his kid was. At practice. *A month ago.*

"Where have you been every night?" he asks.

"Around," Conrad says. "The library mostly."

"I don't get it. Why didn't you tell us?"

327

"I was going to. I've been meaning to."

"I'm sure you would have told us before the first meet," Beth says "When is it, next Thursday?"

"I'm sure I would have told you," Conrad says, "if I thought you gave a damn!"

And the wellspring of anger erupts, engulfing them all.

"What the hell does that mean?" Cal demands.

"Never mind," she says. "It's meant for me. Isn't it? I wish I knew Conrad, why it is still so important for you to try to hurt me!"

"Hurt you? Me hurt you! Listen, you're the one who's trying to hurt me!"

"And how did I do that? By making you look like a fool in front of a roomful of people? Poor Mrs. Jarrett, she has no idea what her son is up to; he lies and lies—"

"I didn't lie—"

"You did! You lied every night that you came into this house at six thirty." She presses her hands tight to her head. "I can't stand this, I can't! If it's starting all over again, the lying, the disappearing, the covering up—I won't stand it!"

"Don't, then!" he snarls. "Go to Europe. Go to hell!"

"Con—"

But he backs away from Cal's hand. "Listen, don't give me that the only reason you care, the only reason you give a damn about it is because someone else knew about it first! You never wanted to know anything I was doing; you just wanted me to leave you alone Well, I left you alone, didn't I? I could have told you lots of things Like, up at the hospital there were rats! Big ones, up on three, with the hopeless nuts! But that's okay; see, I was down on two, with the unsuccessfuls—"

"Con, shut up, stop it—"

"Damn it!" he says. "Tell *her* to stop it! Listen, I know why she never came out there, not once! *I know!* Hell, she was going to goddamn *Spain* and goddamn *Portugal*, why should she care if I was hung up by the *goddamn* thumbs out there—"

"Con! That's enough!"

He takes a swift, sobbing breath, fixing them both with a look of

328

fury. And then he is gone, his feet pounding up the stairs. Moments later, the shattering slam of his bedroom door.

Beth has her back to Cal, her hands clutching at her head. "I won't, I won't!"

He goes to her, puts his arms around her. Her body is stiff. "Somebody'd better go up there."

"Go ahead," she says. "That's the pattern, isn't it? Let him walk all over us, then go up there and apologize to him!"

"I'm not going up to apologize."

"Yes, you are! You always do! You've been apologizing to him ever since he came home!"

"Ah, Beth, lay off, will you? I feel like I've been at a goddamn tennis match tonight! Back and forth, back and forth—"

"Don't talk to me like that!" She twists violently away from him. "Don't talk to me like he talks to you!"

He grabs her, rocks her in his arms. "I'm sorry," he murmurs. "Let's not fight." She lets him hold her, but only for a moment.

"Let's go upstairs," he says.

"No. You go. He wants you. He wants somebody who accepts everything he does. Without question, without criticism . . ."

"And you think that's what I do?"

"I know it is!"

"I think," he says cautiously, "that there might have been a better way to handle this."

"Oh, I'm sure of it." Her voice is bitter. "For openers, he could have come to us and told us the truth."

"No, I meant tonight."

"I know what you meant! You see? Everything he does is all right! And everything I do is—is wrong!"

"That's not true! That's not what I'm trying to say!"

His nerves are raw. "Beth. Please. Let's just go upstairs!"

"No! I will not be pushed!" She moves away to the window, looking out. "I will not be *manipulated.*"

He stands looking at the tree with its strings of lights dangling loose from the branches. "All right," he says. "I'm going."

She does not turn around.

CONRAD LIES FACE DOWN on the bed. Cal snaps on the light. "I want to talk to you."

"I need to sleep," he groans. "Let me sleep."

"In a minute."

He pulls the desk chair over to the bed. Outside the window, heavy flakes of snow make miniature hills and valleys at the lower edge of the sill. "First. I give a damn," he says, "about everything you do."

Conrad rolls onto his back, shielding his eyes with his arm. "I didn't mean that," he says. "I'm sorry. Please. Don't be mad."

"I'm not mad," Cal says. "I'm just trying to figure out what happened down there."

"I don't know what happened! I'm sorry about everything! I—look, can't we talk about it tomorrow, Dad, please! I feel lousy tonight. Tell her I'm sorry, will you?"

"Why don't you tell her?"

"No! God, I can't, I can't talk to her!"

"Why not?"

Abruptly he sits up, clasping his arms about his knees. "Because it won't make any difference."

"What do you mean?"

"It won't change anything. It won't change the way she feels about me."

"Con, she was upset tonight. She was angry. . . ."

"No, I don't mean tonight."

"What, then?"

But he shakes his head. "Everything's Jell-O and pudding with you, Dad. I can't—you don't see things . . ."

"What things?"

He stares out the window at the snow. "All right, then. She hates me. There's nothing I can do about it."

Something terribly wrong. He stares out the window now, too, thinking of last year and Mr. Knight calling him at the office with the grade reports. "Something terribly wrong here, Mr. Jarrett, a straight A student dropping to D's and E's in three months' time. Most of the papers are not completed. Tests not handed in . . ." Cal

330

had asked Conrad, "Why didn't you tell me you were in trouble? It doesn't make sense." And they had looked at each other over the words. *What makes sense?*

"Conrad," he says, "your mother does not hate you—"

"*Okay.* You're right. I just— Please let me go to bed." He jumps up and goes to the closet, stripping off his shirt.

"What do you think of this Dr. Berger?" Cal asks. He tries to keep his voice calm, neutral. "Do you think he's helping you?"

"Dad, don't blame it on Berger! It isn't his fault." He stands facing the closet door. Cal knows he is waiting for him to leave. The snow, piled high against the windows, seals them inside its softness, its silence.

AFTERWARD. The hammerblows of guilt and remorse. He has slandered her. If he could only apologize. All his fault. All connections with him result in failure. Loss. Evil.

At school it is the same. Everywhere he looks there is competence and good health. Only he, Conrad Jarrett, outcast, quitter, stands outside the circle of safety, separated from everyone by this aching void of loneliness; but no matter, he deserves it. He does not speak to anyone. He does not dare to look his classmates in the eye. He does not want to find further evidence of his lack of worth.

Music is his only escape. He can concentrate completely as they practice carols for the Christmas concert. The music fills out the corners of his mind. Not the same as listening to his records. That is dangerous. Flipping through albums gives an eerie feeling of time past, like last year's calendar, carrying too much of the weight of before. And television. Merely patterns of color that jump around on the screen and do not soothe his brain.

"QUITE a recitation," Berger says, biting his thumbnail. "So, how come you're such a rotten kid?"

He stares at his hands. He has dreaded this session, knowing that they would end up talking about it. "I don't know," he says dully.

"Ah, come on. Sure you do."

He gives him a fierce look. "I don't know! Look, if you think you do, why don't *you* tell *me*, and we'll quit going around in circles!"

"That's what happens when you bury this junk, kiddo. It keeps resurfacing. Won't leave you alone."

"Garbage," he says. "I went off the deep end, that's all. I just shouldn't have done it. It didn't make any sense."

"Nope." Berger shakes his head. "There's sense here. Proportion, that's the problem. The stuff came out too strong, and now you won't let yourself buy any of it. The feelings are real enough. Trust that guy in the closet, will you?"

Conrad slides down on the seat of the chair, his legs outstretched.

"Tuesday you felt great, right? You went out for dinner, you bought a Christmas tree, everything's okeydoke, am I right?"

"You're the doctor."

Berger grins. "Hey. The doctor thinks the patient has a bad habit. He takes refuge. He throws out one-liners like 'You're the doctor.' Kiddo, this problem is very specific. It is not necessary to pull the whole world in on top of you, it is only necessary to finish with Tuesday night. Everything's fine until you have this fight with your mother. Then everything's lousy." He leans back in his chair. "So, have you tried to talk it out with her?"

"I can't."

"Have you tried?"

He doesn't answer.

"Tough to be sure if you haven't tried."

"Listen, you don't know her. She— It's impossible. Not that I blame her. I mean, after all the stuff I've pulled . . ."

"What stuff have you pulled?"

He looks down at his hands. "I tried to kill myself, how's that?"

"That," Berger says, "is an old turkey. I am talking about what have you done lately."

"Lately! Listen! I am never going to be forgiven for that, *never!* You can't get it out, you know! All that blood on her rug and her towels—everything had to be pitched! Even the *tile* in the bathroom had to be regrouted. Listen, she fired a *goddamn maid* because she couldn't dust the living room right, and if you think she's ever going to forgive me—"

He stops, staring at Berger, whose eyebrows are raised in mild surprise. The wave of anger recedes slowly, leaving a burning sensation in his chest. With an effort he pulls air into his lungs, clenching his fists, breathing slowly. He gets up, moves to the window, and stares down at the slush in the street.

He hears Berger get up, pour himself another cup of coffee. He turns to watch him. "I think I just figured something out," he says.

"What's that?" Berger asks.

"Who it is who can't forgive who."

RECLINING on the floor, Berger doodles on a scratch pad. Conrad sits beside him, his back against the wall, holding a cup of coffee. "God, am I tired," he says.

"Yeah, well, that's a helluva big secret you've been keeping on yourself," Berger says.

"So what do I do now?"

"Well, you've done it, haven't you? Revelation. She's not perfect. Recognize her limitations."

"You mean, like she can't love me."

"Like she can't love you enough. Like she loves you as much as she's *able*. Perspective, kiddo, remember? Maybe it's hard for her to give love."

"No. She loves my father." He closes his eyes. "She loved my brother, too. It's just me."

"Ah, we're back to the old rotten-kid routine. She can't love you because you're unlovable. So how come your dad loves you?"

"He feels responsible. Besides, he loves everybody."

"Oh, I get it, the guy's got no taste. Give yourself a break, kiddo, why don't you? Let yourself off the hook."

"What d'you mean?"

"I mean, there's somebody else you gotta forgive."

"You mean me? What for? For the other night, you mean? Or for trying to off myself?"

The blue eyes have pinned him to the wall. He shifts uncomfortably. "I haven't done anything else," he says. "I haven't."

Berger smiles. "Okay. You haven't."

333

Conrad gets to his feet and finishes the last of his coffee. "This stuff's rotten, you know that?"

"Damn right. Otherwise, I'd be up to my neck in patients. Listen, kiddo, people don't change on command. You oughta know that, having already given her the ultimate command a year ago."

A hair trigger of release, waiting to be sprung. No more, he is too tired. "That isn't why I did it," he says.

"No? Why, then?"

He is exhausted. Even his bones ache. "I don't know."

"The body doesn't lie," Berger says. "You remember that. So all you gotta do is keep in touch."

"Now, this is what I call a real Christmas," says Howard. "Snowing to beat the band, a turkey in the oven, a real live tree—a lot better than having dinner in some hotel in Florida, right?"

Beth smiles at her father.

"Anyone care for a drink?" Cal asks.

"I would," says Ellen. "A glass of wine, please, Cal." She is sitting next to Beth on the couch. They look more like sisters than mother and daughter. Ellen's hair is thick and silvery, waved expertly. Her body is slim. It is easy to see where Beth gets her looks.

"Howard, Scotch?"

"Fine."

"Beth?".

"No, thanks. Not right now."

"Beth's got a dinner to put on," Howard booms. "We can't have the hostess dipping into the sauce too early, can we?"

No comparing this with Florida, Cal thinks. Last Christmas they had played golf and gone deep-sea fishing and tanned themselves beside the swimming pool at the Sonesta Beach. And each day was more beautiful than the last. Lord, how he had hated it. Like medicine you took, knowing that it had no power to heal. A relief to come back to the gray reality of a Chicago winter.

"Hi. Merry Christmas."

"Same to you, dear!" Ellen holds out her arms and Conrad goes to her obediently for a kiss. He is dressed up today—tan slacks and a tan pullover, his boots polished—a concession to his mother? He looks healthy. The ugly rash is nearly gone.

"You did a great job on this tree," Howard says. "I hear it was all your idea. How long did it take you?"

Conrad grins. "About a month of Sundays." Something is different about him lately. The smile is a good kid grin, with his eyes into it. He looks handsome, with those long, thick eyelashes like a girl's. The build is all boy, though—all angles, elbows, and knees.

Howard rubs his palms together briskly. "Let's get this show on the road, folks!"

Cal and Conrad exchange glances. Cal is reminded of their game, Grandfather Trivia. "What time does he get up in the morning?" "At the crack o' dawn!" "When will he eat liver?" "When hell freezes over!" Jordan had invented the game.

A blessing. Not to know at the moment of impact how far-reaching the shock waves will be. He is achingly aware of Jordan's absence. A year and a half. It is a long time to discover that you are still in shock, still in the infant stages of recovery.

CONRAD, anxious giver, seeks reassurance. "You really like it, Grandmother?"

She holds up the apple-shaped candle for all to admire. "I love it, it smells delicious."

"And the gloves fit okay?"

"Perfect," says Howard.

"Like a glove," Cal says. His mood is buoyant, expectant. He listens patiently as Conrad explains the golf book he has bought for him; it is guaranteed to cut six strokes from his game.

For his mother, Conrad has picked out a bracelet of delicate silver links. "It's beautiful," she says. "It's lovely. Thank you."

They are polite and careful with each other these days. A truce of some kind has been effected. Cal, the fumbling negotiator, has stayed out of it. He cannot bully either of them, he has discovered.

"Hey, isn't there another present down there?" Howard asks.

Conrad picks up a small silver package. "No card. Who's it from?"

Cal says, "It's from your mother and me."

He opens it. Glittering on the nest of white cotton is a key ring with two keys.

Howard nudges Cal in the ribs. He has been like a kid with this. He picked it up with Cal, has kept it in his garage for a week. Now he cannot hide the smile on his face. "Well? Why don't you go look in the driveway?"

They all go to the porch. The green LeMans with its white vinyl top is parked at a jaunty angle in the drive. Howard has wired a huge red bow to the door handle.

"Sneaky, huh?" he crows. "Cal, he looks like we could knock him over with a feather!"

True. Con's expression is totally blank and unreadable, but Cal reads, anyway: I don't think he likes it.

"They had it in a pale gold," Cal says. "You might have liked that better."

"No. This is great." He looks at Cal then, a smile pasted on his face. "I like it a lot. Thanks. It's— I just didn't expect it, that's all."

"Got your license on you?" Howard asks. "Take it for a spin."

"No," he says. Then, "Yeah, okay. I will. Thanks. Thank you both, it's terrific."

And he gets in. It glides smoothly out of the driveway.

"Well," says Howard. "What a surprise, huh?"

Beth and Ellen have already gone inside. The wind pierces Cal's shirt, makes him feel shrunken and old.

"I think he liked it, though," Howard says. "A kid's first car. Always a big deal, right?"

"Right," Cal says.

AND so it had gone wrong. The neat pieces of the day have somehow slipped awry. Cal sits alone on the couch. He has driven Howard and Ellen home, and Conrad is upstairs in bed, asleep. Beth is busy in the kitchen. He stares out of the window at the snow, at the fuzzy jewels of reflection from the Christmas-tree lights. Colored stars in a white sky.

Something terribly wrong, but it was not just the car. It was the whole day. *Well, what do you expect? A family turns inward toward itself in grief; it does not pull itself apart. Like hell it doesn't. Grief is ugly. It is isolating.*

He gets up to make himself a drink, and Beth comes in from the kitchen. She looks tired. We should have gone to London, he thinks. Aloud he asks, "Would you like anything?"

"No. I'm tired. I think I'll just go to bed."

And, knowing that he shouldn't, he says, "I guess he didn't like the car."

She is silent.

"Did he?"

"I think," she says, "you worry too much about him."

"Yeah." And I think that you don't worry enough.

"And you expect too much. From all of us."

"That sounds like the beginning of a lecture. What's it for? I thought I behaved myself pretty well today."

"You want us all to perform for you," she says. "Make the day go right for you."

"Well, I'm willing to do my share. I'll sing and dance and tell crooked-lawyer jokes—it won't be my fault if it falls apart."

"Or mine, either! Or Dad's or Mother's! You didn't have to close up on them just because your surprise didn't work out."

"I didn't close up. What're you talking about?"

"Yes, you did. You moped around here as if your whole day was spoiled over that one thing. I'm tired of you getting your feelings hurt, Cal, because you refuse to see things as they really are."

"And how are things?" he asks, turning around.

"He'll be eighteen years old next month," she says. "For some reason, you think he needs your constant protection. You worry over his every reaction."

"Okay, I'm concerned! I'm *interested!* Are you interested?"

"Oh, sometimes I hate you," she says. "Why couldn't you see this was the way it would work out if we stayed here this year?"

"At last!" he says. "Down to basics! Listen, if my day was spoiled, it was because I had that hanging over my head, so I'm sorry, okay? I'm sorry I didn't take you to London!"

"Are you sorry about giving him a car he didn't want? Sorry about spending thousands of dollars just to make something happen that I could have told you would never happen?"

They look at each other, and he wants to say, But that's not it, don't you see? At least, not all of it. And he knows as she turns away that the day has not gone the way she planned it, either. They are both disappointed. They are both grieving. *And what about tomorrow, then? And all the tomorrows to come? Why can't we talk about it? Why can't we ever talk about it?*

CHAPTER SEVEN

CON has concluded, on this sunny day in January, that what his life lacks is organization. Goals. Standing at his desk, he gazes out his window, pondering, making rapid notes.

1. Finals

Essential that he pass. Only two weeks left. Study like hell.

2. Exercise

Not enough in the last months. His skis, neglected at the back of his closet, reproach him each morning. Someday after school he will drive to Wilmot, take a lesson. No. Pointless unless you have somebody to do it with.

3. Friends

He is definitely in need. He finds each day as he looks around him that he is achingly lonely. Goes over the list again. Lazenby. Truan. Van Buren. Genthe. No. He is not ready for them and anyway they are all seniors now, not interested in their old buddy Jarrett. Besides, their old buddy Jarrett no longer exists. Someone else now. Needing new friends. But how?

4. Job (?)

Doing what? Yard work? (It is January, kiddo.) Volunteer work? Why the hell not? There are plenty of things he could do for other people. Maybe the placement office could give him some suggestions, or he could call the Red Cross, the Foundation for the Blind.

He sits down, looking out at the cedars, the bare gray limbs of maples. Everything slightly out of focus as usual; no, wait a minute,

338

it is not out of focus. It is clear and sharp. His whole life is in place
and it spreads out around him, steady and full of purpose. A mystic
source of energy flooding his body, his mind, all at once. Joy.
Swiftly he notes:

5. *Guitar*
6. *Books*
7. *Girls*

A million years ago, when they were both sixteen, he and Lazenby compared notes daily on their experience with girls. They
concluded that they had none. For him, nothing has changed.
Eighteen years old in two weeks, ye gods, and what does he *know?*

Never mind. Worry about it later. For now, he is too filled with
this good feeling, too filled with *himself*, to care, and he jumps up,
goes to the closet, gets his guitar. And tomorrow he will go to the
library for books. On what? Anything. Everything. He wants to
learn everything, know everything.

Lists. Buck used to find the scraps of notes on his desk, those
stern commands to himself to shape up. He would cop them, and
tape them to the mirror in the bathroom. "The Great Listmaker is
at it again folks," he would tease him. Reverting to old ways—
does that signify a moving backward, or forward? The natural,
sane ticking inside him eliminates all need of an answer.

STANDING in an aisle in the library, Con can feel the eyes on him.
He turns his head to look. A pretty, dark-haired woman. Staring
at him. Guiltily he looks away. Should he know her? Well dressed,
nice figure, nice legs. He looks again, and she is still watching him.

He moves to the next aisle as the familiar cloak of shame settles
about his shoulders. A freak. A one-man sideshow. What *is* this
about him? Still. People shouldn't stare like that.

He checks out his books. The librarian slips his card into the
machine. Even the library is run like a department store now. The
whole world is one big computer, but never mind. They still might
need some people. So ask! He stumbles over the speech he has been
preparing. "Interested in working here . . . wondered about . . .
possibilities of employment . . . ?" She smiles. Oh, yes, they do take

339

on part-time help occasionally. They are fully staffed right now, but if he would like to fill out an application? Yes, he would like to. She gets him a form, and he begins to fill it out, but she waves him away. "Just bring it with you sometime."

So much for a job. *Ah, Jarrett, attaboy, just like you to give up after one try. How about the volunteer work? The placement office? All the things you were going to do.* He zips his jacket against the wind. *Face it, kiddo, things are not gonna be that easy, so grow up.*

A blue Karmann Ghia is parked in the lot beside his car. Bent over, half in, is the woman from the library. The open car door is blocking his path. He waits, his face wooden. He will stare her down this time. She glances over her shoulder. "Sorry." Then she straightens up. He has caught her off guard, but she is still more poised than he. "I embarrassed you in there, didn't I? I'm sorry." She shrugs her shoulders. "But you're very good-looking. I'm sure you already know that."

She gets in her car, backs out carefully, then pulls out into the street and disappears.

He stands, looking after her, while a feeling of total displacement sweeps over him. Mechanically he opens his car door, tosses his books on the seat, gets in. *You're very good-looking.* He observes meticulously all traffic signs, all other cars on the road. He arrives home intact and parks in the circular drive. There is no one home but him. He goes upstairs to his bedroom, drops his books on the bed, goes into the bathroom, and turns on the light.

You're very good-looking. I'm sure you already know that. He studies his face in the mirror. Heavy dark brows and brown eyes. A nose. A mouth. Right, everything there. His hair, decently cut at last; his skin, clear. God, his skin *is* clear; when did that happen? He turns on a foolish, fake smile. Another plus. Straight, even teeth. An outside chance. That she is right.

He turns off the light and sits on the edge of the bed. The freak, the one-man sideshow answer no longer fits. So, what is the catch? What will he have to pay for all of this, for thinking well of himself? He lies back on the bed, staring up at the ceiling. Whatever the price, it is worth it. Even for ten minutes, it is worth it.

"C'MON," BERGER SAYS. "I'm spellbound. You followed her home and she took you into her bed, right?"

"Not exactly." Con takes a bite of the sweet roll he has lifted from the bakery box. "She drove away, and I went home. I told you not to get your hopes up."

Berger sits like a guru, legs folded under him. There are flecks of powdered sugar dotting the front of his sweater.

"Anyway," Conrad asks anxiously, "what d'you think? She probably goes around saying stuff like that to guys all the time, huh?"

"Do *I* know?" Berger raises his palms, flashing a sly smile. "She probably goes around saying stuff like that to guys who are hideously ugly. You know, to make 'em feel better about themselves."

"Okay. You won't take it serious, your loss."

"I take it serious! I want to know something else. What happened when you looked in the mirror? No censoring voices?"

"Not at first. Then later on I heard, 'Conceited, fantasizing, delusions of grandeur,' stuff like that. I ignored it."

Berger laughs. "There's hope for you yet, kiddo. So, how you feeling now? About Christmas. About the car."

"Better, I guess," he says. "I drive it, don't I?"

"You still think it commits you to something?"

"Sort of. Like a bribe. 'There, now be happy.'"

"So, what's the problem? Aren't you happy?"

"Yeah, but I don't want my father depending on me for it. What if I can't live up to it?"

"He doesn't expect you to be happy every minute of the day, does he? He'd probably settle for an hour or two a week. And maybe he gets a kick out of giving you presents. No big contract, just Merry Christmas, period."

"Yeah, maybe." He considers. "It takes a long time to get over the feeling that everybody's watching all the time." He clears his throat. "Listen, there's something else I've been wanting to talk about." Carefully he relates the problem he has now, of female bodies; the fact that the world has suddenly become overpopulated with them.

"Relax," Berger says. "It's normal. Why don't you call somebody up? How about that girl you know from the hospital?"

341

"Karen," he says. "No. She's got this ten-foot pole she'd like to keep me away with."

"Baloney. It's gonna bother her—a good-looking guy wanting to see her? A guy that women proposition in library parking lots?"

He laughs. "I thought psychiatrists didn't give advice."

"Or how about the one in choir? She sounds nice—"

"The problem is," he says, "the only dates I ever had were the all-skate type. A bunch of us going to the show, or getting a pizza after a basketball game. Nobody was *with* anybody else. I don't know how to act, you know, with *a girl,* one to one."

"Simple," Berger says, grinning. "Listen to the expert. It's just like skiing. The first few times you close your eyes and fake it, hope for the best."

"What do you know about skiing? Right from go, there are a million rules."

Berger sighs. "Rules again. They oughta burn every rule book that's ever been written!"

"And where would we be?"

"Out of the box!" He shakes his fists at the ceiling in a parody of rage.

"That box," Con says. "I feel like I've been in it forever. Everybody looking in to see how you're doing."

"Yeah. Not much fun, is it?"

"No. But sometimes I can get out of it now. And then, there's you." He clears his throat nervously. "I never saw you out there. You, I always saw inside the box. With me." He laughs, suddenly embarrassed. He looks at the opposite wall. "What I'm saying . . . I guess I think of you as a friend."

There is movement at the edge of his eye. Berger nodding.

"Well. I think of you as mine, too, kiddo."

"You don't have to say that."

"Right. I don't. So, I wouldn't."

They look at each other, and, abruptly, Con relaxes, grinning.

"You understand, there weren't a helluva lot of people standing in line."

"Good," Berger says. "I hate competition."

CAL FINISHES TYING THE last bundle of newspapers. "Some birthday present," Conrad says, leaning on his broom. "Cleaning the garage."

"Come on. How long did it take?" Cal says. "An hour?"

"One whole hour out of my birthday, when I oughta be blowing out candles, opening presents—"

"Finish the sweeping, then tell me your sad story."

Cal goes inside to make lunch for the two of them, rummages in the refrigerator, pulling out salami, tomatoes, mustard, mayonnaise. Two cans of beer. Conrad comes in as he finishes assembling the goods on thick slices of rye bread.

"No mayonnaise on mine, okay?"

"Oh, hell—"

"All right. I'll eat it." Con grins. "Boy, what a birthday!" He sits at the table, drumming on it with his fingers.

"Thought I heard you playing the guitar last night," Cal says.

"Yeah. Am I rusty."

"Sounded good to me."

He laughs. "You were always easy to please."

"Not me. Good guitar player, lousy garage cleaner, that's my opinion." He picks up his beer. "Happy birthday!"

"Thanks."

The beer slides down his throat, golden and cool. "I used to have to keep an eye on both of you when we did that job," Cal says. "Buck especially. He was a genius at getting out of work."

"Yeah, I remember."

"The only time he worked his tail off was when we did the rec room. Remember the plastering job? You guys wrote dirty words on the wall and then gave it away, laughing so hard."

"They're still there," Conrad says. "We put 'em all back when you left. I'll show you."

And they head for the basement. In a corner near the furnace room, Conrad shows Cal the upside-down obscenities, carefully printed. And another memory slips out then, of lying on the beach while Buck and Con are building a sand sculpture. The sleek lines emerge and he sees the outline of a racing car. When they leave,

343

he goes to view it, sees instead the flaring hips and generously mounded breasts of a giant woman stretching seductively at his feet. "Sex!" he shouts. "Maniacs!" and behind him the laughter becomes obligingly maniacal.

He straightens up, smiling. There is pressure behind his eyes, and the blood is beating in his head.

THEY go upstairs and finish eating lunch.

"You're in a good mood today," Cal observes. "You like being eighteen, do you?"

He laughs. "Yeah, I guess so."

"Tell me something," he says. "You and this Dr. Berger, what do you guys talk about?"

Con looks surprised. "Anything. I don't know. Why?"

"Just curious. What kinds of things?"

"Whatever we feel like. He's easy to talk to. Once in a while he gives a little lecture." He leans back in the chair, in imitation. "'Perspective, kiddo, that's the key word.'"

"What would you think," Cal says, "if I were to talk with him?"

"What for? About me, you mean?"

"No. Just— I don't know. To get a few things straight in my own mind."

Conrad sets his beer down, says with finality, "There's nothing wrong with you, Dad."

"Nice. How do you know?"

"You fishing? You want a grade? Okay, I give you a B plus."

"That's great," Cal says. "I buy you a new car, teach you everything I know—tennis, how to clean a garage—and the best you can do is B plus, that's great."

Conrad laughs. "So, I'm a hard marker."

"Anyway, it isn't important. Just an idea I had."

"See him if you want to. It's okay with me."

But do I want to? What's happening? Nothing is happening, except that now he is imagining. A peculiar stiff set to Conrad's shoulders when Beth speaks to him. But does she speak to him? She issues directives. "Wear the sweater your grandparents gave you

344

for Christmas," she says, walking out of the room, without having any interest in his reply. And Conrad lowers his head in a mocking bow. "Yes, ma'am. No, ma'am." As for himself, he feels undercurrents at work, tremors in the earth.

Last night, in bed, she had whispered against his shoulder, 'You haven't been very friendly lately."

"Friendly?" he said. "I'm always friendly."

"Please. I need you to love me, Cal! Please promise!"

"I love you, Beth. God, you know that."

She clung to him urgently as he stroked her hair, and he was frightened, because it was not like her and because he felt beneath them a fault, imperceptibly widening.

"Coffee?" Berger asks.

"No, thanks." Cal tries to relax. He has never been so nervous. He surveys the room. An overpowering air of disorder dominates, weighs him down.

The man sitting opposite him has a wild look: his hair is a dark, fuzzy halo; his eyes, a sharp, stinging blue. Cal shifts uneasily in the chair. "I don't really believe in psychiatrists," he says.

Berger laughs. "Okay. What do I do now? Disappear in a puff of smoke?"

"I didn't mean that. I meant that I don't believe in psychiatry. As a panacea for everybody, you know?"

"Okay," Berger says. "Me neither."

"I'm not putting you down. Or what you've done for Con. He's better, I can see that."

"Well, he's working at it now."

He feels trapped. "I knew something was wrong," he says. "Even before. But I always thought that intelligent people could work out their own problems. . . ." He looks down at his hands. "I wish," he says, "that I knew what the hell I was doing here."

Berger gets up and goes to the table in the corner. "I'm getting a feeling from you," he says, "of heavy guilt. About missing the signals. Am I right?"

"Yes," Cal says, "sure." It is easier now that Berger's back is to

345

him. It was the eyes that were making him nervous. "You don't have something like that happen and not feel the responsibility."

"Guilt."

"Guilt. Yes." He takes the cup of coffee Berger is holding out to him. "Well, I am guilty. And lucky, too. I was there at the right time. I could have been at a meeting, we could have both been at meetings."

"Your wife was there, too?"

"Yes."

Banging on the door, begging to be let in, while Beth called for an ambulance. "He wouldn't, Cal, oh, he wouldn't!" "Just call!" he had directed her over his shoulder.

"So, you think of yourself as a lucky man."

"I used to, before—before Buck's accident. Hell, all life is accident—who you fall in love with, what grabs you, and what you do with it."

"That sounds more like the philosophy of a drifter than a tax attorney from Lake Forest," Berger says.

"Okay, I'm a drifter," he says. "I can see myself— I see Beth and Con drifting away from me while I stand there watching. And I don't know what to do about it."

"What do you want to do about it?"

"Nothing! I don't want to do anything but sit here on the fence. Until I fall off. On one side or the other."

"You see them on opposite sides of the fence, is that it?"

"Yes," he says. "No. I don't know."

Berger strokes his lip with the edge of his coffee cup.

"I see her," Cal says, "not being able to forgive him."

"For what?"

He shrugs. "For surviving, maybe. No, that's not it. For being too much like her. Hell, I don't know. I don't know what the hell I'm talking about. I'm not a drifter. I'm not on any fence. I'm not any of those things. Except maybe a lousy husband and father."

"Ah." Berger nods. "Well, maybe rotten sons deserve lousy fathers. Yours tells me twice a week what a rotten kid he is."

"He shouldn't. It isn't true." He rubs his face with his hands.

346

"He used to call the hospital the zoo. I asked him if coming to see you was like going to the zoo, but he said no, it was more like the circus."

Berger laughs. "That's either a compliment," he says, "or damn poor PR, I don't know which."

Cal takes a deep breath. "I think I know why I came here. I think I really came to talk about myself."

"Okay," Berger says. "Why don't we do that?"

CHAPTER EIGHT

EXAM week. The first day dawns, sunny and below zero. Con pulls into the school parking lot, leaves the car unlocked. Someone might want to take a cigarette break in it, cry in it, who knows?

English. Miss Mellon has written across the chalkboard: RELAX. NO BIG DEAL. Nice. She really is a nice person. He sits down near the window. Shadows of trees, blue on the snow. Everything glittering out there. She has not been trying to smother him after all; just trying to be nice. *Don't get distracted!* He looks down at the three essay questions and takes out a pencil. His mind goes stubbornly blank. Well, that's that. Three lousy questions to sum up one's semester's work. What does he have to say about them? Nothing. *Concentrate, damn you, Jarrett.* He has read the books. Okay, so he is no less equipped than anybody else. "Relax," she says. *Okay. Okay.*

AT HIS locker, he notices a group of girls at the end of the hall. Someone calls out, "Hi." He waves and sees them head for the exit doors. All but one of them. Jeannine. She is tying a scarf about her head. He has not spoken to her since Christmas vacation. He wonders now why he ever put girls on the list. To frustrate himself, for sure.

He takes another cautious look; she is gone. *Nice going, kiddo. Another opportunity missed.* So easy, too. She was by herself; no one to hear him stammer around— Ha. No one but her. This is worse than any exam. He stares fixedly into his locker, wasting precious seconds; then he slams it closed, sprints down the hall, and bursts through the double doors, breathless.

Jeannine is standing in the lobby pulling on her gloves, her books balanced on the radiator.

"Hi." He sets his books next to hers as he zips his jacket.

"Hi." Cool and reserved.

And rightly so. Exactly what has he to offer someone like her? "What did you have today?"

"History. You?"

"English. It wasn't too bad. How was yours?"

"Easy."

"Big smart senior." He grins at her. She smiles.

He opens the door for her, and the air hits them. She shivers, gripping her books. "'By. See you."

"Would you like a ride home?"

She hesitates, gives him a small, grateful smile. "Oh, that'd be nice. Thanks."

In the car, he turns the radio up; it relieves him of the need to talk. Ragged piano blues. They listen.

"I didn't know you had a car," she says.

"Christmas present. My folks."

"It's nice."

He pulls to a stop in front of her house. Her hand is on the door handle. "Thanks a lot."

"Welcome."

"I'd ask you to come in, but my mother—she's funny about that. She works. . . ." She turns suddenly to face him. "There was something I wanted to say to you. That day we— I said a stupid thing. I didn't know about your brother then. I'm sorry."

Stunned, he sits there, not moving. He had almost forgotten the incident. Now it rushes back to him. An embarrassed silence. He stares out at her house, she at her hands.

"You know the rest of it, too? I mean, about me?"

"Yes."

Should have told her. Should have known someone would tell

348

her. Sometime. Sure. Bring it up over a Coke. "Oh, by the way . . ." *Whip out the newspaper clippings.* "Police chief . . . reasonably certain . . . no drugs involved . . ." *No drugs. Part of the shame. Somehow it is not such a personal failure if you are on something. Anybody can do something crazy if he is stoned, but crazy on your own time is much more serious.*

"There are worse things," Jeannine says, still looking at her hands. "People do worse things than that."

"Yeah." He wants to help her through the awkwardness of the moment, but it comes out rudely, as if he is cutting her off.

"Well," she says. "Thanks again for the ride. I'd have frozen." She is out of the car, turning away, hurrying up the steps.

Nothing to be ashamed of. Maybe not. Nothing anybody particularly wants to be associated with, either.

THE driveway is choked with cars. He parks in front and lets himself in through the garage.

Mrs. Lazenby confronts him in the kitchen. "I thought I heard somebody trying to sneak in!"

He smiles awkwardly. "Hi, how're you?"

"I'm fine, you dreamer. Thinking you could get up the back stairs without saying hello to anybody, huh?"

He grins. "That was the plan."

She takes his hand, leads him into the dining room. He is greeted by his mother's bridge club, smiles politely. His mother sits quietly through his ordeal.

"He's thin, Beth," Mrs. Truan says. "You should fatten him up."

She smiles. "How was your exam?"

"Not bad."

Mrs. Lazenby hands him a piece of chocolate cake on a napkin. "Here. For being such a nice boy, humoring the old ladies. Where've you been, anyway? We miss you."

"I've been meaning to stop by," he lies. "I've been busy."

"Well, don't be so busy," she says sternly. "Come over some night; I'll make lasagna."

"I will," he says.

He escapes then to his room, where he sits staring out of the window. The problem of connecting is partly that of fitting mood with opportunity. When he sees Lazenby's mother, he remembers their house, all warmth and friendliness; eating toast with peanut butter, playing catch in the backyard, he and Lazenby and Buck. If Lazenby were here this minute. Passing each other in the hall doesn't do. The mood is wrong; too much clanging—of locker bells, echoes of other conversations. It wouldn't work.

Likewise, Jeannine. But if there were a telephone number here on his desk pad. So that when the feeling hit, he could go directly to the telephone without stopping to think; just dial the number and it would be done.

He goes to the telephone table in the hall, flipping through the telephone book. D. Pratt on Wisconsin. Carefully he notes it down. On the desk pad in his room is another number, written month ago. Under it: *Karen.* He looks at it for a long minute. Then he gets up and goes again to the telephone.

The telephone is answered on the first ring.

"You want Karen? Who is this?"

"It's— I'm a friend of hers. From the hospital."

The voice goes flat. "Well, she's at school. Don't you go to school?"

Her mother, of course. Nobody else would take the trouble to cross-question him or sound so worried.

"Yes," he says. "I do. But we're off this week. Exams. Would you tell her I called? My name is Conrad—"

"I'll give her the message."

The receiver bangs in his ear. "Thanks very much," he says politely to no one. Replacing the receiver, he goes to his room, to fall face upward on the bed. Nice. A nice cool zero for the day. Well, she wouldn't have wanted to talk to him, anyway. Why should she? Why would anybody? He rolls onto his stomach, hands behind his neck, then rises grimly from the bed. *Get it over with. Cross off both numbers in one afternoon.* He dials Jeannine's number.

"Hello?" Her soft voice musical even over the telephone.

He clears his throat nervously. "Hi. This is Conrad. Jarrett."

"Oh," she says. "Oh, hi."

"Listen, I was wondering. Would you be interested in going out sometime?"

A long pause. "You mean, with you? Like, on a date?"

Eyes closed, he grinds his forehead deliberately against the wall, a bubble of laughter loose in his chest.

"Yeah," he says, "well, it wouldn't have to be a real date. We could fake it. See how it goes, sort of."

She giggles. "Okay, that was dumb, I agree. Just pretend I didn't say that. Start over."

He grins at the receiver; obligingly he clears his throat. "Hi," he says. "This is Conrad. Jarrett."

"I'd love to," she says. "When?"

CAL stretches, glancing at his wristwatch. Eleven thirty.

"Working this late is ridiculous," Ray says, rolling down his sleeves. "Want to grab a sandwich?"

"Sure."

They lock up and walk to the Carriage Grill, a fancy name for a dull spot. Ray looks at him over his coffee cup. "Cal, I like to be let in on what's happening with you off and on, you know?"

"With me? What d'you mean?"

"You haven't been around the last couple of months, that's all."

"Around? What are you talking about?"

"Cal, I've known you for over twenty years, you think I can't tell when something's wrong?" He looks down into his cup.

The waiter approaches with their corned-beef sandwiches.

"Everything's fine," Cal says. "You want me to stop by your office, hum a few bars from *The Sound of Music* every day?"

"Why are you worrying, then?"

He laughs. "I'm not. In fact, I'm thinking about taking a couple of days off in March to play in the lawyers' tournament in Dallas."

"Well, great. Why don't you do it?"

"I'd be leaving you with all this work."

"Don't be dumb, I'd do it to you in a minute." He takes a bite of his sandwich. "Beth going with you?"

351

"Yeah. We'll stay with her brother and his wife."

"That's good," Ray says. "I think it'd do you both good to get away for a few days. That's the answer."

The answer to what? Life reduced to the simplest of terms. Formulas. Get away for a while.

"Look, I'm sorry," Ray says. "It's none of my business. But you worry too much about Con. You got to let go sometime, buddy. In another year he'll be off—"

"I'm not worried about Con," he says.

"Who, then? Beth? Is something wrong between Beth and you?"

"No!"

Ray is wearing an uncomfortable look. "Listen, Cal, Nance and Beth had lunch together last week—" He breaks off.

"Next time," Cal says, "try for more directness. What are you supposed to tell me?"

"I'm not supposed to tell you anything," Ray says unhappily. "But Beth is pretty upset. She says you're obsessed with Con's problems. You can't think about anything else."

"That's ridiculous," he snaps. "She can't think about them at all. Now what does that say to you?"

"It says nobody's normal," Ray says. "Look, Cal, forget it. I'm feeling very existential tonight. People are born. Then they die. In between they perform a lot of meaningless actions."

"Ray, you don't believe that."

He grins. "Oh, yeah, when I'm sober, I believe it a lot. What do you believe, buddy?"

"I believe I'll go to Dallas, play some golf, maybe get blind one night with my brother-in-law."

"Do it," Ray says. "My blessings."

Cal thinks back to that Christmas in Florida, to the day when the telephone call had come from Howard. They had gone to play golf, leaving Con on the beach with some kids he had met. After they left, Con had gone upstairs to the room, called Lake Forest to ask if his grandfather remembered how many strings of lights he and Buck had put on the outdoor tree at their house last year. The telephone had been ringing when they walked in. It was Howard

352

frantic. "Cal, don't leave Con alone down there, something's wrong. I know it. You'd better have a talk with him."

And so he had. He went immediately next door, and Conrad was on his bed reading a magazine, calm and relaxed. Yes, everything was fine. Yes, he had called his grandparents to wish them Merry Christmas, why?

And for some reason Cal had bought that. Even though, like a single frame of film flicked on the mind screen and then off, it had been there that day. The knowledge of the thing that Con would do to himself someday.

Obsessed, Beth said. Maybe she is right, maybe he is. One thing for sure, Ray is not right. Life is not a series of meaningless actions. Some of them are so far from meaningless as to be beyond reason, maybe beyond forgiveness.

STANDING on the front porch of Jeannine's house, Con nervously shoves his hands in his pockets, pulls them out again. Too casual. Wouldn't want her mother to get the wrong impression. He glances at his watch. Eight thirty. He is right on time. Her mother is strict, she says. Maybe she has a rule about her not being out after midnight. He hopes so. The evening now stretches lengthily ahead. What is the problem? No problem. He is in great shape. He has just been cut down to once a week by his analyst. He finds on waking each morning no terrible urgency to escape his thoughts. They are harmless. They concern a report he has to write, a section of tenor melody he is learning, small goals to purify his days.

Berger yesterday had grinned lecherously at him over a sugar doughnut. "Psychiatry has its advantages. I expect to hear all about it on Tuesday."

He had laughed. "Yeah, well, I didn't hear all about how it went with my father, did I? What did he want, anyway?"

"He wanted," Berger said, "the name of a good allergist. Listen, you want me to tell you what he wanted?"

Con decided he didn't want that, after all. Respect for privacy was what he wanted. And now he is on a Tuesday-only schedule. "Gee, coach, I hope I make it," he had said on his way out.

353

Berger had sighed. "And I just ordered a couch; how'm I gonna pay for it?"

With a start he realizes he has forgotten to ring the doorbell. *Nice beginning, Jarrett.* He rings and the door is opened by a pleasant-faced woman with red hair, a wide smile. "Hi. You're Conrad, right? I'm Jen's mother."

She ushers him into the small, tidy living room, where a small boy sits cross-legged on the couch, watching television.

"Mike, this a friend of Jen's. Conrad . . . ?"

"Jarrett," he supplies. "Hi, Mike."

"Hi." The eyes do not move from the screen.

"Sit down. Jen's almost ready. She got home late from work. You're new here, aren't you?"

"Me? No. We've lived here for about ten years."

"Oh." She is puzzled. "Aren't you the one that works at the music store in Lake Bluff?"

"No." He smiles.

"Well, then, did she meet you at the Evanston concert?"

He shakes his head. How many are there, anyway? "I go to Lake Forest," he says. "I gave her a ride home from school once."

"Oh, you're the tenor!" she says.

He gazes about the room. Plants everywhere. "You must like plants," he says. *Oh, brilliant, Jarrett. Brilliant.*

She laughs. "Well, they make nice pets." She gets up. "I'll just hurry Jeannine along."

Con is left with the small boy.

"I'm gonna take guitar lessons," Mike says.

"Are you? Good," Conrad says politely.

"But I might take karate instead."

Jeannine appears in the doorway. Behind her the command is issued: "Don't be late!"

"I won't!"

In the car, they drive in silence for a few minutes.

"I'd better warn you," she says. "I'm a horrible bowler."

"That's okay."

"Well, it's not, really. You haven't seen me."

354

"Look, we don't have to go bowling if you'd rather not."

She glances quickly at him. "No, I'll go. If you want."

"What would you rather do?"

She shrugs, then abruptly she laughs. "I just hate to do something that'll make me look silly."

"You won't look silly," he promises. "I'm a great teacher; you'll look like you belong to a league in twenty minutes, okay?"

"Okay."

And it is all right after that. She is right; she's a lousy bowler but a quick learner. And besides, she looks terrific up there. He notices that she is wearing the blue skirt she wore the first day he saw her. And he notices how she sits with her legs tucked back, her hair a smooth river of silk.

"You were a natural," he tells her across the table at McDonald's afterward.

"Oh, sure. I'm also a Gemini, so be careful."

"Why?"

"Because. We are two-faced and unpredictable. What are you?"

"January tenth."

"Capricorn. That's a good sign. Dutiful. Responsible. Serious. Capable." She grins. "Late bloomers."

He laughs. "For sure."

On the way home, Con slides his hand across the seat and holds hers lightly. She talks: about her parents' divorce; about her father, who lives in Akron; about her mother, who is a nurse. In front of her house, they talk some more.

"Well, what d'you think?" he asks. "Did this work out okay? You want to try it again?"

"Sure."

So they set up the following Saturday night. And, as casually as the earth one day spun itself loose from the sun and off into whirling space, he kisses her, his hands on her shoulders, her mouth under his, cool and firm. Berger is right: the body doesn't lie. He says against her cheek, "I'll call you tomorrow, okay?"

"Okay," she whispers. Her breath is warm against his ear. "Two phone calls in one week. You are swifter than I thought."

CHAPTER NINE

ON IMPULSE, Con attends a swim meet after school, sits alone be
hind a group of freshmen.

"Boy, do they stink!" one kid says in disgust, and Conrad feel
oddly hurt by the remark. But it is true. One win, four losses. The
should be better. He feels a twinge of regret; maybe he could hav
helped.

Afterward he heads for the exit. It is dark outside, and he has t
pick his way around pools of half-melted snow in the parking lo
Behind him the doors burst open. Shouts of laughter push outward

"Glad you can laugh about it, Genthe, it sure as hell wasn'
funny."

"Ah, come on, we weren't that bad."

"Face it, we got waxed! We stunk!"

"Truan, no kidding, I don't know how you can listen to that lec
ture one more time about Buck Jarrett, the all-time great swimme
of the world."

"You think he's ever gonna quit kissing the guy's picture—"

An abrupt silence. It stabs deeper than the words.

Someone says, "Shut the hell up, will you?"

Con continues across the parking lot, his throat tight. He step
into a puddle, and icy water oozes through the seam of his boot.

"Hey, Con." Lazenby comes up behind him.

He turns, gives him a blank smile.

"Could've used you today, buddy," Truan says.

"I don't think so."

Lazenby laughs. "He's right. Nobody could help us today."

"How's it goin', Jarrett?" Stillman checks out the LeMans. "You
old man's so loaded, how come he didn't get you an Eldorado?"

"I tried not to let it ruin my Christmas." He is surprised when
they laugh.

Truan says, "I heard you were going out with Pratt."

"No kidding," Lazenby says. "Since when?"

He cannot answer.

Stillman flashes the grin. "Got what you wanted yet?"

356

"Do me a favor," he says. "Try not to be such a jerk. I know it won't be easy for you."

They stop walking and eye each other warily.

"Hey, you guys," Lazenby says.

"Man," Stillman says, "you're the jerk. Guys like you who think you're so damn special, you give me a pain in the—"

Something explodes inside his head, the red brick building behind him, the white doors, gray cement—all dissolving into broken bits of color as he slams his fist hard against that face—a sweet rush of mindless ecstasy washes out everything and makes him whole again. The rough feel of cloth tearing in his hands as he holds on, shoving, pushing, and they go down together on the gravel. Stillman's arm is around his neck, his hand punching at his back. "Goddamn you, Jarrett!"

Con hits him again. And again. Miles away, someone calls his name. "Con . . . Con . . . Connie!" and he is grabbed from behind. "Cut it out!" someone says. "Cut it out!"

It is Lazenby holding him. He straightens slowly, looks at Stillman lying on the ground, legs sprawled, an elbow crooked high over his face. A handkerchief in his fist. Truan and Genthe help him up. Stillman looks at the handkerchief, moaning. Blood pours from his nose. There is sound, but it's garbled and he cannot understand it. He doesn't want to.

He walks away, his knees trembling. He gets into his car and sits, holding on to the steering wheel. His hands hurt. The knuckles are scraped raw. He feels for his keys in his back pocket. They are not there. They are somewhere in the parking lot. With his books. He rests his forehead on the wheel.

The door on his right opens. His books are tossed in on the seat. Lazenby leans across and hands him his car keys.

"Thanks." He takes them without looking.

Lazenby gets in, slams the door. "I want to talk."

Con stares at the dashboard.

"The guy's a nothing," Lazenby says. "A zero upstairs. You know that about him, Connie. Since fourth grade you've known it."

"So?"

357

"So. You make yourself look stupid when you let him get to you
like that."

"So, I look stupid," he says. "Is that the message?"

"No." Lazenby looks away, staring out into the darkness. "What
is it with you, man? We've been friends for a long time."

"Laze," he says, "we're still friends."

"Are we?" Lazenby's voice is flat, strained. "Look, I don't know
why you want to be alone in this. I miss him, too."

A blow he is not expecting at all. He concentrates on the car keys
under his hand, against his thigh.

"I can't help it," he says. "It hurts too much to be around you."

The keys dig into his thigh. Next to him, Lazenby sits, elbow
against the door. What he said is true. The three of them were always together; why does he think of it as only his grief? *Because,
damn it, it is.* His room no longer shared, his heart torn. *And there
is no way to change it.*

His heart pounds painfully. "I've got to go," he says.

Lazenby stirs, not looking at him. "Yeah. Okay."

The door opens and he is gone. Conrad holds himself tight; control is all, he will not, will not. Not here. Not again.

HE LETS himself into the house with his key. The house is quiet,
empty. Wednesday. His father is working late; his mother is playing tennis. Good. He does not want to talk.

There is blood on his jacket and his shirt. He goes to the kitchen,
strips to his undershirt, and works at the stains. He lays the jacket
on the counter and throws the shirt in the dryer. Since they were
little, they have done this; getting rid of the evidence, Buck called
it. He shivers suddenly. The house feels cold.

Now he searches the refrigerator, gets out the TV dinner bought
for him for Wednesday. "Take the dinner out of the cardboard
envelope, tear back foil to expose chicken, cook 35-40 minutes."
Obey all rules and do as directed, punishment may be lessened.
Don't doubt that there will be punishment.

Punishment? Of course, for losing control. Always.

He looks in the cupboard for the coffee. Sees Stillman suddenly lying on the ground, his mouth a round O of surprise. His prickles with fear. *How many times did I hit him?*

He sits at the table to eat his dinner. No TV tonight. Each sm punishment he inflicts could lessen the larger one.

The telephone rings, and his stomach knots. He lets it r Eleven times. His father, maybe. Who else would it be?

He looks down at his dinner and quickly looks away. It was S man's father, calling from the hospital. His nose is broken, his is broken. He sees Mr. Knight telling his father they must ex him. He is dangerous. No control, it is shameful, terrible— *Oh, C I didn't mean to!*

He picks up his dinner and flushes it down the disposal. He sta out the window into the chill February darkness. *How many ti did I hit him?* And how will he be punished? He doesn't wan think about it.

He retrieves his shirt from the dryer. It is clean, warm, and slips it on and goes to sit on the couch in the den. He leans head back. His body feels churned up, brutalized. He need move around, but he will not allow this; he will allow himself comforts tonight. Waiting is part of the punishment. So he wait

EXHAUSTED after working late, Cal pulls into the driveway. Co car is there; Beth's is in the garage. Good; everybody home. He himself in through the kitchen and makes his way toward the c where a light is burning.

Conrad is asleep on the couch, sitting up, his head back. ' television set is off. Cal sets his briefcase down and touches C rad's shoulder gently. "Hey."

Con snaps upright, his eyes blinking. "Time's it?" he says.

"Twelve o'clock. What're you doing down here?"

"I couldn't sleep."

Cal laughs. "I see that. Let's go to bed, okay? I'm bushed."

"Wait a minute," he says. "I need to talk to you."

A note of urgency in the voice. "What's the matter?"

He does not look at Cal directly. "Something happened today school. I got in a fight."

360

"A fight?" He sits down in the chair. "Who with?"

"Just a guy. Kevin Stillman."

"Sure, I know him. Diver on the swim team, isn't he? What was the fight about?"

"Nothing. I don't know. He's just a jerk, but I didn't— I shouldn't have— I know that's no excuse. . . ."

"What happened?" Cal asks. "Did you get hurt?"

He looks up. "Me? No. I think I hurt him, though. There was a lot of blood. His nose—"

"Was he on his feet?"

"Yeah. I mean, not at first, but he was when I left. Lazenby took him home, I think."

"And it wasn't about anything?"

He shrugs. "I guess it was about how he bugs me and I bug him."

"Well, now you know it," Cal says. "Maybe you won't have to fight about it anymore, huh?" He rubs the back of his neck with his hands. "I called you around seven. You weren't here."

"I was here."

"Why didn't you answer?"

"I don't know." He looks at the floor. "I thought it might be somebody else."

"Relax," Cal says. "Stillman's all right."

"How do you know?"

"I know," he says. "Guys have been getting in fights since school was invented. Think about the last fight you were in."

"I was never in one," he says. "This is the first."

"You're kidding!"

Con shakes his head.

Cal looks at him. "Listen, I'm telling you, he'll be there tomorrow. Once, I broke my finger in a fight, knuckling a guy on the head. Doctor told me next time to use a baseball bat." He laughs, and Conrad looks up at last, grins faintly.

"You're not mad, then?"

"Mad? No," he says.

"I shouldn't have gone out of control like that," he says. "I shouldn't have blown up."

361

"You never blow up," Cal says, then corrects himself. "Hardly ever. You owed yourself. So, forget it."

Not just to comfort, it is the truth. A disposition like an angel's, the boy's grandmother Ellen used to say. Sunny and sweet, he never got mad. And that wasn't good. He kept everything inside. Cal has learned a thing or two from Dr. Crawford: razoring is anger; self-mutilation is anger. So this is a good sign; he is turning his anger outward at last. But something bothers him still. "You don't want to tell me what it was about?"

Conrad shrugs. "I told him he was a crummy diver. The guy's got no sense of humor."

Cal undresses in the dark, listening to the silky rush of her breathing. She did not stop in the den on her way to bed. Maybe she assumed the light had been left on for him. She must not have looked in Con's room, either, or she would have noticed that he was not in bed. He had asked on their way upstairs, "Did you hear your mother come in?" Conrad had said no.

Wouldn't she think it strange, Con sleeping on the couch at whatever time she had come in? Wouldn't she have wakened him to ask—at least—*What the hell is wrong with her?*

CHAPTER TEN

"Okay, I guess we're off," Cal says. "You've got the number, haven't you?"

Con helps his father load the last of the suitcases into the trunk. "Yeah. Have fun. Play good."

"I'll try."

Not a trip to Europe, but Cal can do this for her; take her to visit her brother. Ward Butler is big and loud, nothing like his sister in looks or temperament. Married a woman just like himself. Easy people to like and to be with. And she is as close to Ward as she to anybody. *As close as she is to me?*

Con slams the lid down. Then his mother comes out of the house. She is wearing a dark green dress, banded with white at the throat.

and wrists. Her hair falls loosely, hiding her face, but Con knows the expression she is wearing: a remote look reserved for airports and other public places. They are a complete contrast in attitudes: his father jokes with ticket agents and passengers, his mother remains cool and aloof. It is not her fault. She can't help it if she is afraid of strangers.

"Good-by, Mother," he says.

"Good-by. Be nice to your grandmother." She gets in the car.

"The flight gets in Wednesday at four," his father says. "You wait here, okay? We'll go out for dinner."

"Okay."

"Listen, don't let your grandmother push you around too much. You can stand it for five days, can't you?"

"Right."

"You got plans for this weekend?" he asks.

"I thought I'd cruise through town, run a few red lights, smoke some hash, get a couple girls in trouble, nothing special, why?" He smiles. "Quit worrying. You're making me nervous."

"I'm not worrying. Just take care, okay?"

"I will. See you Wednesday."

He waves them out of the driveway, then goes upstairs to get his own suitcase, thinking with longing of playing the stereo in his room and eating salami sandwiches, drinking beer, coming and going as he pleases, but his father wouldn't go away under those conditions. He loves his grandmother, but talking to her is like being on a loaded quiz show; her questions defy answering. "Have you completely lost your senses?" is a favorite. Maybe that is where his mother learned that there is danger in revealing too much.

Seated across from Con at dinner, his grandmother eyes him sternly. "You're letting your hair grow, aren't you?"

"I don't let it, Grandmother, it just does it. On its own."

"Well, I hope you're not turning into one of those hippie freaks. Howard, he needs some more meat."

"No, thanks. I've had plenty." Hippie freaks. She is ten years behind the times.

"Where's your appetite? How can you put on weight, eating like that?" she demands. "At least have more potatoes and gravy."

He allows her to refill his plate, doesn't really mind her bossing him around. Last year, when the hole was closing over his head there were no lectures from anyone. He reads this as a statement of his good health. Today he is capable of improvement.

"How were your grades last semester?" she asks.

"Not bad. Two C's, a B, and an A."

She shakes her head. "Whatever happened to all those A's? What are you doing with your time?"

"Nothing much," he says.

"I don't believe you appreciate your advantages, Conrad. Being born into a good family. Having a head on your shoulders—"

"Is it fair to count that? Everybody's got one, Grandmother."

Her lips fold in. "All right. Make fun. It's the thing you do best."

He grins, coaxing a smile from her. "Thanks. It's nice to be good at something."

THAT night he picks Jeannine up at the bakery shop where she works. He remembers what she told him the first time he came to pick her up: that the woman behind the register thought he was planning to stick up the place. "He has a furtive look," she had said. He liked that image of himself as the bakery rip-off man: the girl cowering behind the bread, the cinnamon buns. "Okay, girlie, get those Danish twists into the bag, no funny business!"

In the car, Jeannine slides over closer to him, squeezing his arm. "Your parents get off all right?"

"Yeah, they left. What'll we do? Good movie in Lake Bluff."

"I should go home first," she says. "Just to let her know."

As they round the corner to her house, she suddenly sits up very straight. "Damn," she says. "Oh, damn."

A black Buick is parked in the driveway.

She gets out of the car the instant he pulls to the curb. He reads the car's Ohio license plates.

"Is it your father?"

"No," she says. "Not my father."

364

Her mother stands in the doorway. "Hi, honey. You remember Mr. Ferrier, don't you?"

The man is light-haired and heavyset, with a rough, outdoor look about him. He smiles broadly. "Jen, you're prettier than ever. Nice to meet you, Conrad."

He smiles at the man. He always admires these take-charge guys; they make awkward situations fast and simple. He glances at Jeannine. She is not smiling.

Mrs. Pratt says, "Paul and I were thinking about going to get a quick bite to eat. Honey, would you mind keeping an eye on Mike?"

"We were going to the show," Jen says stiffly. "It's up to Con."

"I don't mind," he says.

"Good, then," Paul says. "See you later." They are gone. The door slams behind them.

From the couch Mike says, "Can we have popcorn tonight?"

Jeannine doesn't answer; she stares at the television.

Feeling awkward, Conrad peels out of his jacket. "Let's make popcorn," he says.

She looks at him. "I'll make it, you stay here."

She disappears into the kitchen, and Conrad sits beside Mike on the couch. "What're you watching?"

"Nothin'. Hey, you wanna hear me play the guitar?"

"Hey, yeah. When did you start?"

"Couple weeks ago. Mom bought me one."

He listens to the chords: C, G, D, E minor, A minor. After each one Mike looks up expectantly.

"Fantastic." He rewards him. "Terrific."

"Nah. But I don't think it'll take me long to get good." He hands Con the guitar. "Now you play something," he orders.

He plays a Simon and Garfunkel tune, then some John Denver. "Hey, you're really good, you know?"

"It's not hard," he says. "You'll be able to do it in a while."

He hands the guitar back, goes out to the kitchen. She has her back to him, all business.

"Jen, what's the matter?"

"Nothing. I'm acting dopey tonight. Just ignore it, okay?"

365

"Okay. He seemed like a nice enough guy to me."

"Well, he's not!" she snaps. "A man who dates a married woman, in my opinion, is not a nice guy."

"I thought your parents were divorced."

"They are. Now! They weren't before he came along—" She stops abruptly. "I'm sorry. I don't like acting like this over it, especially in front of you."

"Why, in front of me?"

He moves toward her. She is crying. "I'm sorry," she says, "I can't help it."

He puts his arms around her. "It's all right," he soothes. "It'll work out all right."

"I don't think so. I kept hoping they would get back together, and I know, *I know,* that's just stupid! They don't love each other, so why do I make such a big deal of it?" She pulls in her breath, and her arms are around his waist, her head on his chest. He holds her, tests the feeling of someone looking to him for support. He feels as if he could stand here holding her forever. He lifts her chin and kisses her. Her face is tear-streaked, her mouth loose under his. He has never felt so strong, so needed.

WARD's wife, Audrey, pours Cal a cup of coffee when he returns from playing golf. "Not much to celebrate with, is it?" She smiles at him. "Ward's going to stop for beer on his way back. He and Beth went riding."

Cal leans back, relaxed. "That's okay, I can wait."

"Seventy-one, that's really good, isn't it?"

"It's the best I'll do in this tournament, I'm sure. God, it was beautiful out there. Summer comes early around here, doesn't it?"

"This isn't summer! Summer is absolutely *unbearable!*"

"Where are the boys?" he asks.

"They're right outside. In the pool."

"Gee, they look great."

Their sons, Charlie and Kerry, are ten and seven. They are lively boys, large for their ages.

"Charlie's such a daredevil," she says. "Kerry's more cautious."

366

Like his own. Buck was the one he had to watch. Conrad had all the common sense.

"How is Con?" Audrey asks.

"Pretty good."

"I tried to talk to Beth last night, but she made me feel like it was off limits. Then I started to worry a little."

"No, he's fine." A lot of subjects are becoming off limits. On the flight down, he had attempted a discussion of their summer plans. Would she like to go to London? Dubrovnik? She answered with polite indifference. Whatever he would like to do was fine with her. He took it as delayed punishment for Christmas. Okay, fair enough. But his try for a talk about the conversation he had with Ray in the restaurant was greeted with stony silence. She definitely did not want to hear any of that.

"If you don't know, Cal, it's hopeless for me to try to tell you."

"Oh, great, it's hopeless," he said. "Terrific."

And she had twisted toward him in the seat, saying, "Please! Can't we just have a good time for these few days? Let's just relax and have fun for a change."

So, okay, he blamed himself. He would relax. He would quit nagging her to confide in him.

But it surprises him that she would be as reserved with Audrey. She likes Audrey. And it was an honest question. Why duck it? He is discovering that he never knows how to read her, and there are fewer and fewer openings into the vast obscurity of her nature. He is on the outside, looking in. Has he always been?

"I know," Audrey says, "that you have to be careful with Beth. I mean, emotion is her enemy. She wants everything to go smoothly, the way she's planned it."

Is it that obvious? He remembers Carole Lazenby's words at lunch that day. "She's a perfectionist. . . . She never lets herself get trapped." Oh, God, once she was trapped and she knew it. A hot night last August. She had gone out for a walk. Alone. He sat in the living room, thinking about the set of her shoulders as she walked away from the house; she had looked so small, so sad. And he had found her in the backyard, weeping, and trying not to weep. Those

367

dry, tight sobs. It was the only time he saw her cry. She had not cried at the funeral. He had cried. Howard and Ellen had cried. But she and Con had been stony and calm throughout. The scene in the garden had come later. After Con. She had grieved then. At last.

Neither of them had cried that night on the dock. Too catastrophic for tears. That murderous lead-colored moon. The black water all around them. The people who didn't know who they were, only that something terrible had happened. "Those kids never should have been out there without power." A man next to him had answered, "Doesn't make any difference. The lake whips up like that and it doesn't make any difference, power or not." And the radioed message from the cruiser: "We found her, sir. She's dismasted. Only one on board. Sorry."

"They'll find him," Beth had said, gripping his arm. "They'll find him." They did not find Buck for two days.

Morbid thoughts. He looks at Audrey, who is frowning at him.

"Is something wrong, Cal? I mean, something else?"

"No," he says. "What could be wrong? Here I sit with my lovely sister-in-law, on the way to winning the first tournament of my career, what could be wrong?"

A car has pulled up in the drive, and Ward's voice booms. "Hey, you big-city dude, what did you shoot?"

Beth follows Ward into the kitchen, looking like a sixteen-year-old in jeans and a red checked shirt, her hair in pigtails.

"Seventy-one," Audrey says.

"Seventy-one! Oh, Cal, that's marvelous!" Beth says. "Oh, you *are* going to win it this year!"

"Hey," he says, "you'll jinx me."

"Nobody did better, did they?"

"Not today. Still two days to go, though."

Ward sets down a case of beer. "What you need," he says, "is an early ride tomorrow to set you up."

He laughs, looking at Beth. Her eyes are alive, her cheeks burned from the sun.

"Listen, I had her on the biggest damn horse you ever saw today, and she was beautiful! She's got great hands—"

368

"Oh, shut up, Ward!" She looks at him, laughing.

"Buy her a big Appaloosa, keep it in your backyard over there in leafy Lake Forest—"

"Why is it that Texans always confuse big with best?" Cal teases. "Just like that crazy airport. Ten thousand acres of concrete! Ask a security guard where the baggage is, and he tells you, 'I have no idea.'"

They all laugh.

"What are we doing for dinner tonight?" Beth asks. "I'm starved!"

"Let's just throw some steaks on the grill, how's that? And whip up a salad." Ward ruffles his sister's hair. "Hey, I'm glad to see you so cheerful, Sissie. Things going good for you again, huh?"

A pause, a half step off the beat. She does not look at Cal. "Yes," she says. "Things are going fine."

"Good. I'm glad you could come. So how's Con doing?"

"Everything's fine, Ward."

"He seeing anybody? Like an outpatient sort of thing."

"He's seeing a doctor in Evanston," Cal says. "Twice a week. No, once a week now. He's coming along."

Beth is studying her wristwatch intently.

"Listen," Ward says, "tomorrow morning, before you tee off, a good, brisk ride. It'll do great things for you!"

He laughs. "No, thanks. You two go ahead."

"Didn't I tell you not to marry a dude, Sissie? Hey, you do well tomorrow, or we'll send you back east by yourself!"

ON SUNDAY, at breakfast, his grandmother asks, "What time did you get in, Con?"

"I don't know. Twelve? Twelve thirty?"

"One thirty," she says.

"One thirty, then." Con nods amiably, helping himself to toast. His head sings with an intricate melodic line—Telemann? Marais? He cannot remember, but he loves those unfamiliar instruments— the recorder, the harpsichord—their simple statements of truth.

"How can you expect to get a decent night's sleep, coming in at that hour?"

"I give up. How can I?"

It is a perfect day. And tonight he will go to Jeannine's to study. Thinking about it makes his skin ripple pleasantly. Last night he took her out again: the old Saturday-night-show date. Afterward, at Lombardi's, they had run into Phil Truan and Shirley Day, and they had talked about the four of them going bowling sometime.

Truan is a nice guy. That is the truth.

And another truth. That there are no secret passages to strength, no magic words. It is just something you know about yourself. Since last night—no, before last night—it is as if he knew it all along. He is strong, he is able, because he is.

AFTER dinner he and his grandfather sit in the living room, reading the Sunday paper. Con leafs through his section casually while he waits patiently for the sport section.

An article on page three suddenly leaps out at him. GIRL TAKES OWN LIFE. Oh, God. He skips to the middle. "Carbon monoxide poisoning . . . nineteen-year-old Skokie girl . . . dead in her car early Saturday morning . . ." He goes back to the beginning. "Karen Susan Aldrich . . . dead on arrival at Skokie General Hospital . . . hose attached to the car's exhaust pipe was drawn through a rear window . . ."

His body is suddenly numb. The words swim before his eyes. *Oh, God. Oh, no.* He trembles. " 'We are in shock . . . ,' father told reporters. 'Everything going so well, I can't believe . . . ' "

He folds the newspaper carefully, holds it on his lap, rocking slowly. He feels dizzy and sick at his stomach.

"Conrad? What's the matter?" His grandfather stands over him. "Are you all right?"

"I'm all right." He can hardly hear himself, the sounds inside his head are so loud. His grandmother's hand is on his forehead.

"You don't feel hot to me. Is it a headache?"

"Yes," he says, getting up. "I need to go to bed. I'm tired."

"Bed?" his grandfather asks. "At seven o'clock?"

Fully awake, he lies in the bed. *What happened? A stone bench outside the hospital, where they sat for hours soaking up spring*

370

sunshine, Karen's legs swinging back and forth, and the blue dress clings to her slim body. Her shiny hair, long and black, freshly washed. She is smiling at him. What happened? Crawford, you liar, you promised. You said you were never wrong. Oh, God, please, I don't want to think about this. Let me sleep. God, let me sleep.

He wills his mind to let him pass into dreamless sleep.

He sits against the cool bathroom wall, in only his shorts. The door locked. He draws the blade down into his left wrist, a deep vertical cut. The artery bubbles up like a river. Does it to his right arm. Warmth and color flood the room. He is free at last, comforted. It crosses his mind to compose himself for dying. Awkward, there is nowhere to put his hands, the blood makes everything slippery. Lies on his side, using one arm as a pillow. He sleeps. And then, arms tied, his jaw aches, something hard between his teeth to keep him from swallowing his tongue, they say. He knows better. It is how they punish you for failure here, and someone crying, "Lord, what has he done? What has he done to himself?"

HE AWAKENS to fear again, his mouth dry. For terror-filled seconds he doesn't know if it is happening all over again. Numb with fear, he scrambles out of bed, pulling his clothes on.

The house is dark. He fumbles for his jacket in the hall closet, quietly lets himself out the front door.

He walks swiftly, without direction. To calm himself. To get away from dreams, from thinking at all. He remembers another newspaper article. About him. The police chief was quoted. He couldn't understand why a kid would want to hurt himself like that. Crawford had let him read it. He had tried to explain that he had not been trying to hurt himself, he had merely been trying to die.

No. You do not slash yourself if you are merely trying to die. Nor do you overlook the sleeping pills beside the razor blades in the medicine chest. Not for him. Too easy. And too neat. *Oh, God; why, then?*

He stops walking. The sidewalk is shadowy, the air still and cold.

Ahead of him, a car approaches, pulls to the curb opposite him. Police car. He has a sudden urge to run, but stands still as the cop crosses the street.

"Where you headed?"

"Nowhere." He wets his lips nervously. "Just taking a walk."

"Pretty late, isn't it? After two. Where do you live?"

"Fourteen thirty Heron Drive." He is surprised at how calm, how normal his voice sounds.

The cop frowns. "Long way from home, aren't you?"

He has given his home address. "I'm staying with my grandparents. On Green Bay Road." For a moment he panics; he cannot remember the number. "It's a gray house with black shutters. Fifty-one thirty-five."

"What's the name?"

"Butler. Howard Butler."

"Yeah, okay." The cop smiles then. "They know you're out?"

He shakes his head. His hands are sweating. Will they take him to the station? Call his grandparents?

"What's your name?"

"Jarrett. Conrad Jarrett."

"Well, Conrad, I wouldn't walk around here this late. Too many nuts in the world. You'd better head back."

The cop drives off. He lets his breath out slowly. *Too many nuts.* Meaning you aren't one of them. All the outer signs must be right, then: hair the right length, polite answers. *You're all right, kid. Ordinary.* He zips his jacket up; turning, he follows the disappearing taillights, two red eyes in the darkness.

HE SLIPS inside, goes in the dark to the den at the back of the house. No going back to bed. Not safe there. He sits upright in the chair by the door, arms along the armrests, not leaning back.

Unforgivable. It is unforgivable. They wrestle with the boat together, the sails snapping like rifle cracks in the wind. "Get it down! Get the damn sail down!" Grabbing at a billowing mass, sticky and wet against his face. A loud crack and the terrible rolling begins, the water closing over his head. He fights his way to the surface,

372

screaming, emptied of everything but fear. "Buck! Buck!" In front of him a hand stretching out along the upturned hull, water crashing against him, pushing them apart. Buck yells, "Kick off your shoes!" Mindless, he obeys, chokes as water closes him off again from the moon, from everything. They collide in the water. Buck grabs his shirt. "Hang on, I'm gonna go under, have a look!" He screams at him, "Don't go, don't go!" but Buck is already gone and above him the sky is black. It is painful to breathe, terrifying. He must turn his head away from the hull, from safety, to do it. Buck surfaces beside him. "We screwed up this time, buddy!" They stare at each other, and Buck breaks into a grin. "Well? You got any ideas?" He shakes his head, then finds his voice. "It's not so goddamn funny, Buck!" He soothes him. "Okay, okay. They'll be looking for us, for sure, just hang on, don't get tired, promise?" He says, "Don't you, either!" and they stop talking then, address themselves to the task of enduring. And it starts to rain. Hours into the night they hang off the sides of the boat. Hands numb with cold, the water is icy. "How long you think it's been?" "I dunno. An hour? Two?" "Hell, longer than that, don't you think?"

When did it happen? When did they stop calling to one another from opposite sides of the stern, where they hung for better balance? Did he think it was over? Man, why'd you let go?

His grandmother crying at the funeral. "Poor Jordan, he didn't want to leave us like this!" And he had answered her, saying coldly, "Why did he let go, then? Why didn't he hang on?"

And he was punished for that, because afterward everything made him ill. Food, and people eating it. Smells. And, for weeks, not being able to sleep. That was punishment, too, being forced to submit over and over to a hopeless rerun of that day, to what could have been done to make it different. Nothing. That is the nature of hell, that it cannot be changed.

HE IS awake again. *No more. No more.* Tears fill his eyes, run down his cheeks. Nearly morning now. Outside the window he can see faint streaks of light separating the trees from their background of sky.

He goes to the bathroom, stares at himself in the mirror. His heart is pounding, and a cracking headache has ignited behind his eyes. He leaves the bathroom, goes to the telephone. Seven. Not too early to call. He looks up the home number and quickly dials.

It is Berger's voice at the other end. "Hullo."

"This is Conrad," he says. Tears blind him. "I need to see you," he whispers.

"Yes. Okay. Can you make it to the office in half an hour?"

"Yes."

He replaces the receiver, goes upstairs for his wallet and keys. He leaves a note for his grandparents by the telephone. "Had to leave early. See you tonight after school."

Nearly light as he gets into the car. He wipes his eyes. *This is how people get in accidents, keep calm, keep calm.* He grips the wheel tightly, fighting panic. *Now a red light, now stop, now watch the car in front of you.* He focuses carefully on the road.

BERGER is filling the coffeepot. "You made good time."

Con stands motionless in the doorway.

"It might help if you just let it out, Con."

The use of his name releases him, and he sits down on the floor slowly. The tears roll down his cheeks.

"I need something...."

"Okay," Berger says. "Tell me."

"I can't!" he cries. He drops his head. "You make me talk about things I can't talk about!"

"Is that what you came here to tell me?"

He lifts his head, holding himself tight. Control. Control is all. He tries to stifle the sound, but he cannot, and he begins to sob. There is no control anymore, everything is lost, and his body heaves.

"Ah, God, I don't know. I don't know, it just keeps coming, I can't make it stop! It's all hanging over my head!"

"What's hanging over your head?" Berger comes over and joins him on the floor, giving him a cup of coffee.

"I don't know!" He looks up, dazed, drawing a deep breath. "I need something, I want something—I want to get off the hook!"

374

"For what?"

He begins to cry again. "For killing him, don't you know that? For letting him drown!"

"And how did you do that?" Berger asks.

But it is coming from some part of him that is separate and unknown. "I don't know, I just know that I did!" He sobs. Can't think, no way out of this endless turning and twisting. Hopeless.

"You were on opposite sides of the boat," Berger says, "so you couldn't even see each other. Right?"

He nods his head. He scratches his cheek, staring at Berger through the slits of his eyes.

"And he was a better swimmer than you. He was stronger, he had more endurance."

"Yes."

"So, what could you have done to keep him from drowning?"

Tears flood his eyes again. "I don't know. Something."

It is always this way. He cannot get by this overpowering burden. "You don't understand. It has to be somebody's fault. Or what was the whole goddamn point of it?"

"The point of it," Berger says, "is that it happened."

"No! That's not it! That is too simple. . . ."

"Kiddo, let me tell you a story," Berger says. "About this perfect kid who had a younger brother. A not-so-perfect kid. And all the time they were growing up, this not-so-perfect kid tried to model himself after his brother, the perfect kid. It worked, too. After all, they were a lot alike, and the not-so-perfect kid was a very good actor. Then along came this sailing accident, and the impossible happened. The not-so-perfect kid makes it. The other kid, the one he has patterned his whole life after, isn't so lucky. So, where is the sense in that, huh? Where is the justice?"

"There isn't any," he says dully.

Berger holds up his hand. "Let me finish. The justice, obviously, is for the not-so-perfect kid to become that other, perfect kid. For everybody. For his parents, his friends, and, most of all, himself. Only, that is one hell of a burden, see? So, finally he decides he can't carry it. But how to set it down? No way. A problem without a solu-

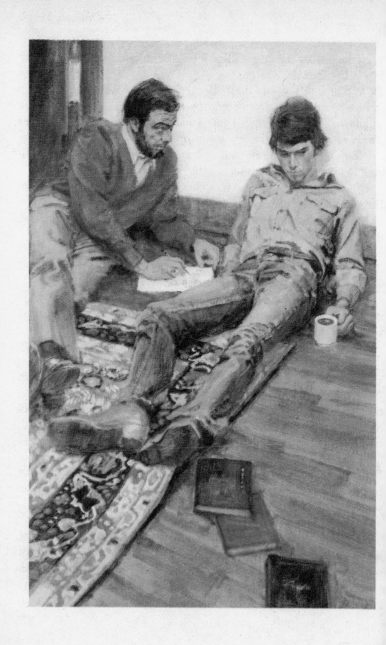

tion. And so, because he can't figure out how to solve the problem, he decides to destroy it." Berger leans forward. "Does any of this make sense to you?"

"I don't know," he says. "I don't know."

"It is a very far-out act of self-preservation, do you get that, Con? And you were right. Nobody needs you to be Buck. It's okay to just be you."

"I don't know who that is anymore!" he cries.

"Yeah, you do," Berger says. "Con, that guy is trying so hard to get out! Let him talk. Let him tell you what you did that was so bad. Listen, you know what you did? You hung on, kiddo. That's it. That's your guilt. You can live with that, can't you?"

He cannot answer.

"The thing that hurts you," Berger says, "is sitting on yourself. Not letting yourself connect with your own feelings. It is messing you up. You get any sleep last night?"

He shakes his head.

"How about food? You had anything to eat since yesterday?"

"No—" He starts to say that he is too tired to eat, but Berger is heading for the door, and he stumbles behind him, dragged along by the force of Berger's monologue.

"Jeez, if I could get through to you, kiddo, that depression is not crying and *giving vent*, it is plain and simple *reduction of feeling*. Reduction, see? People who keep stiff upper lips find that it's damn hard to smile."

The restaurant has a neglected look about it, but inside it is clean and cheerful. Berger picks out a table and orders for them both: orange juice, bacon and eggs, coffee. Conrad sits exhausted, his eyes swollen, looking down at his hands. Narrowing his eyes, he blends everything to gray—the curtains, the walls, the dark gorilla-like man across the table from him.

"The little girl in Skokie is what started all this, am I right?" Berger asks quietly. "Crawford called me last night. He was pretty shook, too. But, kiddo, you know the statistics. Out of every hundred, fifty are gonna try it again. Fifteen eventually make it."

He covers his face with his hands. "Don't," he says.

The waitress brings their breakfast, and Con props his elbows on the table. "She was okay," he says. "Into everything at school, and happy. She told me to—to be less intense. It isn't fair!"

"You're right. It isn't fair," Berger says. "I'm sorry for her, the poor kid." He runs his hands through his hair. "Listen, eat. You'll feel better once you eat."

"I can't," he says. "I don't know what I would have done if I couldn't have gotten you this morning. I felt so shaky."

"And now?"

He closes his eyes. "Still shaky."

Berger laughs. "That's what I like about you, kiddo. You got style. Listen, what happened this morning was that you let yourself feel some pain. And the world is full of pain. Also joy. Evil. Goodness. Horror and love. You name it, it's there. Sealing yourself off is just going through the motions, get it?"

He opens his eyes to study the ceiling, too tired to comment.

"Go home and get some sleep. You look whipped."

"I can't. My grandmother would hassle me all day."

"So, go to your own house. You've got a key, haven't you?"

He sits up. "Yeah, I do. I should have thought of that."

"You would have. When are your parents due back?"

"Not until Wednesday."

"Okay, go home, rest, eat something, hear?"

"It's okay for me to go? You don't think I'll do anything crazy?"

"Like what?" Berger asks. "You're a big boy. You're not gonna punish yourself for something you didn't do."

"All right."

"And anyway, punishment doesn't make the guilt go away, does it? And it doesn't earn you any forgiveness."

"No," he says wearily.

"So, what's the point of it, then?"

Berger walks him to the car. As he gets in, tears well up again. For so long he has shielded himself from hurt. Suddenly all his senses are raw, open to wounding.

He wipes his eyes. "I'll see you tomorrow."

"Drive carefully."

HE LETS HIMSELF in through the kitchen. He goes upstairs to his bathroom, turns on the shower, and strips down. He gets in, adjusts the water to as hot as he can stand it. He does his best thinking in here. The heat relaxes the clots inside his brain, and he leans his forehead against the wall as the warmth spreads downward from his neck to his shoulders and back.

Guilt is not punishment, Berger said. Guilt is simply guilt. Years ago he and Buck had a run-in with a clerk in a drugstore. He wouldn't believe they had paid for two comic books. He had threatened to call their father. "Go ahead," Buck said with scorn. "My dad knows we don't take things. What do I care what you think?" But Conrad had cared desperately, and had felt, even as he knew he was innocent, guilty and shamed by it. Why?

Because it has always been easier to believe himself capable of evil than to accept evil in others. But that doesn't make sense. The clerk in the drugstore wasn't evil, just mistaken. Bad judgment doesn't make you evil—can he only see these two opposites, good and evil? Innocence and guilt? Is it necessary to believe others guilty in order for himself to be proved innocent? There is a way through this, if only he can find it.

"C'mon, you promised!"

"Why do I always have to go first?"

They are eight and nine, in the garage, with the door closed. Buck is abruptly disgusted with him.

"Ah, forget it, baby! I said you could do it to me after!"

As always with freedom in sight, Con opts for prison. He stands obediently still as Buck ties his hands behind his back, sits as the rope is lashed around his ankles. Buck pulls a handkerchief from his pocket. "First we torture you. Then we make you talk." He forces Con back against the floor and ties the handkerchief around his mouth. Terrified, Con struggles to free himself, fights the gag; then the garage door opens. "What the hell is this?" He is pulled to his feet, the ropes loosened, the gag snatched from his mouth. Not relief but horror, as he sees Buck's pants jerked down, his father's hand cracking across the bare bottom. Buck howls in protest while he stands in terror waiting for his punishment. But then his fa-

379

*ther's anger is spent, and he says, "Don't you ever do a thing like
that again, Bucky, you understand?"*

For some inexplicable reason he was left out of this. His shame
and guilt ignored. He had to suffer alone. But what for? It was just
a boy's game, dangerous maybe, but not evil, and nobody's fault.
It happened, that's all. Not so frightening, is it? To believe them
both innocent. *Oh, God.* Tears leak out. Resigned, he lets them
come as he soaps himself carefully. Finished, he gets out, towels
himself dry. Slowly he turns his arms up to look at the insides of his
wrists. Then at his long line of life, curving beside the heel of his
hand almost to his wrist. He draws a ragged breath, wondering
about Karen, about her line of life. Was it a long one, too?

Tears of grief this time. *Not fair!* No, but life is not fair always.
It just *is*.

He puts on underwear, continuing to blink his tears back. Reduction of feeling. He is not guilty of that today. He climbs into bed.
Cleanliness surrounds him, its smell cool and seductive. He rolls
to his face and, without a thought, he sleeps.

CHAPTER ELEVEN

THE air is balmy as they sit on the patio, watching the boys swim.
Ward raises his glass to Cal. "To your low total the first day."

Audrey says, "To that thirty-foot putt on the fifteenth today. I
was poking everybody in sight. 'Hey, that's my brother-in-law!'"

"You did look good, Cal," Beth says.

He grins. "At isolated moments."

"Well, you didn't really expect to win," Ward says.

"Hell, no!"

But that is the funny part. After Saturday, when he saw that he
could do it, he had tightened up. *You didn't expect to win.* Maybe
that's it. You get what you expect.

"Why don't we go out to the Captain's Table and celebrate, anyway?" Ward asks.

"That'd be nice," Audrey says.

"I'll check to see if we need reservations."

Audrey gets up, too. "I'll put some hamburgers on for the boys. Keep an eye on them, will you?"

Beth nods, and they are left alone on the patio.

"Having fun?" he asks her.

She smiles. "Yes. Are you?"

"Sure."

"I've been thinking," Beth says, "that we should play more golf together. Maybe our next vacation should be strictly golf. We could go to Pinehurst."

"Sounds great," Cal says. "I bet Con would like that, too."

A short silence. Then, "Do you do that deliberately? Or is it a reflex action? I'm curious."

"Do what?"

"Insert him into the conversation. Whenever I mention you and I doing something together."

"I'm sorry," he says. "You said vacation. I guess I assumed that you meant him, too."

"I'm surprised that you haven't called him yet."

"I was going to tonight."

She laughs. "It must be hard to grow up when your father is breathing down your neck all the time. I think I would hate it."

Cal gets up, goes to stand near the edge of the pool. He hears the patio door slide open. Ward says, "Everything's all set. Nine thirty. We've got time for one more round, folks."

"I don't think I'll have another," Beth says. "I'm going to dress."

"Nothing fancy, Sissie. You look fine just the way you are."

Cal turns and hands his glass to Ward. "I'll have one."

AND again he drinks too much. Out of anger at her, maybe. Out of fear. Out of whatever it is that is happening to them that he does not want to see and doesn't see when he is high.

"One more!" Ward is gay when they arrive home, he and Audrey giggling together as if they didn't know how they had been used tonight. Intermediaries. Beth would not look at him all night. Now they sit on opposite sides of the living room, the silence between them hostile. "There's a bottle of Tia Maria in the garage," Ward.

381

is saying to Audrey. "Come on with me. I've got some things to whisper to you."

Laughing, she goes with him, and they are left with the silence. Beth picks up a magazine, and his anger ignites.

"Why don't we finish it?" he asks.

She looks up. "Finish what?"

"What you started out there tonight."

"I started? By suggesting we go away together on a vacation? You were the one who walked away from me, remember?"

"What the hell was I supposed to say to that? The old song and dance—I overprotect, I breathe down his neck."

"You do."

"It's a matter of opinion."

"Right. So there's no point in discussing it further."

"I think there's a point."

"Why are you so obsessed?" she snaps. "God, I am sick of talking about *him!* He controls you, even when he's not around."

"Oh, stop it. We haven't exchanged a dozen words about him in months. *He* isn't the problem. So let's talk about what's really bothering you."

"Oh, no, let's talk about what's bothering *you!* That's what you want. That's why you go around moping and depressed—just the way you used to, dragging everybody down with you!"

"What the hell are you talking about?"

"I'm talking about last spring, when you couldn't answer the phone, couldn't open your mail without wondering if it would be the hospital with more bad news."

"God damn it, sure I was depressed! But I wasn't too depressed to take you to Spain and Portugal—" He struggles for control, his senses blurred. "I am asking you to tell me," he says slowly, "what I've done that's made you so angry with me."

"It's not what you've done," she says. "It's what you think *I've* done."

"What you've done." He lets the words sink in, trying to get the message. "I don't know what you mean. I don't think you've done anything."

382

"Oh, you liar," she says bitterly. "You do. You blame me for the whole thing."

"For what whole thing?"

"That whole vicious thing! He made it as vicious, as sickening as he could! All that blood! Oh, I will never forgive him for it! He wanted it to kill me, too!"

And suddenly she is crying. Painful, desperate sobs that shake her shoulders. Her hands are over her face, her head bent to her knees. Frightened, he kneels beside the chair, trying to put his arm around her, but she will not permit it.

"Leave me alone! You got what you wanted, leave me alone!"

"I got— Beth, I love you, honey, please, let me help."

Her head jerks up. She looks at him stiffly. "Help? What do you mean, help? I can help myself."

Ward and Audrey are standing in the doorway. "Hey," Ward says softly, "I'm sorry about this. We don't want to butt in."

"You're not butting in!" Beth says. She starts to cry again, and Cal stands up, close to tears himself.

"Don't you understand what Conrad was saying?" she asks. "He was saying, 'Look! Look what you made me do!'"

"Why?" he asks. "Why was he saying that?"

"I don't know!" She sobs, and then her voice is calm. "I just know how people try to manipulate other people."

"Oh, God, Beth, I don't believe that! I don't believe he went all that way to try to manipulate us! What he did, he did to *himself!* Can't you see anything except in terms of how it affects you?"

"No! Neither can you! Neither does anybody else! Only I'm willing to recognize that I do it. I don't know what he wants from me. Does he want me to throw my arms around him when he passes a chemistry exam? I can't do it! I can't respond when someone says, 'Here, I just did this great thing, so love me for it!' I can't!"

"I don't think he wants that," Cal says. "I think he just wants to know that you don't hate him."

"Hate him? How could I hate him? Mothers don't hate their sons! But he makes *demands* on me!" She looks up at him. "Where did you get that? About my hating him? Did he tell you that?"

"Beth—"

"You let him say that to you?" Her voice is trembling. "I don't know what you want from me anymore, Cal. I don't know what anybody wants from me!"

"Honey, nobody wants anything from you," Ward says. "We all just want—Cal and Con and everybody—we want you to be happy."

"Happy!" She looks at him. "Oh, Ward! You give us the definition, will you? But first you'd better check on those kids. Every day, to make sure they're good and safe, that nobody's fallen off a horse, or drowned in that swimming pool you're so proud of!"

"Beth!" Audrey says, her hands to her face.

"And then you come and tell me how to be happy."

Cal closes his eyes, not listening anymore, remembering last year, when he stood outside the bathroom door, begging to be let in. *Con, open the door! Let me in!* His shoulder crashing against the door, the jamb splintering, giving way to the nightmare of blood, the towels and floor soaked with it. Con's arm curved, hiding his face.

And in the hospital, strapped down in the high, criblike bed, his face pale against the green emergency-room sheets. *I want to die.* And himself in shock, watching the bottle drain healing liquid into that arm. In shock, already broken by the note they had found on his desk: "I wish I knew why but I just don't."

After the accident, after they had towed the boat in, he had moaned over and over, "Mama, I'm sorry! Dad, I'm sorry, I'm sorry!"

That second time there had been no apology. A bloody, vicious thing. She is right. It hasn't killed her, but it has done something to her, something terrible. Circles and more circles, where does it end? How can it end?

THE air smells of darkness, of endless space, as Cal stands on the porch. Beth is inside reading, Conrad upstairs doing homework.

This afternoon, on the plane, she had sat untouchable beside him, and he had left her alone, knowing that if he tried to approach her, she would simply move her seat. But tonight, at dinner, she had been perfect. The perfect wife, the perfect mother. Conrad

384

picked the restaurant and did all the talking, while she and Cal listened, quietly attentive. Once she reached out to pull the collar of Con's shirt from under his pullover, and he sat, not moving, drinking in every ounce of her attention, knowing that, mysteriously, he had done something right tonight.

And, when he refused dessert, even her correcting his table manners seemed right and proper. "You don't need to say, 'I'm full.' Just 'No, thanks' is sufficient."

"Wait, let me write that down, will you?" he teased her.

Now he stands on the stairs as Cal comes inside. "See you in the morning," he says. "I'm tired. It was sort of a rough week."

"Your grandmother give you a hard time?"

"No. She was fine. I'm just— I'm glad you're back, that's all."

And he goes to *her* then; it is what he has come downstairs for, obviously. He puts an arm around her in a quick, clumsy embrace. "G'night." His voice is thick. He exits swiftly, his face turned away.

She sits on the couch, the book in her lap, just as he has left her. She is staring off into space. Then, after a moment, her head drops over her book again, her hair spilling over her shoulder. Her face is hidden from Cal, also.

"ALREADY I'm thinking about next fall," Jeannine says. "Isn't that dumb? I don't want to go away now."

They are sitting on the floor in her living room, their backs against the couch, as Conrad picks out chords on Mike's guitar. He has Mike's cowboy hat on, pulled down on his forehead.

"I don't want you to go, either," he says. "Why don't you hang around here for another year? Wait for me?"

"I can't," she says. "Did you write that, Con? It's beautiful. Play it again."

And he plays her the song he has composed over the past week. She listens, elbows on her knees, chin in her hands.

"I love it. You should write words for it."

"I'm not too good at that."

"You used to write poetry, didn't you?"

"Who told you that?" he asks. "Lazenby?"

385

She nods. "I said to him, 'Tell me everything you know about Conrad Jarrett.' So he did."

He laughs. "The hell you did!"

"Suzanne Mosely asked me today if I was still going out with you. I said yes. Then she asked me if I was serious, or was I just having a good time. She said you were the only nice boy in the whole school, and she would be very disappointed in me if I were just fooling around with you."

"I can't believe she said that. She never even talks to me."

She laughs. "You don't accept compliments gracefully. Like, when I told you how much my mother likes you—"

"I'm just waiting for the rest of it. My mother likes you, my brother likes you, thanks for everything, and I'll see you around."

"Oh, you're hopeless, you really are."

But she is not laughing. Instead she is looking at him with a solemn, wide-open expression. His head suddenly feels light. He turns toward her, puts his arms around her gently. Her mouth opens under his, her breath is sweet-smelling, like apples. He gathers her against him as warmth spreads through his whole body. His face in the hollow of her neck, he rocks her slowly, gently in his arms.

SHE turns his arm up and brushes her fingertips against the scar on his wrist. "Did it hurt?"

"No," he says. "I don't think so. I don't remember."

"Would you rather not talk about it?"

"I don't know. I've never talked about it. To doctors, but not to anyone else."

Her fingers on the scar send out strange vibrations from nerve endings that are not completely healed. He wonders if they will ever be.

"Why did you do it?"

"I don't know. It was like falling into a hole and it keeps getting bigger and bigger; you can't get out. And then all of a sudden it's inside you, it *is* you, and you're trapped."

"I know. I know that feeling." She holds his hand lightly.

"I don't feel that way anymore."

387

"Con, do you believe people are punished for things they do?"
"Punished? You mean by God?"
"Yes."
"I don't believe in God," he says.
"Not at all?"
"It isn't a question of degree, I don't think. Either you do or you don't."

They are silent for a moment. "I believe in God," she says.
"Okay."
"What do you believe in?"
"Oh, tennis courts, wallpaper, Miami Beach—"
"Liar," she says, her arms sliding around his neck.
"You," he says, kissing her.
"Liar again, but that's nice."

And he squeezes her tightly, feeling the sense of calm, of peace slowly gathering, spreading itself within him. He is in touch for good, with hope, with himself, no matter what. Berger is right, the body never lies.

CHAPTER TWELVE

BETH left the telling of it up to him.

"You're the expert in human relations. You handle it." Said calmly, as she was packing. Cal had felt the accusation behind it.

"I don't understand why you're leaving!" he says.

"Because I can't stand the way you look at me. I can't stand that 'poor Beth' expression on your face."

"I don't believe you. I'm not looking at you any differently."

"When you suggested a counselor," she says, "I knew."

"Counseling! I said counseling for both of us."

"No! You're the one who isn't happy anymore, can't you see that? You see a counselor; you do what you need to do."

"What I need," he says, "is for us to talk to each other! I want to talk to you, Beth, but when I try, you freeze me out."

"Well, what do you expect from an emotional cripple?" she blazes. "That's what you've been trying to tell me, isn't it? That's

388

what you really think of me. I won't have it, Cal. I won't have you wringing your hands over me, the way you have over him."

There is too much that he doesn't understand anymore. There is a private core within her that is so much deeper than he ever imagined it to be. He has no such core; at least he cannot find it, if it is there.

Nightly they argue. Daily she gets up, spending hours at Onwentsia organizing the tennis tournament. Over there they think of her as a marvelous miracle.

Marvelous miracle, his wife, but her outer life is deceiving. She gives the appearance of orderliness, but inside, what he has begun to glimpse is not order, but chaos.

The other night he had shouted in her face, "Do you love me, Beth?"

"Stop it!" she said.

"Tell me! I want to know!"

"I feel the same way about you," she said, "that I have always felt! You are the one who's changed!"

He sits this morning across the breakfast table from his son, who has made breakfast for them both, while outside the sun is shining thinly. Spring is slow in gaining strength this year. The middle of May already. The mornings are still chilly, like fall.

"Want to go outside?" Conrad asks.

"Sure." Although he really doesn't want to, shivers as he sits, hands around his coffee cup, on the patio steps. Conrad remarks about how warm it is. Also remarks that the lilacs are in bloom, and isn't this the time they usually fertilize the lawn? Not that he is looking for a job, but he was just curious.

A good opportunity to tell him. Start slow; say they won't fertilize this year; they are planning to sell the house, it is too big for them.

"It's always been too big, hasn't it?" Conrad asks.

Right. Only now there are other things to spend money on—college expenses next year, some investments he's been contemplating. The trip that Beth is taking.

"What trip?"

"Your mother's going away for a while."

"What d'you mean? You mean, not with you?"

"No. I can't get away right now."

"I don't get it. Who's she going with?"

"No one," he says. "She wants to go to Greece. Maybe Italy."

"What is this, Dad?" Conrad asks abruptly. "Has something happened?"

"No." There is nothing definite, no talk of divorce, and to say the words could make it so. "I've rented a house. In Evanston. Down by Centennial Park, near the lake."

"That doesn't sound like anything she'd like."

There is an uncomfortable pause. "The thing is, this trip could last for a while." Beautiful. Beautiful story. Just a couple of holes in it so big you could put your fist through them.

"What're you saying?" Con asks. "When is she leaving?"

"She's left," he says. "This morning, before you were up."

"Was she in such a damn hurry she couldn't even say good-by?" His voice is bitter. "Never mind. I know why."

"No, you don't."

"Yeah, I do. And I see your problem, too. You can't just come out with it, can you? First you have to check around, make sure there aren't any razor blades—"

"That's not funny! You think that's funny?"

An ugly silence, while they look at each other. Then Conrad looks away. "No," he says, "I'm sorry."

"You want the truth? I don't know why she left. And neither do you, because a lot of things happen in this world and people don't always know the answers! I'm no authority on her! You're no authority, either!"

Conrad stares at him, stricken.

In despair, Cal hears himself go on. "You're no authority, period. You just think you are. You make the judgments, don't you? But nobody's supposed to make a judgment on you! Do you think that's fair?"

"No," he whispers, his eyes fixed on Cal's face.

"I don't want you to say anything like that to me again," Cal says. "I don't like jokes about it."

390

"Dad, I'm sorry. I really am. I mean it."

"No." Abruptly his anger recedes. "I'm sorry, Con. I don't know what I'm yelling at you for."

"You were right. You ought to do that more often."

He gives a short laugh. "Oh, yeah?"

"No, really. Tell me to shape up." A slight pause, a change of key. "The way you used to do with him."

Cal looks up in surprise. "Buck needed it. You didn't. You were always so hard on yourself, I never had the heart. Besides," he says, "you were the good kid. The easy one to raise."

"Ah, Dad, don't."

"It's the truth. You were the one I never worried about. That was the problem. I should have been worrying. I wasn't even listening."

"I don't think I was putting out many signals, then," Conrad says carefully. "You couldn't have done anything."

"Maybe not." He gets up and walks to the edge of the patio, hands in his pockets. Behind him Conrad sighs.

"What happened, Dad? How did everything fall apart like this? Was it me? Dad, is it me now?"

"No," he says wearily. "It's nobody. Nobody's fault." Over and over this same lesson to be learned; it is the way things are.

"Listen," Conrad says, "it's not—somebody else?"

God, he is young. I forget sometimes how young he is.

"No," he says. "Nothing like that." And he comes back, sits beside him on the steps again. "I told you the truth," he says. "She wanted to go away for a while. Beyond that, I don't know."

"You know," Conrad says, "I used to figure you for a handle on everything. You knew it all, even though you grew up alone, with nobody looking after you."

"I was looked after. Where'd you get that idea?"

"Yeah, but nobody was responsible," he insists. "Nobody helped you with the decisions. I really admire you for that."

"Well, don't admire people too much," he says. "They disappoint you sometimes."

"I'm not disappointed," Conrad says. "I love you, man."

He winces, and his throat is tight, his eyes filled with sudden

tears. "I love you, too." He hooks an arm around his son's neck and
is at once caught in a fierce embrace. He strokes the dark head
wedged against his shoulder.

Conrad pulls away, straightening himself, arms on his knees,
head down. "You think she'll be back soon?"

"I don't know," he says.

"You think she's coming back at all?"

"Yeah, of course!" Of course she is. *At all, God!* That is not a
thought he needs to handle today.

"She'd better," Conrad says. He wipes his hand swiftly over his
eyes. "I'm a lousy cook."

No need for any more words. The sun is warm on his back. He
could fall asleep here, maybe he will, waiting for whatever comes
next.

EPILOGUE

LAZENBY's house looks the same to him; the red maple, tinged by
a late August frost, is the same size he remembered. Somehow he
has expected change. He gets out of the car. Nervous. He said
good-by to Berger today; maybe this is too much of a good thing.

Berger had raised his arms in the familiar gesture of confusion
and benediction. "Listen, you're my prize pupil. How about if I
use you in one of my ads?"

"Hey, don't start depending on me," he warned.

Berger just laughed.

Con had tried, then, to thank him properly. "I want you to know,"
he said, "that on your scale of one to ten, I give you a nine."

They laughed, and Conrad issued the invitation. "The house
we've moved into is only six blocks from here. You ought to stop by.
I mean, if you do that."

"What, visit friends? Yeah, I do it occasionally. Hey, you can do
the same, you know."

And right then he had gotten grabbed, missing him already. He
had taken off fast, before he acted like some six-year-old who just
fell off his bike.

Now, standing on Lazenby's front porch, he has that same funny feeling in the pit of his stomach. A tall blond girl answers his ring. Here is change at last: Lazenby's sister, Katy, all grown up. "Yes?" she asks. Then, "Connie! Oh my gosh, Ma! Guess who's here?"

They beam at him, Katy and her mother, and he is overcome with shyness.

"Joe around?"

"He's out in back, I think," Mrs. Lazenby says.

"I'll go see."

He moves off the porch and around to the backyard. Lazenby is practicing chip shots into a tree hole. "Forward press," Conrad advises.

Lazenby looks up. Then he lowers his head, steadying himself, dropping the shot neatly into the hole.

"How's it goin'?" Conrad asks.

"Okay." He leans the nine iron against a tree. "How about you?"

"Good."

"I heard you moved."

"Yeah. To Evanston."

"You like it?"

"Yeah, I like it fine. We've got a house over near the big U. In case you want to drop by sometime."

"Maybe I will."

They look at each other. Conrad says, "I've been thinking."

"Good." Lazenby nods approval.

"I'm thinking I'd like to beat you again at golf."

"That's interesting," Lazenby says, "considering you haven't beaten me yet. What makes you think you can?"

"That swing I just saw."

Lazenby laughs. There is a sudden, awkward silence.

"So," Conrad says. "How about it? You want to play?"

"I don't know," Lazenby says. "Ma's got a pile of things lined up for me to do today."

"Okay." He backs off at once. "Next week, maybe. Call me."

"You don't want me to try and get out of 'em, huh? I mean, well, it's worth asking."

Con grins. "Yeah, ask."

He waits in the backyard while Lazenby goes inside. He studies the shades of green, light and shadow that edge the lawn, those sharp, precise measurements, signifying order. And other things that make him feel good: the clean flight of the ball on a good drive, the graceful blue-and-orange swallows that swerve across the fairways. Gestures. He is learning to interpret them now. In a letter his mother wrote to his grandmother she said, "The Aegean is bluer than the Atlantic, and rough and bumpy. It looks just the way the boys drew it on those funny school maps." For she had saved them all—the maps and papers and a valentine trimmed with Kleenex lace that he had made for her—and packed them away in a box he had found in the basement. Do you save stuff like that if it means nothing to you?

Last year. Another time dimension. He had often punished her in his mind. *They tortured us at the hospital, you know. Mostly at night with boiling water from the ceiling. I always slept with the covers over my head.* Lies, to ease his own hurt.

A window opens behind him, and Lazenby says, "Ma says it's okay. She says first you got to come in, have some peanut-butter toast. She wants to rap with you."

He looks up at the window as Lazenby rolls his eyes. *Mothers.* Con grins. "Be right there."

He will see her when she comes home, maybe drive over to his grandmother's house some morning and say hello. Just hello, nothing important. No point in it, anyway, because she knows it all, knows just as he does that it is love, imperfect and unordered, that keeps them apart, even as it holds them somehow together.

He follows the sound of Lazenby's voice. "Hey, anybody seen my golf hat? Katy, you seen my golf hat?" Con picks up the nine iron, swinging it lightly through the grass as he walks toward the house.

Judith Guest

Much of the excitement surrounding the publication of *Ordinary People* stems from the fact that it is the first unsolicited manuscript (one not submitted by an agent or established author) published by its American publisher in twenty-seven years. Judith Guest recalls her family's reaction when the news came that her first novel had been accepted:

"Our house was a scene of total chaos. My eldest son went to the mailbox and from the kitchen I heard him say, 'Hey, here's a mailgram for Judith Guest. Who calls you that?' [Miss Guest is married to Larry LaVercombe.] I went flying out to the porch, snatched the mailgram right out of his hand, read it, and immediately burst into tears. My youngest son thought somebody had died. Then, when all three boys had read it, one kid chinned himself on the archway into the dining room, and another went tearing around the house yelling, 'We're gonna be rich! We're gonna be rich!' As for me, I was thrilled, awed, overwhelmed!"

The warmth and vitality of Judith Guest come through in her writing. "I wrote *Ordinary People* as a short story in 1972, then decided I wasn't ready to give those people up, and so I expanded it into a novel. If Conrad resembles anyone, I suppose it would be my brothers—not their experiences, but their personalities. I've thought about writing a sequel, because Con is still on my mind, but I'm working on two other novels now."

She began writing four years ago when her youngest son entered school. "Now," she says, "writing has become my escape, my terror, my compulsion."

Has her new-found career changed her life or her family's? "Once, when my eldest son wanted something done, he said, 'Why do you always have to be writing that dumb book?' But later he said, 'I'm sorry I called your book dumb.' Lucky for me, all of them are very patient."

A BAG OF MARBLES

A condensation of the book by
JOSEPH JOFFO

Translated from the French by
MARTIN SOKOLINSKY
and JUDITH LANDRY

Illustrated by Ben Wohlberg

PUBLISHED BY MICHAEL JOSEPH, LONDON

Here, in one of the most unusual memoirs to come out of World War II, is Joseph Joffo's account of two high-spirited Jewish boys fleeing the dreaded Gestapo in Nazi-occupied France.

Joe was only ten years old, his brother Maurice twelve, when their father told them they must leave Paris—alone—and escape to the Unoccupied Zone. So, with little money, no papers, but unlimited grit, these two cocky kids set off on what was to become a three-year odyssey across the French countryside.

Incredibly, they managed to enjoy themselves as they bluffed their way to safety time and time again. But they also knew stark, stomach-wrenching fear, for they travelled with the certain knowledge that one false step would land them in a German death camp.

Chapter 1

I rolled the marble around at the bottom of my pocket.

It was my favourite marble and I never parted with it. Oddly enough it was the worst-looking of the lot, nothing in comparison with the magnificent whirling specimens that I would gaze at in the window of Monsieur Ruben's shop at the corner of the rue Ramey. My marble was made of clay, and the glaze had chipped off here and there, making it rough in places and somehow patterned, like a diminutive version of our classroom globe. But I was fond of it; it was good to have the earth all tucked away in one's pocket, with the mountains and seas.

"Come on, don't take all day about it."

Maurice was waiting, sitting on the pavement in front of the delicatessen, his socks as usual so hopelessly twisted that Father calls him "the walking accordion". Between his legs was a little pile of marbles, three in a triangle with the fourth on top.

Old Madame Epstein watched us from the doorway, a Bulgarian grandmother wrinkled like a prune, with the coppery complexion that came from the wind of the steppe. She sat there in the doorway, on her straw-bottomed chair, smiling at the children on their way home from school. People said that she had crossed Europe on foot, fleeing from pogrom to pogrom until finally, when she came to this part of the eighteenth *arrondissement* of Paris, she had met up with other fugitives from the East: Russians, Rumanians, Czechs, intellectuals and craftsmen. Her hands rumpled the worn serge of her apron, as black as my own. In those days all schoolchildren wore black, a childhood in mourning. It was a foreboding in 1941.

"But what are you *up* to?"

Not surprisingly, I was hesitating. Maurice was horribly good. I had shot seven times already and missed completely. His pockets were bulging with marbles he had won at break. I was down to my last one, my beloved.

"I'm not going to crouch here all night, you know," he growled.

The marble trembled slightly in the palm of my hand; I shot and missed. I should have known that a miracle was unlikely. Now it was time to go home.

The shop fronts along the rue Marcadet were heaving weirdly. I turned my face to the left hoping to avoid Maurice's eagle eye.

"Stop sniffling," said Maurice promptly.

"I'm not."

"When you look away I know that's what you're doing."

I gave my eyes a cursory wipe and walked faster. We'd be getting a ticking-off anyway; we should have been home half an hour ago.

Home was in sight now—the shop on the rue Clignancourt with the big, broad lettering on the front: JOFFO – COIFFEUR.

Maurice nudged me. "Here you are, you idiot."

I looked at him and took the marble he was handing me.

A brother is someone who gives you back your last marble when he's won all the rest.

So I got back my miniature planet. Tomorrow I would win a whole pile of marbles from him. He mustn't be allowed to think that he could bòss me around just because he was two years older. After all, I was ten now.

Then we went into the barber's shop and were greeted by the familiar smells. Every childhood has its own particular smells, but mine seemed permeated with the whole range from lavender to violet. I can still see the jars on the shelves, still smell the clean towels, still hear the snipping of the scissors.

Business was brisk when we came in. As usual, Duvallier tweaked my ear. He seemed to spend his whole life in the shop. He was old and a widower, living in a small fourth-floor flat which was probably far from gay. So he came down the street and spent the afternoon with the Israelites. When all the customers had gone, he would settle into his usual barber's chair. "Just give me a shave," he used to say. It was Father who used to shave him. My spell-binding father, king of the street. My doomed father.

We did our homework; I had no watch in those days, but it couldn't have taken more than forty-five seconds. Then we hung around in the bedroom so that Mother wouldn't catch us and send us back to work. Then we went out again.

Porte de Clignancourt, 1941. Paris was a children's paradise. A murky city lit by shop windows, with strips of sky above, the narrow pavements blocked by dustbins to be climbed on, hallways to hide in, doorbells to ring—we had everything, horses and carts, the flower-woman, and the terrace cafés in summer, a maze, a sea of intersecting streets. "Where to?" Maurice asked when we were outside.

I was about to answer when I saw them coming. You couldn't miss them. Two huge men, dressed in black and swathed in complex leather straps, their high boots polished and shining.

"SS," Maurice murmured.

They moved slowly and stiffly, as if on parade.

"A haircut, d'you think?"

The thought struck us both simultaneously. We glued ourselves together in front of the shop window as if we were Siamese twins, and the two Germans went in.

We started to laugh. What we had blocked out was a small notice stuck to the window, saying, in black letters, *Yiddish Gescheft*.

Inside, in the deepest silence ever to descend upon a barber's shop, two SS men sat primly among Jewish clients, waiting to bare their defenceless napes to my Jewish father or to my Jewish brothers.

Outside, two small Jewish boys were doubled up with laughter.

HENRI BRUSHED the bits of hair from Bibi Cohen's collar; Bibi got up from his chair and went over to the till, behind which Maurice and I were now lurking anxiously. Perhaps we had gone a bit far.

Henri turned to the first German.

"I believe you're next, monsieur."

The SS man settled himself in the chair, his cap on his knee.

"Shall I make it fairly short?"

401

"Oui, la raie à droite, s'il vous plaît." (Yes, the parting on the right, please.)

I nearly choked when I heard that: a French-speaking German! He had a tiny pistol in a highly-polished holster. In a few minutes he would realize where he was and pull out the gun and start shooting and massacre the lot of us, even Mother, upstairs.

By now I was terribly frightened. I remember only one thing: it was Albert who took the plunge while sprinkling lotion on his client's shorn neck.

"This war's not much fun, is it?"

The SS man gave a start. It must have been the first time any Frenchman had spoken to him, and he jumped at the opportunity. "It certainly is not."

They went on talking; the others joined in and the conversation became quite friendly. The German translated for his mate, shaking the head that Henri was trying to control. It wouldn't do to slash the cheek of this lord of the Teutonic race.

An advance glow spread over my bottom from the hiding that would come the minute the Germans left the shop.

"It's you now, monsieur." My father was dealing with the second one.

Samuel came in.

He would often call by in the afternoon, on a friendly visit. He ran a junk stall in the street market down the road. His speciality was old clocks, but he had miscellaneous jumble on his stall as well.

He was in excellent spirits. "Hello, everybody."

Father flicked a towel open sharply before putting it round the SS man's neck. Samuel had just enough time to catch sight of the uniform. His eyes grew rounder than my marbles. *"Oh,"* he said. "Oho, oho . . . ."

"Yes," said Albert, "it is rather crowded today."

Samuel smoothed his moustache. "Never mind," he said. "I'll come back later."

As he left he seemed to be walking on eggshells.

Thirty seconds later, from the rue Eugène Sue to the borders of Saint-Ouen, from the Yiddish restaurants to the backs of the

kosher butchers, everybody knew that *le père* Joffo had become the Gestapo's official barber.

In the shop, the conversation grew increasingly friendly. The SS man glimpsed our two protruding heads in the mirror. "Are those your little boys?"

Father smiled. "Yes, they're little horrors."

The SS man nodded. "Yes," he said, "the war's a shocking business. It's the Jews' fault."

Father gave two final snips with one eye closed like an artist's. A flick of the wrist to remove the towel, a quick proffering of the mirror. The SS man beamed with satisfaction. "Very good. Thank you."

They went up to the till to pay, and Father went behind the desk to give them their change. Squeezed against him, I saw his face high above me, beaming. "Are you pleased with your haircuts?"

"They're excellent."

"Well," said my father, "before you leave, I'd like to tell you that everyone in this shop is Jewish."

He had done some acting when he was young; when he told us stories he used to mime with sweeping gestures. At that instant, no actor could have stood behind the footlights with greater majesty than Joffo behind his counter. In the shop, time seemed to stand still. Duvallier put down his newspaper. We got to our feet. Suddenly the SS man's lips seemed thinner.

"I was talking about rich Jews."

The change clinked against the counter; then there was a noise of boots. We were frozen, petrified; as if a wicked fairy had changed us into statues. The Germans had probably reached the end of the street when the spell was finally broken. My father allowed his hand to stray over my head and Maurice's, and I knew that I had escaped a thrashing. I closed my eyes so that my brother wouldn't see me cry twice in the same day.

AS SHE DID every evening, Mother had come to inspect our teeth, our ears, our nails. Plumping up the pillow, she tucked us in, kissed us and left the room. And, as usual, no sooner had the door closed behind her than my pillow flew through the darkened room and hit Maurice, who cursed like a trooper.

I listened intently. A rustling of sheets told me that Maurice had left his bed and was preparing to pounce. I tensed my negligible biceps, gasping with joy and terror; I was ready for the battle and . . .

The light.

Dazzled, Maurice leapt into his bed and I tried to give an impression of deep slumber.

It was Father. Pretence was pointless; he was never taken in.

"Next instalment of the story," he announced.

That was the best thing that could happen. All children love stories but these were something special. The hero was my own grandfather whose moustachioed face peered from a daguerreotype in the living room. My grandfather had twelve sons; he was a rich and generous man respected by the inhabitants of a large village in Russian Bessarabia. He lived and reigned happily over his tribe until the pogroms began.

I was weaned on stories of his adventures. I saw rifle butts smashing doors, breaking windows; peasants fleeing wildly, houses in flames. I saw a whirlwind of sabre blades, the breath of charging horses, the glint of spurs and, towering over the whole scene, the gigantic figure of my grandsire, Jacob Joffo.

My grandfather was not the kind of man to stand around while his friends were massacred. In the evening he would put aside his beautiful robe, and put on the boots and clothing of a *muzhik*. He blackened his face with soot, then set out alone to the area of the soldiers' barracks. He would lie in wait in the shadows and then, when he saw three or four of them, without haste or anger, he would knock their heads against the walls, then go home, humming a Yiddish air.

We listened that night as we always did: open-mouthed. The lamp threw shadows on the wallpaper, and Father's arms were seen waving on the ceiling. As the massacres intensified the walls became peopled with refugees, who left dark, rainy towns with strange architecture, travelled through an inferno of tortuous passes and freezing steppes until, one day, they crossed one final frontier, and came upon a beautiful plain, steeped in sunshine, with birds singing, wheat fields, trees, and a village with red roofs and a church steeple. Over the doorway of the biggest house was written: *Liberté, Egalité, Fraternité.* Then all the refugees put down their bundles and the fear left their eyes, for they knew that they had arrived in France.

I have never found the love of the French for their own land surprising. But I know that no one ever loved that country as much as my father, born eight thousand kilometres away. We never went past the town hall without Father's grip tightening over my hand. He would point to the letters on the façade.

"You know what those words up there mean."

By the age of five I could repeat them to him.

"That's it, Joseph. And as long as they're written up there we'll be all right here."

And it was true that we were all right. One evening when the Occupation had begun, Mother had raised the question. "You don't think that there will be trouble, now that they're here?"

We knew what Hitler had already done in Germany, Austria, Czechoslovakia and Poland, where race laws were coming in one after the other.

Father made his broad comforting gesture. "No, not here. Not in France—ever."

But his confidence had been shaken when they had brought in the law requiring identity cards and, most of all, since two men in long raincoats had stuck up that notice on the shop window.

"Good night, children."

Father closed the door again, and we were left snug in the dark. It was just an ordinary night, a night in 1941.

Chapter 2

"Your turn now, Jo."

I came up to the table, holding my jacket. It was eight o'clock in the morning and still pitch-dark outside. Mother was seated at the table, holding a needle and some black cotton; her hands were

406

shaking. Under the lampshade, Maurice was standing, smoothing down the yellow star sewn to his left lapel and embroidered with the word: JUIF.

Maurice looked at me. "Don't cry. You'll get your medal too."

Of course I would get one; everybody in the whole neighbourhood would get one. And once you had one, there was not much for you to do: you couldn't go to the cinema or on the train; possibly you wouldn't even be able to play marbles any more. It could be that you no longer had the right to go to school. Now that would not be so bad! Mother nipped the thread with her teeth, and I was branded.

Father had finished shaving, and the smell of soap and aftershave wafted in with him. He stopped me before I reached the door.

"You've got to be top of the class now. And you know why."

"I know," Maurice answered. "To make Hitler sick."

Father laughed. "You could put it like that," he said.

It was cold outside; our wooden soles clattered on the paving. Maurice marched ahead, puffing hard so that he could see his own breath. The marbles clattered in his pockets. Less than two hundred yards away were the school railings, the courtyard with its chestnut trees, black in winter.

"Hey, Joffo!"

It was Zérati calling me. He had been my friend since infants' school. He ran to catch up with me, his nose red with cold.

"*Salut.*"

"*Salut.*" He stared at my chest, and his eyes grew round. "Goodness, you're lucky," he finally murmured. "That star is lovely."

Maurice laughed and so did I. I felt a wave of relief. All three of us walked into the courtyard. There were groups of children running madly in and out of the columns.

"Hey, you lot! Have you seen Joffo?" Zérati didn't mean to be unkind. He just wanted to show me off a bit to the other boys in the school.

The others formed a ring around me. Kraber smiled. "You're not the only one—some of them in the second year have got stars

407

too." There was a stirring in the shadows and two unsmiling faces pushed through.

"Hey, are you a yid?"

It would have been hard to say no when it was written on your lapel.

"It's because of the yids that we're in the war."

Zérati didn't flinch. He couldn't have weighed more than five stone, but he turned to face the bigger boy.

"You're a real idiot, you are. Is it Jo's fault that there's a war?"

"That's right. The yids should be thrown out."

Mutterings. What was happening? I was a child like any other, with marbles, spankings, lessons to learn. Then suddenly they stuck a few square inches of cloth on me and I became a Jew.

What was a Jew anyway? I felt anger swelling up in me.

The ring tightened around me. "Look at his beak!"

On the corner of the rue Marcadet there was a huge poster. It showed a spider crawling over a globe, a huge hairy spider with bulging eyes, and a fearful nose like the blade of a scimitar. Underneath, it said, "The Jew attempting to take over the world." The poster didn't worry us in the slightest. We didn't look like that. I was rather fair, with blue eyes and a nose like everybody else, so it was simple: I wasn't the Jew.

"What's the matter with my nose? Has it changed since yesterday?"

Before the big oaf could answer the bell rang. I saw Maurice at the other end of the courtyard. He looked angry too.

The first lesson was geography. Monsieur Boulier hadn't questioned me for a long time and I was nervous. His eyes slid over us but they didn't stop at me. It was Raffard who went to the board and bit the dust. That seemed bad to me: perhaps I didn't count any more. What did they all have against me?

"Take out your exercise books. Date in the margin. Heading: 'The Rhone Trench'."

I had to have it out with him. I needed to know whether I still existed.

Boulier had an obsession for silence. When he heard talking or a pen falling, he would point his finger at the culprit and the

408

sentence would come down like the guillotine: "You will stand in the corner during break and conjugate the verb 'to make less noise'."

I put my slate down on the corner of the desk. Cautiously, I pushed it. The slate teetered then fell with a crash.

He was writing on the blackboard and turned round. He looked down at the slate on the floor, then at me, and his gaze became vacant. Slowly, he picked up the big ruler and pointed to the map. "The Rhone Trench separates the ancient mountain masses of the Massif Central from the younger mountains . . . ."

The lesson had begun; and I saw that, as far as I was concerned, school had ended.

At break in the courtyard I was suddenly at the centre of a whirlwind.

"Yid! Dirty yid!"

Someone shoved me from behind and I bounced onto someone else's chest; there was another push and I went sailing backward. I managed not to fall, and tried to break the chain. I saw Maurice fighting twenty yards away. I lashed out and took a bad punch on the ear. The teacher in charge blew his whistle and everything stopped.

"All right, what's going on here? Now get out and fast!"

I felt my ear swelling. Maurice had a bloody handkerchief knotted round his knee. We couldn't exchange a word; it was time to go back to our classrooms.

Over the blackboard, was a portrait of Marshal Pétain. A fine, worthy-looking face topped by a *kepi*. Below were the words, "I keep my promises, even those made by others." I wondered who could have promised to make me wear a star.

What I remember of that morning—more than the blows, more than the indifference of the adults—was that feeling of not being able to understand. I was the same colour as they were; my face was the same. I'd heard of different religions, and that people had fought about this long ago, but I had no religion. On Thursdays, I even went to the church club with the other children of the neighbourhood. Where then was the difference?

Eleven thirty. I put on my coat and went out. Maurice was

waiting for me. We didn't say anything; there was nothing to say. We went up the street together.

"Jo!" Somebody was running after me. It was Zérati, all out of breath. He was holding a small linen bag. He proffered it to me.

"I'll swap," he said.

"What for?"

"For your star."

It had been sewn with big stitches and the thread wasn't very strong. I worked one finger underneath and tore it off. "Here you are."

Zérati's eyes shone.

My star. For a bag of marbles. That was my first business deal.

FATHER hung up his overall on the coatrack behind the kitchen door. Before sitting down at table he inspected my swollen ear and Maurice's knee. Plunging his spoon into his noodles, he swallowed with difficulty and looked at my mother, whose hands were trembling on either side of her plate.

"No school this afternoon," he pronounced.

Maurice and I dropped our spoons.

"Do you mean it? But what about my satchel?"

"I'll get it. Don't you worry about it. You're free this afternoon, but be back before dark. I have something to say to you."

I remember the joy that flooded over me. A whole afternoon to ourselves, while the others were mouldering over maths we would revel in the joys of our street kingdom.

We ran up towards the Sacré-Coeur; there were long flights of steps there with handrails made expressly for children to slide down. In front of the Sacré-Coeur there were German officers wearing long capes, laughing and taking photos. We made a detour to avoid them.

At Boulevard Barbès we sat down to catch our breath. "Shall we have a go at the till tonight?" Maurice said.

I nodded.

Every now and again, when everyone was asleep, we would creep downstairs to the shop, barefoot. Not a glimmer of light filtered through the shutters. In the darkness my fingers moved over the packets of razor blades, until they reached the cash desk. There were always piles of loose coins in that drawer . . . .

We agreed: tonight would be one of those nights.

During our hours of wandering, we forgot what had happened that morning; we loved to amble through the neighbourhood smoking eucalyptus cigarettes. In a France deprived of tobacco or at best limited to a tobacco ration, I would go into a chemist and gaze glumly at the proprietor.

"I'd like some eucalyptus cigarettes please. It's for my grandfather; he has asthma." Usually it worked.

Maurice got up suddenly. "We'd better go home, it's getting dark."

It was true; the first evening mists were rising behind the dome of the Sacré-Coeur. At our feet the city spread like the already fading hair of an ageing man. I didn't know that I wouldn't be seeing that familiar landscape again through a child's eyes, or that, in a few hours' time, I would no longer be a child.

WE RETURNED that evening to find the shop closed. Many of our friends had already left Paris some time ago; Father and Mother used to whisper privately and I overheard names of regular customers who had gone. Other words cropped up: *Ausweis, Kommandantur*, demarcation line . . . and names of cities, too: Marseilles, Nice, Casablanca. My brothers had left at the beginning of the year. I hadn't really understood why.

Still, this was the first time that Father had actually closed the metal shutters in the middle of the week. He was in our room stretched out on Maurice's bed; his hands were clasped under his head looking at our room as if he were trying to see it through our eyes. Maurice and I sat on the other bed and he began a monologue that still echoes in my ears.

"Many evenings," he began "I've told you stories, true stories that members of your family played a part in. Today I realize that I've never told you about myself." He smiled and went on. "When I was little I lived in Russia, where there was a very powerful leader called the czar. This czar was like the Germans today; he liked to make war, and he had the idea of sending emissaries to the villages to round up little boys like me and take them away to camps where they became soldiers. They were taught to march and obey orders without question and also to kill enemies. So, when I was old enough to go, my father spoke to me like . . . ." his voice grew hoarse, "like I'm doing, tonight."

Outside, it was almost dark; but none of us made a move to light the lamp. Father went on. "'My son,' he said 'do you want to be a soldier of the czar?' I said No.

"'So you don't have much choice,' he said. 'You're no longer a child; you're going to leave, and you'll cope very well because you're no fool.'

"I said I would go, and after saying goodbye to him and my sisters, I left. I was seven years old.

"I earned a living and kept out of the hands of the Russians; and believe me, it wasn't easy. For a crust of bread I shovelled snow with a shovel that was twice as big as I was. I learned to use scissors and became a barber; three days in one town, a year in another, and finally, I ended up here, where I've been happy.

"Your mother's story is a bit like mine. I met her in Paris, we fell in love, we got married and you were born." He hesitated, and his voice became less clear. "Do you know why I'm telling you all this?"

"Yes," said Maurice. "It's because we're going to go away, too."

Father took a deep breath. "Yes, boys. Today it's your turn. The Germans are getting tougher with us all the time. I know that you aren't afraid, but there's one thing to bear in mind: when you're not the strongest, when you're two against ten, twenty or a hundred, the bravest thing to do is to swallow your pride and run away."

A lump was rising in my throat, but I knew that I wouldn't cry; perhaps even the day before my tears would have flowed, but now things were different.

"What about you and Mother?"

He leant forward to place a hand on each of our shoulders. "Henri and Albert are in the free zone. You are leaving tonight. Your mother and I have a few matters to sort out here and then we'll leave." He laughed. "Don't worry—the Russians didn't get me when I was seven, so the Germans won't manage it now that I'm fifty."

I relaxed: so we were going to be separated, the war could not last for ever, then we would come together again.

"Now," said my father, "you must listen carefully. Take the *Métro* to the Gare d'Austerlitz, and buy a ticket for the town of Dax. From there, you'll have to cross into unoccupied France. You won't have the papers, but just outside Dax there's a village called Hagetmau; there are men there who will take you across. You're safe as soon as you get to the other side. Your brothers are in Menton—it's just near the Italian frontier. You'll find them."

Maurice piped up. "How do we get on the train?"

"Don't worry, I'm going to give you each five thousand francs. Make sure you don't lose it or let it get stolen."

Five thousand francs! I'd never had more than ten francs in my pocket. What a fortune!

"Look, there is one last thing you must get straight," Father said. "You are Jews but you must never admit it, do you understand? *Never!*"

We nodded in unison.

"You mustn't even whisper it under your breath—always deny it. *Always!* Are you a Jew, Joseph?"

"No."

With a sharp crack, his hand landed on my cheek. He had never struck me before. "Don't lie. Are you a Jew, Joseph?"

"*No!*"

My father rose to his feet. "That's it," he said. "I think you know what you're up against."

My cheek was still smarting, but one question kept running through my mind.

"Father, what is a Jew?"

Father scratched his head. "Well, it's rather embarrassing to have to say this, Joseph, but I'm really not very sure. Long ago, we had a country; we were driven out, so we scattered all over the place. There are times, like the present, when this still happens. You might say that the hunting season is on again, so

we have to move off till the hunter gets tired. Well, it's time fo
supper, and you'll be leaving immediately afterwards."

I remember the clink of spoons against the rims of bowls, th
murmur of voices asking someone to pass the salt, the water, tha
sort of thing. Our two haversacks were on a chair near the doo
stuffed with underwear, sponge-bags, folded handkerchiefs.

The clock in the corridor struck seven.

"Well then," Father said, "You're all ready. The money's i
the pocket with the zip, and so is a piece of paper with you
brothers' address. Say goodbye to Mother and off you go."

She helped us into our coats and knotted our scarves; she gav
our socks a last pull. She was smiling all the time, and all the tim
the tears streamed down her face. I felt her damp cheeks agains
my forehead.

Then Father broke into the least convincing burst of laughte
I'd ever heard. "Now really," he exclaimed. "Anyone would thin
they were going off for ever and were just little babies. Off yo
go, children, and see you soon." A brief kiss, and he thrust u
towards the staircase.

Long afterwards, when everything was over I learned that m
father remained standing there, rocking gently backward an
forward with his eyes closed, nursing a grief as old as time.

Chapter 3

At the Gare d'Austerlitz there were hardly any outbound train
and the platforms were seething. I followed Maurice clutching m
haversack.

The bells of the luggage trolleys rang out under the glass roof
bicycles were tied together in stacks. We positioned ourselve
behind a charging porter who plunged into the crowd, pushing hi
trolley before him. This was a good move for us because, a secon
later, we found ourselves at the booking-office window. Th
queue twisted away like a snake.

"Which of the five people at the front looks the nicest?"
Maurice asked.

414

"The young bloke in the third place, with the polo neck."

Maurice went up to him. "M'sieur, my little brother's got a bad
eg . . . do you think you could . . ."

The fellow inspected us sharply. For a split second I was afraid
e was going to refuse. Then he made a weary gesture.

"Go ahead," he said. "Goodness knows when my train will
eave."

Maurice thanked him and entered the front of the queue.

"Two singles to Dax, third class."

I noticed that no one paid any attention to us; two rather
orlorn children alone in a crowd; I supposed they had worries of
heir own, and thought that our parents were somewhere around
he station.

Maurice pointed to the departure boards. "Platform seven," he
aid.

Steam filled the vast hall, the tops of the iron columns
isappeared into the smoke, and the train drew in. Maurice
ursed. The coaches were jam-packed. There were three empty
ompartments reserved for German soldiers. The empty seats were
nost enticing, but it would be courting disaster.

"Come on, we'll try here."

The steps were very high. I worked my way along the corridor.
'wo men argued about reserved seats, waving cards bearing the
ame number. The tension was mounting; it was pointless to look
or seats.

"Here's a place," said Maurice, "It won't be too bad." It was a
ttle space walled in on one side by a huge cardboard suitcase.
Ve put our haversacks on the floor and sat on them, leaning
gainst the partition.

We settled down side by side. I peered into my haversack and
ame up triumphantly with a package containing an enormous
am sandwich; Maurice had one too.

"Keep your head down while you eat that, or there'll be a
iot."

After two mouthfuls I was thirsty. I would have given ten years
or a glass of ice-cold *grenadine*. For the first time I had a fortune
n my pocket and I couldn't even treat myself to a *grenadine*. Our

415

ten thousand francs had been considerably dinted by the price of the tickets, and what was left had to last for some time. But money could be earned: when we reached the unoccupied zone we would look after ourselves somehow.

Our train started. We were off. I stood up and glued my forehead to the window. A tangle of rails sailed by; we slid under footbridges, past piles of coal gleaming in the moonlight. Around us people were talking. Seated on the big cardboard suitcase, a kindly-looking elderly lady was observing us; she looked like the grandmothers in the pictures in my reading-book; white hair pinned in a neat bun, blue eyes, wrinkles, lace collar, grey stockings.

"Are you going far, children?" She was smiling. "Are you travelling all alone? Don't you have any parents?"

Maurice mumbled into his sandwich. "Yes, we do. We're going to meet them. They're ill; I mean my mother is."

I was almost angry with Maurice for lying to her, but he was right—for the time being we had to mistrust everybody.

Still smiling, she leaned down to the wicker basket to pull out a bottle of fizzy lemonade. "I daresay you're thirsty after that sandwich."

Maurice unfroze. "I am rather," he admitted.

Lovely lemonade tickled my tongue and palate. We were moving fast now. Beyond my own reflection in the window pane I now saw flat land, rolling away at every curve. Maurice closed his eyes; his head was resting against the door of the compartment and wobbling with the vibrations. Farther on, behind the grandmother, there was laughter; snatches of song. We were nice and snug; there was nothing to worry about until Dax, where the Germans would be checking papers. But I mustn't think about that, yet.

There were eight lucky people in the compartment. One of them, a man whose face I could just distinguish was looking at me with sadness in his eyes. He had on a cassock. I don't know why, but the sight of him reassured me. Whether this train was taking me to life or death, I was going to fall asleep under the protective gaze of an old priest . . . .

DAX.

The name lashed my ear. The brakes screeched and the blocked wheels slid on a little farther and then stopped.

Maurice was up; his face the colour of aluminium in the early light.

I gazed around me. The corridor was almost empty. In the compartment behind me there were empty seats, but the priest was still there.

Maurice anticipated my question. "Lots of them jumped off while the train was slowing down."

The loudspeaker blared out a long sentence in German and I saw a dozen German policemen on the platform, coming towards us. Maurice grabbed me by the arm and we went into the compartment and sat next to the priest. He was pale, too, and his whiskers had sprouted during the night. Next to the window, a gaunt woman was already clutching her pass; I could see the round black stamps and signatures. The grandmother was also there, her suitcase in the rack above her head.

"*Halte!*"

The shout came from outside and we rushed to the window. At the other end of the train a man was running in the open. A whistle blew and a group of soldiers fanned out across the tracks. The man stopped as they shot, but he wasn't hit. He raised his arms and two soldiers hustled him off towards the waiting room, I saw one of them club him with a rifle butt. Others were being caught too; helmets and rifles glinted in the dawn light.

Suddenly I realized that the priest's hand was on my shoulder. Slowly, we went back to our seats. The train was quiet now; the Germans had blocked the exits.

The words came to my lips of their own accord. "Father, we haven't any papers."

He looked at me and smiled. "If you go around looking so frightened the Germans are going to know without your telling them."

"Papers . . . ."

They were still a long way off, at the beginning of the carriage; there seemed to be a lot of them. I could understand quite a bit of

417

what they were saying; Father and Mother spoke Yiddish and was very like German.

"Papers . . . ." They were coming closer. The doors slid as the opened and closed. The grandmother had her eyes shut.

Now they were in the next compartment; I had a curious feelin in my stomach. I mustn't show fear. I dug into my haversac extracted the remainder of my sandwich and was biting into when the door opened. Maurice glanced up with beatif innocence; I observed this with a surge of admiration.

"Papers . . . ."

The gaunt woman held out the white sheet. My far-away hea was beating powerfully. The German scrutinized the sheet paper, then extended his hand towards the grandmother wh handed him a green paper and an identity card.

"Is that all?"

She smiled and nodded.

"Take your suitcases and go out into the corridor."

The priest stood up, took down the suitcase and th grandmother went out. One of the policemen took her basket. I the light of day, her flat white chignon shone for a split secon then she disappeared behind the uniformed backs. Goodby grandmother. Thank you, and good luck.

The priest showed his papers. I continued chewing. Th German looked carefully at the photo and compared it with th original.

"I've lost a little weight," said the priest, "but it *is* me.

A faint smile flickered across our German's face. "What with th war and the rationing . . . ." He handed back the paper. "Bu priests don't eat much."

"There you're mistaken, at least in my case."

The German laughed and pointed towards me. The pries flicked my cheek. "The children are with me."

The door had closed after a lightning salute from the jovia German. My knees began to tremble. The priest stood up.

"We can get out now. And since you're with me, we'll hav breakfast together. What do you think?"

I noticed that Maurice was more affected than I was; you coul

418

at him to pulp without producing a tear, but at the first pleasant ord he simply crumpled.

The buffet was a gloomy place, high ceilinged, with marble-pped tables. Waiters stood waiting, holding shiny trays.

"We'll have *café au lait* and bread and butter," the priest said. But I warn you—the coffee is made from barley, the sugar is ccharine, and there isn't any milk.

I coughed to clear my throat. "Maurice and I would like to ank you for what you've done."

For a moment, he was disconcerted. "But what have I done?"

Maurice took over, a hint of mischievousness in his voice. "You ed to save us by saying that we were with you."

Slowly, the priest shook his head. "I didn't lie. You were with e just as all the children of the world are with me. That's one of e reasons why I'm a priest—to be with them." There was a oment's silence then the priest asked, "And now where are you oing?"

I felt that Maurice was hesitant, but I couldn't let this priest ink that we didn't trust him. "We're going to Hagetmau to try cross the demarcation line there."

The priest put down the cup.

"I understand," he said. He took a big wallet from his pocket nd produced a slip of paper from among the religious pictures. Vith a blunt pencil he scrawled a name and address on it and anded it to us.

"You'll get across," he said. "And if you should ever need me st write to me."

Maurice put it into his pocket. "We're going, Father. There ay be a bus for Hagetmau soon, and we should hurry."

He held out his hand and we shook it in turn. Maurice headed or the door. But I felt a pang of unease. I turned back to the riest, there was something I had to ask him.

"Father, what did they do to the old lady?"

"Nothing. She didn't have any papers, so they sent her back ome. That's all."

Outside Maurice was waiting for me. There was a ray of cold unlight and he had lost the wan look he had had earlier. I felt

better too—as if the light had washed away the exhaustion of t[h]
journey.

The bus station wasn't far. The man behind the counter didr[n]
bother to look up.

"Two tickets to Hagetmau please."

Here we are again with two tickets in our pockets. We haven['t]
much money left, but that doesn't matter: free France isn't far o[f]

Chapter 4

The bus stopped just outside the village. On the way, a c[ar]
filled with German officers had passed us. I was briefly terrifie[d]
but they paid no attention to our rattletrap bus.

The sky had cleared, the countryside was very flat and t[he]
houses huddled around the church. The air was sharp and t[he]
wind seemed to roar straight into our lungs.

Maurice hitched up his haversack. "Let's go!"

We marched briskly across a narrow bridge over a tiny river,
mere trickle of water, mostly boulders.

The main street ran slightly uphill. Our wooden heels clattere[d]
on the uneven cobblestones and we came to a fountain under
porch. There wasn't a soul on the streets; an occasional dog sniffe[d]
our calves. The place smelled of cows and wood-smoke. Tw[o]
grocery shops on the main street, both closed.

"Goodness," growled Maurice, "they're a lively lot."

The silence was beginning to alarm me, too. After the din of th[e]
train and the commotion of arrival, we felt as though someon[e]
had stuffed cotton into our ears.

Over our heads, the church clock struck. "Of course," Mauric[e]
said, "it's midday and everybody's eating."

That was a word he should never have mentioned: th[e]
sandwiches had vanished long since, the morning coffee was lo[st]
in history. When I closed my eyes, I could see steak and chips.

We wandered aimlessly round the village and came acro[ss]
another square, smaller than the first. Opposite a building tha[t]
must have been the town hall was a café-restaurant. I looke[d]

wards Maurice anxiously. "Perhaps we could get something to eat?"

Maurice hesitated a little. "O.K." he said finally. "No point in ropping dead from starvation."

The streets might have been empty, but not the café. At least a undred people were crowded around the tables. Three aitresses were running between them carrying plates and utlery. The place was heated by an enormous earthenware stove nd there were three groaning coatracks behind the door.

"What can I do for you boys?" One of the waitresses, red-faced nd dishevelled, pushed her hair out of her eyes.

Maurice replied, "We'd like to eat."

She pushed us to a bare wooden table on which she put two lates. "We've got lentils with bacon and stuffed aubergine. For essert, there's cheese and fruit. Is that all right? I can give you adishes with salt to start with."

"Yes, fine."

She was off towards the kitchen as another waitress emerged ith a plate of lentils in each hand; there wasn't much bacon on nem.

I looked at the other diners. They weren't country people, more ke men and women from towns. There were children too, even ery young ones.

Maurice leant over his plate. "We'll be bumping into half the ie Marcadet in here."

They must have been people like us, Jews on the run. But what ere they waiting for? Perhaps it was going to be harder than we ought.

Our waitress came back with three radishes at the bottom of a owl. She placed the salt cellar between us.

I asked her, "Is it always as crowded as this?"

She shrugged. "Believe me, the day that the Krauts put that ne a kilometre from here, they made certain parties richer than would have thought possible . . . ." I followed her eyes and saw ie *patronne* fastidiously drying a coffee cup behind the bar. She ad carefully dyed hair and wore jewellery.

"With what she makes here, she could spend her whole life at ie hairdresser's."

She cleared away our empty plates. Nothing goes faster tha radishes when you're hungry.

"What about . . . is it easy to get across?"

She shrugged again. "Most of the time they get across witho trouble . . . only you've got to wait until it's dark because it's to dangerous during the day. Excuse me."

She came back immediately with the lentils, put them in fron of us and went away again. The aubergine that followed w: stringy and the stuffing non-existent. The cheese was flat and dr the apples were withered, but our waitress made the mistake leaving the basket near our table. The apples ended up in m haversack.

Gradually the dining room emptied. We paid our bill, whic seemed outrageously high, and went out again into the streets Hagetmau. A sharp, unpleasant wind was still blowing.

"Listen," said Maurice, "we'll try and cross this evening– there's no point in staying here. So let's find out where we ca get a *passeur* and how much he'll want."

I couldn't quarrel with that. Fifty yards away was a boy about fifteen on a huge black bicycle with a wicker basket. H stopped in front of a house, rang the doorbell, handed over package from his basket and said loudly, "Good morning, Madam Hudot. Here's your order." Whistling, he got back onto h bicycle and watched us coming towards him. He had red hand and filthy finger-nails.

"We'd like a little information."

He laughed, revealing a mouthful of terrible teeth. "You wan to know where the *passeur* is, don't you?"

Maurice stared at him. "Yes, that's right."

"Well, it's easy. You leave the village by the main road, g three hundred yards, and at the first farmhouse on your right, as for Bédard. Only it's five thousand francs each."

I paled; Maurice was stunned too. The delivery boy grinned. " can take you over myself for five hundred francs. How's that?"

We laughed with relief. He was a good chap all right.

"Look, here's what I suggest: I give you my basket and yo finish my round. It's just some meat, and the addresses are on th packets. You'll find the houses easily and they give you tips. I'm going to take a look at my traps and tonight at ten we'll meet under the bridge, near the arch."

Maurice handed me his haversack and took the basket. The delivery boy climbed on his bicycle and rode off.

I turned to Maurice. "Have you got a thousand francs?"

He nodded, "Of course, but only just. Once we've paid him, we'll be almost broke."

"That doesn't matter! Once we're in the free zone we'll manage all right."

That was the beginning of one of the oddest and happiest afternoons of my life. We went from farm to farm, two brats from the Paris gutters suddenly breathing the fresh country air. While Maurice was giving the farmer his joint of mutton, his *entrecôte* or his steak (all of which implied that the black market was humming in that part of the country) I gazed at the rabbits in their hutches, played with puppies and piglets. And then there were horses: not many—most of them had been requisitioned—but there were still one or two old cart-horses.

The basket was almost empty. Coins jingled in Maurice's pocket; people were surprised not to see their usual delivery boy, Raymond, but they gave us tips all the same. There was only one more delivery left, a leg of lamb to take to a house behind a small wood.

My legs were feeling heavy, but we were moving at a good pace when we came abreast of the trees.

"Psst . . . ."

The whistle froze the blood in my veins. Maurice stopped in his tracks.

Behind a tree, a thick-set balding man motioned to us, but seeing us petrified, he smiled and came towards us. By the look of him I knew he was a fugitive like ourselves. His haunted eyes, his nervous hands, everything advertised a refugee.

"Excuse me, do you live around here?" he asked.

"No."

"Are you Jewish?"

Maurice shifted the basket to his other hand. "No."

The man's jaws tightened instantly. "I am. I've got my wife and mother-in-law hiding in the woods. I'm trying to get across." He slapped the knees of his trousers, which were green with moss.

"What happened to you?"

His hands flapped hopelessly. "It happened yesterday, about thirty kilometres away. I had the address of a *passeur* that they'd given me in Bordeaux. I found the man; he charged twenty thousand francs for the three of us and took us out at night. After we'd been walking for a long time he squatted down and told us to wait while he went to see if the coast was clear. I told him that I'd go with him. At that point he hit me with his stick and ran away. We spent the whole night in the woods and we've been walking since daybreak."

Maurice seemed to be weighing up the pros and cons.

"Listen," he said "we're going to cross too, but we don't know if the fellow who's taking us will agree to take you. But you could come and ask him. Ten o'clock under the bridge at the other end of the village."

"Thank you. Thank you so much." He stammered out a series of disconnected words, and disappeared back into the wood.

Maurice had set off again.

"Do you think Raymond might . . .?" I asked.

He shook his head. "I don't know, but I'm going to watch out."

THE NIGHT was clear, soon the clock would strike ten. The time had come. I didn't know whether to be pleased or alarmed.

I moved very slowly to avoid snapping a dry branch; beside me Maurice was holding his breath. On the other side of the arch I could make out the three cowering silhouettes of the Jewish people we had met earlier.

The Germans were on the other side of the wood; funny that they hadn't already fired on us; I felt terribly exposed.

"Listen . . ." At night, bicycles make a noise. It's the friction of the little headlight dynamo against the tyre. But this cyclist was whistling a merry tune. That was the last straw. This nocturnal cyclist was going to give us away to the Germans. He stopped—it was Raymond.

424

He made no effort to keep his voice down. "Well, shall we go?"

Maurice handed over our money, which Raymond stuffed into his shirt, and pointed to the three silhouettes.

"These people want to get across too. They're exhausted and they've got money."

Raymond rubbed his hands. "I'm having a good night. Usually the other *passeurs* don't let me have this many. Well, let's get going."

I stood up carefully, trying hard not to let a single joint creak. I heard Raymond snicker. "Don't worry, lad, no need to play Indians. Just walk behind me and do what I do."

We started off. I was sweating like mad and, as we crossed the fields, it seemed to me that our column must have been visible thousands of yards away. At last we entered the wood. Raymond marched forward through the ferns, making the brittle stalks crackle.

As soon as we were under the trees, I had the feeling we weren't alone. "There's somebody to our left."

Raymond didn't look round. "I know, a dozen of them. Old Branchet taking them across."

"Is it far now?" whispered Maurice.

Raymond gestured vaguely. "Not as the crow flies. But we've got to go round the clearing."

The sand underfoot seemed finer now and rose up in gentle banks; there were pine needles on the ground and I slipped several times on my wet soles. How long had we been under way—two minutes or three hours? It was impossible to say. The wood grew lighter ahead of us; the trees opened out. Raymond summoned us around him.

"See the lane over there? You follow it for about two hundred yards and you come to a ditch. Watch out. It's deep and full of water. Then you come to a farmhouse. You can sleep there, if there are no lights on—the farmer knows what's going on."

"You mean . . . that's the free zone over there?" Maurice said.

Raymond laughed softly. "The free zone? You're in it already!"

I had a feeling of frustration. The line! I had imagined it as a wall, crammed with sentry boxes, machine guns, barbed wire, with patrols creeping through the dark and floodlights searching every blade of grass. And instead of all that—precisely nothing.

Near us the Jewish trio congratulated one another and thanked Raymond, who assumed a modest air. I couldn't resist asking Raymond if it was always this peaceful.

"Usually it goes fairly smoothly. The guard posts are far apart and there are blind corners where they can't see us. The only danger is when they send out patrols." He hitched up his trousers and shook hands. "But don't imagine that it's easy as this everywhere—there are places less than ten miles from here where people were killed not so long ago, and it's getting tougher all the time. Well, good luck!" He vanished into the trees.

We continued our way, alone now. Maurice held my hand; it wouldn't do to get lost. A night in this wood would not be very pleasant, particularly as the temperature was dropping every minute. We crossed the ditch and saw the farmhouse before us. The three Jews came up and we entered the farmyard. I jumped: there was a tall man there, motionless, in the dark, with a fur collar hiding his ears and the wind ruffling his hair.

"O.K. This is the place." His voice was harsh. "You'll find straw in the shed. There are blankets behind the door; they aren't much to look at but they're clean. I ask only one thing: if you have any matches or a lighter, give them to me, because I don't want to see my hay go up in smoke with you inside."

We shook our heads.

"Fine, then. If you need anything, just tap on that little window, that's where I sleep. All right. Good night."

"Good night, monsieur."

The wooden door creaked on its old hinges and a warm smell of the clean dry hay made my eyes grow heavy. I climbed on a bale and buried myself in another. I hadn't the strength to go and get the blankets. A greyish light filtered in through the skylight. Our companions were whispering together at the other end of the barn.

I heard Maurice coming and rough material scraped my cheek. "Roll yourself up in this."

I could just about make it. The weight of my eyelids was pulling me down into a black world. I fell asleep.

426

When I opened my eyes again I didn't need to feel the place beside me.

I already knew that my brother wasn't there.

EVER SINCE Mother had decided that she no longer needed my cot beside her, Maurice and I had shared a room. I had always known when he went to get a glass of water, slipped out of his bed for whatever reason. And at that moment I knew that at a time when he should have been sleeping, Maurice had disappeared.

The most plausible explanation was that he'd gone to the lavatory. But we'd peed together against the farmhouse wall before coming in here. So where had he gone, without telling me?

There was a sound of whispering outside. I listened intently and pushed back the blankets.

What if it were the Germans? Impossible—we were in unoccupied France . . . . What about thieves? Gangs of hooligans?

In my stockinged feet, I stole noiselessly across the earth floor and opened the door a crack.

Shapes were approaching and I recognized one of the men who had been in the restaurant. There were two children in the group, one being carried and a little girl in white socks. What a mistake to wear those socks—they could be seen a hundred yards away. They brushed past me in the darkness and collapsed in the hay.

Still no Maurice. What could he be doing? I went out. The night was cold, and I plunged my hands into my coat pockets. My fingers touched a piece of paper that hadn't been there before.

The moon was bright enough for me to read the scrawled lines: "I'll be back. Don't say anything to anyone. M."

I felt relieved. I still didn't know where he had gone, but I knew that he was coming back, which was the main thing. I went back to my place in the hay and slept for several hours.

When I woke, it was light enough for me to see that the barn was full of refugees—about fifty of them, perhaps more. They were all sleeping. But still no Maurice. Near me, I could see a woman with a woollen coat crying in her sleep.

More people came, a big group this time. Then suddenly, he was there.

427

"But where on earth . . ."

He put a finger on my mouth. "Not so loud. I'll tell you."

What he had done was very simple and he described it with considerable complacency. He had gone back the way we had come, made eight trips across the line, brought forty people over and made himself twenty thousand francs.

Twenty thousand francs! A fortune.

"But Maurice, what if you'd been caught?"

He ran his fingers through his hair. "You heard what Raymond told us—there isn't the slightest danger."

I wasn't entirely satisfied. "Yes, but don't you think it was rather mean to take those people across for money?"

Maurice stared at me. "First of all, I didn't make anyone come with me. Second, at five hundred francs instead of five thousand, I don't think they can say that I robbed them. And there's something you seem to forget: we're going to need money if we want to get to Menton."

"But we could have . . . ."

But Maurice was off, and there was no stopping him. "You think that because we're in the unoccupied zone people are going to feed us for nothing? Last night it was me, but the next time it will be up to you to work something out . . . . Don't think that just because you're the youngest you're going to sit around twiddling your thumbs . . . ."

"Stop yelling for goodness sake. It's O.K., I get it."

But Maurice was really screaming now. "Do you think it was fun? Do you think I wouldn't rather have had a good night's sleep? And now you put on airs and tell me I shouldn't have done it!"

I jumped to my feet. "I never said that!"

Angrily, he pulled the wad of crumpled notes out of his pocket. "Here, go ahead, give them back their money if you want to."

Taken aback, I stared at the money he had made by risking his life, which would enable us to continue our journey. I smoothed out the notes and handed them back to him without saying a word. He had calmed down now; his chin on his knees, gazing at the rising sun.

"Are we going to take the train again?" I asked.

He must have sensed from my voice that I was trying to make conversation and to get him to forgive me. "Yes. I talked it over with a fellow I brought across last night. The nearest station is at Aire-sur-l'Adour. We've got to be careful because the police are all over the place and they've got orders to arrest any Jews." I was astounded. Why had we made this journey if we were right back in the same mess?

"Some of them let you get away, some take bribes. From what the man told me, we should be able to get through with our eyes shut."

I was hungry; it had been a long time since the lentils. "Don't you think we could ask the farmer to give us some bread and milk? We could afford that now, couldn't we?"

Maurice massaged his stiff legs. "I agree, we deserve something."

Ten minutes later we were seated in the low room that served as kitchen, bedroom and dining room combined. Two thick earthenware bowls of milk and two long loaves of coarse bread, sliced lengthwise and covered with that luxury of luxuries, a layer of butter. We were alone with the farmer, everyone else had left at dawn.

"Are you going far?"

With my mouth full, I answered, "We're going to take the train to Marseilles." He was undoubtably a good man, but I had already realized that the less you said, the better.

He looked at us almost affectionately. "When I was a boy at school the teacher made us read *Two Children on a Tour of France*. There were drawings for each chapter. You look a bit like them."

Maurice swallowed. "What happened to them in the end?"

"I don't remember—they had all kinds of adventures. All I remember is that it had a happy ending." He paused and then added, "But there weren't any Germans in the story."

We had finished and Maurice stood up. The man took a clasp knife from his pocket, and cut two large chunks from the bread.

"Put them in your bags, for the journey," he said.

429

THE BACK ROAD wound through empty fields past a few houses. A dog followed us. He seemed delighted by our company.

> *Vingt-sept kilomètres à pied, ça use, ça use . . .*
> *Vingt-sept kilomètres à pied, ça use les souliers . . .*

We hadn't actually done twenty-seven kilometres on foot—barely three, but it was the twenty-seventh time we had sung the song. If it hadn't been for the blister on my heel I could have walked all the way to Marseilles.

Another kilometre post: Aire-sur-l'Adour 19. Another eighteen stones still to pass.

"Do you want a piece of bread?"

Maurice shook his head. "Any athlete knows you mustn't eat in the middle of an event. It makes you all out of breath."

We trudged on, and the sky clouded over. Clear and black a while ago, our shadows now became indistinct.

Vingt-huit kilomètres à pied . . . .

"Are you limping?"

"Don't you worry about it."

The milestones seemed to be getting farther and farther apart. It was too much for me—my leg was trembling up to the thigh, and I could feel the pricking of the blister rubbing against my sock. But stopping was out of the question. I might walk my ankles to the bone, but nobody should be able to say that I had slowed us down. I gritted my teeth and whistled.

Aire-sur-l'Adour 17.

Suddenly, Maurice sat down by the roadside. "I've got to stop. I didn't get enough sleep."

What an unexpected piece of luck! "Sleep for a bit—you'll feel better soon. There's no rush."

He curled up on the grassy bank and I took the opportunity to remove my shoes. It was as I'd feared: the wool was stuck to a blister the size of a one franc piece. If I pulled the sock free, I would make it bleed. I took out a handkerchief, folded it and used it as a makeshift bandage.

His muzzle on his paws, tongue lolling, the dog watched me. He looked like a good-natured Parisian mongrel. Perhaps he was a refugee too; perhaps he was a Jewish dog.

430

I heard the sound of wheels. I saw that it wasn't a horse and cart but something more elegant. It looked more like the sort of open cab one saw in films about the old days.

The distinguished-looking driver had a whip beside him, but he wasn't using it. In view of the age of the horse the whip wouldn't have been much good; each step seemed like its last. But the carriage was headed towards town, so I limped forward.

"Excuse me, monsieur, you aren't going to Aire-sur-l'Adour by any chance?"

"Yes. To be exact, I'm stopping two kilometres this side of it."

"And would you . . . I mean, could you give my brother and me a lift in your cab?"

The man frowned. Clearly I had said something I shouldn't. "Young man, this vehicle is not a cab—it is a barouche."

I stared open-mouthed. "Oh, I see. I'm sorry."

He seemed touched by this politeness. "It's unimportant really, my boy, but it's good to call things by their proper names. Yes, you and your brother may share this carriage."

"Thank you, monsieur."

I hopped back to Maurice and woke him roughly. "Hurry up! Your barouche awaits you."

"My *what?*" He rubbed his eyes, and stared blankly at the waiting vehicle. "Goodness," he murmured, "where did you find that?" But he greeted our driver respectfully and we climbed in.

The man clacked his tongue to the horse and we set off. He turned towards us. "Let me introduce myself: I am the Count de V."

A count no less. He was the first count I'd seen.

"I used to own a car, but it was requisitioned six months ago," he said. "As for this horse, if I may use the term loosely, it's the only one that hasn't been taken over by the *commune*. I should add that his days are numbered. I won't be able to put him in harness much longer."

Aire-sur-l'Adour 16.

We were hardly going faster than on foot. Now our coachman was chatting non-stop. We took it in turn to utter monosyllables so that he wouldn't get the feeling that he was talking to himself.

431

"You see, children, when a country loses a war as decisively as we have lost this one, it is because the leaders of that country have not proved equal to their task, and I make no bones about it: the Republic was not equal to its task." One finger pointing skyward, the count was holding forth. "France was great only during the time of the kings. No king would ever have consented to see his people taken over from within by all manner of foreign elements, which have dragged the nation to the brink of the abyss . . . ."

He went on with his discourse, but I had stopped listening.

Aire-sur-l'Adour 7.

"What France lacked was a large-scale national movement which would have enabled her to rekindle her faith and find the strength to throw the Teuton back beyond our borders. But this time, we lost . . . ." His voice fell off sadly; he was acting a part, without actually believing what he was saying. "Words came along, new words: *liberté, égalité, fraternité*, and they helped to blind the eyes of succeeding generations. Those words concealed the true values of the French spirit: the values of greatness, sacrifice, order, purity . . . ."

Out of the corner of my eye I saw Maurice yawning.

Aire-sur-l'Adour 2.

I prepared to get out, but he turned to us again. "My young friends," he said, "all the way here you have listened to me attentively and courteously, and I don't doubt that these words will make their mark sooner or later on your minds. I shall take you all the way to town."

With a regal air, he shook the reins against the protruding ribs of his old horse.

Chapter 5

I scarcely remember anything about the journey to Marseilles, other than the fact that it had nothing in common with the one to Dax. We slept like logs and in the middle of the night ate veal cutlet sandwiches and hard-boiled eggs given by a fellow passenger. There had been changes, long waits on the platforms of unknown stations where railway-men chalked up the delays on big blackboards. It was a slow journey, but I went through it in a kind of pleasant dream. We had money and time; nobody thought of asking us anything, two children in a war made by the adults.

I remember seeing policemen go by, and overheard them say that they, too, had been ordered to arrest Jews and send them off to special camps.

And on that peerless winter morning, under a sky swept clear of clouds by the *mistral*, we found ourselves in a great city, but how different from our own! We stood at the top of the great stairs in front of the Gare Saint-Charles, dazed by the wind and sun, the city sprawled at our feet, swarming beneath the plane trees, the poles of the trams ploughing through the leaves. We went down and entered Marseilles through the Boulevard d'Athènes.

I later learned that the great port was a centre of gangsterism, drugs, vice—a European Chicago, so the books, films and articles said. This might have been true but I never liked to hear it. Marseilles for Maurice and me was, that morning, a great, riotous, windy celebration.

Gusts of wind hit us obliquely and we moved forward crabwise, laughing. We walked on down a boulevard full of people and shops. At one corner there stood a huge cinema with portholes like an old steamer. We looked at the advertisements: it was a German film, *Baron Munchausen*, with Hans Albers, the big star of the Third Reich. One of the photos showed him riding on a cannonball; in another, he was having a sabre-fight with a gang of cut-throats.

I elbowed Maurice. "Hey, look, it doesn't cost much."

He looked at the sign below the ticket-office window. "It doesn't open until ten . . . . We'll go for a walk and come back."

We carried on down the wide boulevard; past pavement cafés where men in grey felt hats were reading newspapers and smoking cigarettes. And then, suddenly, the street opened out; there was a gust of wind, and we stopped dead in our tracks. Maurice was the first to speak. "Hey look! It's the sea."

We had never seen it before and we'd never imagined we'd

come across it like that, so suddenly. But there it was, stretching away as far as the eye could see, dotted with tiny islands bright with sunlight. Before us we saw the great bridge that spanned the Vieux Port, flotillas of small craft, and the ferry, making one of its first trips of the day. We went right up to the edge of the quay.

"Well boys, how about a trip to the Chateau d'If? Hop aboard and we'll be off."

He looked a bit of a fake, bundled up in a pea-jacket, a cap with gold braid and skinny legs in huge white trousers. He pointed to a yellow boat with red seats and tatty-looking rails.

I felt sorely tempted by the Chateau d'If: a castle in the sea sounded magical, but regretfully Maurice shook his head.

"But why not? It's half-price for children. You're not going to tell me that you haven't got the money?"

"No, it rolls too much; we'd be seasick."

The man laughed. "Yes, I think you might be right." He had clear, kind eyes; he looked at us more attentively. "From the way you speak," he said, "I can tell you aren't from around here."

"No, we're from Paris."

"Paris! Oh, I know Paris. My brother moved there; he's a plumber at the Porte d'Italie."

We chatted for a bit; he wanted to know what was going on up there. He showed us the slack in his belt. "In a year, I've lost a stone and a half. I say, if you like I'll show you the motor of my boat."

Delighted, we went aboard. The motor was in the bows, in a glassed-over shed. He was a great enthusiast and chatterer—we had a job getting away.

We walked along the port around the Quai de Riveneuve; there were barrels and coils of rope and a salty smell, the smell of adventure. I expected to see legions of pirates.

Across the quay was a jumble of tiny alleys with washing stretched from one side to the other. The roads rose in steps and dishwater ran down the middle in a gutter.

I began to feel uneasy; women were chatting in shadowy doorways, sitting on rush-bottomed chairs.

Suddenly Maurice shouted, "My beret!"

435

A huge giantess had snatched it from him; she had a vast bosom that trembled when she laughed. I took off my own beret and stuffed it in my pocket.

Maurice's beret really made the rounds. Within seconds the fat woman had thrown it behind her to a second girl half-naked in the shadows of a corridor. Then, in a window on the second floor, a woman even fatter than the first was holding the precious headgear between her podgy fingers. She was laughing too.

"Come up and get it, sweetie."

Maurice watched his beautiful Basque beret twirling on the forefinger of the fat lady. "I can't let her have it! I'll have to go up there."

I was not very old, but I knew about life. There were girls like this near Clignancourt and the big boys in school often talked about them during break. I held him back. "Don't go up. They give you diseases and they take your money."

The girls were still laughing; now they started on me. "Look at the little one. Isn't he sweet? He took his beret off straight away; he's no fool."

As we stood hopelessly in the middle of the street, a red-haired woman opened the door of the café nearby. She shouted at the woman holding the beret. "Maria, aren't you ashamed of yourself, going for children? Go on, give it back to him."

Maria went on laughing, then good-naturedly she threw down the beret.

Maurice caught the beret and we ran through the street as fast as our legs would carry us. What with the sea, the boat and the prostitutes, we had quite forgotten the cinema. We came out at the harbour and walked up the big boulevard called Canebière. Three minutes later, we were sitting three rows from the screen, our haversacks in our laps, our hands deep in our pockets.

We were virtually alone and the vast place was unheated. I remember that the news came first. We saw German tanks in the snow, awaiting the spring to attack Moscow. The newsreader said that it was very cold but that the men's morale was high.

Then there was a bit about Paris fashions—with women with black lips, very high hairdos and high-heeled shoes. They had been photographed in the streets, in front of monuments like the Eiffel Tower, the Arc de Triomphe and the Sacré-Coeur. For a few seconds we saw our own neighbourhood, and that reminded me that I'd hardly thought about Mother or Father since leaving home. I would have loved to tell them that tomorrow we would reach our destination safe and sound.

During an interminable interval Maurice and I asked each other riddles, traded insults, and exchanged a few kicks under the seats. Then the film began.

We saw it three times in a row. I've seen films since then—some very bad, some very fine, but I've never again experienced the wonder of that occasion. The Nazi film industry succeeded in creating a work that gave two young Jews a day of enchantment.

It was four o'clock when we left the cinema, eyes full of dreams. We were ravenously hungry and Maurice marched straight into a *pâtisserie*. On a glass shelf stood unlikely-looking cakes made without eggs, butter, sugar or flour. The result was a pinkish foam with a soggy core topped by a crystallized cherry.

We each gobbled down four of them.

Afterwards we wandered along the dock railings like two emigrants hoping to stow away. Maurice waved his hand. "Over there, it's Africa."

I stared in that direction as though I might see monkeys, a lion, masked dancers in grass skirts. "And where's Menton?"

He pointed to the left. "It's right over there, near Italy."

"They'll be at work when we get there."

"We'll find them. There can't be that many barbers' shops."

"What if they're doing some other kind of job?"

Maurice looked up. "Why do you always complicate things?"

"Oh, it's me who complicates everything, is it? I suppose I'm the one who had my beret swiped?"

We swore at each other for a couple of minutes, then set off again. This kind of slanging match had always done us good; we felt better afterwards.

Dusk. It was time to go back to the station. At the top of the stairs I turned round to have a last look at Marseilles, a city of sunlight, sea, cinemas, boats and a stolen beret.

437

I went down to the lavatories in the tiled basement. The place smelt of chlorine and my wooden soles echoed fearsomely. Coming back I saw two huge policemen were blocking the entrance, their backs were turned to me.

Should I try going back downstairs? No, absolutely—they'd hear me.

I slipped between them, taking care not to bump them.

"Excuse me . . . ." They let me go past and I trotted off innocently.

"Here, you, where are you off to?"

I felt the sweat break out from every pore. I turned and went back. They looked most unpleasant. I raised my beret politely. This act, and perhaps the fact that I had washed my face and hands and slicked my hair down a little, may have worked in my favour. There are times when the smallest thing can decide the way things will go.

"I'm going on the train."

They had their hands behind their backs and were rocking backwards and forwards on their heels.

"Have you got your papers?"

"No, Father has them."

"Where is your father?"

I turned round. The station was crowded, especially at the other end, near the left luggage. "Over there, with the suitcases."

"Where do you live?"

"Marseilles."

"What address?"

"On the Canebière, above the cinema." The best lies are those that come out automatically. I went on, "My father owns the cinema."

They weren't impressed, but the next question was asked in a different tone. "So you must go to the cinema a lot?"

"Yes, every time there's a new film. At the moment it's *Baron Munchausen*. It's very good."

I wouldn't have believed they could smile, but they almost did. "O.K. off you go."

"*Au revoir*, messieurs." I put my beret back on and went off.

438

But now I had to watch out; there would be trouble if they followed me.

Maurice was sitting on a bench outside the waiting room. I walked straight to the place where my father was supposed to be, picking my way through groups of passengers and manoeuvring it so that the last carriage of the train acted as a screen between me and the two policemen. I made no sign to Maurice, who didn't move; he must have understood that there was something wrong.

Suddenly I saw them coming. My heart stopped beating. I should have known they wouldn't let things drop: the moment you think you've won is always the most dangerous time.

They slowly drew closer, their hands still behind their backs. The man looking at the train timetable couldn't be more than thirty; he could be my father . . . . I put on a lively expression and asked him the time.

He looked surprised. He must have wondered why I was smiling so broadly.

"Can't you tell the time?"

I broke into laughter which surprised him even more. Soon he'd assume I was completely mad. The policemen were abreast of us now, a few yards away; but with the hubbub of the station, they couldn't hear what we were saying.

"Of course I know how to tell the time."

"Well, just look up there and you will see a clock."

The policeman glanced at us and went past; and the man never knew that, for a few fleeting seconds, in their eyes he had been the owner of a big cinema and father of a ten-year-old boy.

I felt a hand on my shoulder. It was Maurice. He looked uneasy. "I've heard people talking. The police are checking all over the station. Loads of people have been arrested. They're checking everyone."

"What shall we do?"

"We could go out of the station, but we'd lose our tickets; we can only use them tonight. I'm not so keen to stay in Marseilles. Where could we sleep?" He suddenly nudged me. "Look!"

A whole regiment of police had just come in; the fellow leading must have been a captain at the very least. The gendarmes fanned out and began asking people for their papers. It was a round-up, and we were right in the thick of it.

At that moment, the loud-speaker announced the arrival of our train. There was pandemonium; there were few passenger trains and they were always overcrowded. We were among those leading the charge. Luck was with us: the ticket inspectors hadn't locked the doors and we climbed aboard the train.

In the corridor, Maurice said, "If they come round checking, we'll hide under the seat."

But they didn't come round and after a half-hour's delay, the train moved off. We breathed a sigh of relief—we were on the last lap of the journey.

We crawled along at a snail's pace, with frequent stops in the countryside for no apparent reason. Railway workers walked along beside our carriage and, half asleep, I heard voices, their Provençal accents, their curses.

The sun rose near Cannes and I must have fallen asleep after that. Maurice woke me up. After stepping over the bodies of sleepers in the corridor, I found myself standing on a square planted with tall palm trees, the first I'd ever seen.

DURING THOSE wartime months, Menton was still a small town whose fortune had been made by the English, aided by some tubercular millionaires who had come there to live out their last days in the sun. The grand hotels and the sanatorium were now inhabited by the Italian occupation forces who lived there like princes. The town cast a spell over me the moment I entered it, with its charm, its arcades, its Italian churches, its old stairways, and the ancient jetty from whose tip you could see the old town and the mountains which plunged steeply into the Mediterranean.

When we arrived, we immediately began the search for our brothers.

The barber's was a smart-looking place on the corner of a broad street leading to the museum. In spite of the reflection on the window I could see inside. The large fellow running the clippers over an inclined neck was Henri, the eldest. He hadn't changed, a little thinner perhaps, but only a little. He hadn't seen us.

440

"Come on, let's go in."

The little bell over the door jingled; Henri turned round, and stood for a moment with his clippers suspended in mid-air.

"Well," he said. "Well, well, if it isn't the hooligans!"

He bent down and hugged us; he smelt as good as ever. "Sit down. I'll be ready in a couple of minutes."

A last touch of the scissors to even up behind an ear, a whisk of the feather duster on the collar, a lightning parading of the mirror, and he whipped the towel from the neck of his customer.

"Will you excuse me for five minutes, Madame Henriette? I've got to cope with these two."

The proprietress nodded her assent and out we went.

He took our hands and pulled us along in the wake of his long strides.

"What about Mother and Father? How did you get across? When did you get here?"

We walked up towards the church of Saint-Michel through narrow winding streets, with flights of steps leading to the sea. They were living on the rue Longue, which reminded me of Marseilles, with washing-lines stretched between the second floor windows; a small arch spanned the street.

Almost under the arch, Henri went through a low door. There was a staircase going down; the steps were steep and narrow. "Don't make any noise; we'll give him a surprise."

We found ourselves in a small dining room furnished with a huge Provençal dresser, a round table and three chairs. Through the half-open bedroom door, we saw Albert reading on his bed.

"I've brought you some friends."

"Oho," he said, "It's the hooligans."

We flung ourselves around his neck.

They gave us some lemonade, bread—and chocolate. Seeing my amazement at such a delicacy, Henri explained that you could manage quite well if you used your wits.

We recounted our adventures from start to finish. Henri's five minutes became an hour.

Finally Albert said, "Now we must concentrate on you. For the moment you can sleep on a mattress in the dining room."

Henri went back to work and Albert heated water for us to wash in. It had been a long time since our last bath. We put on clean underwear from our haversacks. I had never felt better.

"Now," said Albert, "here's the money and a list. We're going to celebrate tonight."

Armed with string bags, we flew down the steps, crossed the street, and onto the beach of Les Sablettes, at the foot of the old town.

It wasn't a very big beach, but there wasn't a soul there—just a few fishing boats with their nets drying, and little waves lapping. We ran, jumped, danced, shouted—drunk with joy and freedom. Our hair and shoes full of sand, we ended up flat on our tummies; then we went paddling for a bit and finally left, regretfully.

In tiny squares, fishermen were playing *boules*, cursing in the local *patois*, which sounded like Italian. In the shops people asked our names and Maurice answered, "We're the brothers of Albert and Henri."

Everyone seemed to know them and without asking for a single ration book the butcher handed us a huge steak, and the grocer gave us four kilos of potatoes, six eggs, a lettuce and some flour. We went back to Albert loaded like mules.

All three of us prepared the feast. When Henri came home with a bottle of wine, the table was set, and the potatoes were browning in the pan.

I don't remember that meal. Albert gave me half a glass of wine and that must have finished me off. I heard Maurice telling about the yellow star, and I fell asleep on the table, my head on my arms. I slept for seventeen solid hours.

The next three days were marvellous.

Henri and Albert would leave early in the morning; we would get up about nine o'clock and, after breakfast, we'd go onto the beach to play football with a ball our landlady lent us. Maurice was goalie. We marked the goals with our coats and I would practise until I was breathless, shouting with triumph when I scored.

In the afternoons we used to go exploring. On our second day, on a slope of the Bay of Garavan, we came across an immense villa all boarded up. The iron gate was locked but we scaled the wall and found ourselves in an overgrown garden. There were statues half-hidden by climbing plants and an empty pool. We played in the garden the whole afternoon, scaling the statues and fighting endless duels, until suddenly the church clock of Saint-Michel struck six.

We raced back to the flat, because we were supposed to set the table each evening and tidy up.

That night when we were in bed, Maurice burst out, "Listen Jo. I know we're having fun, but don't you think we could try to earn a bit of money?"

Maurice had given our brothers the remains of the twenty thousand francs, but he was right: we couldn't let them support us until the end of the war. And since leaving Paris we had discovered that fending for ourselves was more interesting even than football or exploring deserted villas.

Sometimes in the afternoons we met boys of our own age. We came in for a bit of teasing because of being "Parisian brats", but football proved an ice-breaker. I made friends with a boy called Virgilio, who lived in a decrepit house on the rue de Bréa. He confided to me about a job looking after the cows on a hill farm above Saint-Agnès. It wasn't badly paid and the farmer was nice.

I decided to talk it over with Maurice that very evening. Bursting with pride at having a plan I met him on the rue Longue: he had on a blue apron and his hair and eyebrows were white with flour. Resourceful as always, he was already working in the baker's shop at the end of our street.

I borrowed some money from Henri and the next morning at eight o'clock I went down to the market place and took the bus to Saint-Agnès. My forehead pressed against the window, I watched the sea sink into the distance as the bus climbed the series of hairpin bends at a maximum of ten miles an hour.

In Saint-Agnès, a typical little postcard Provençal hill-town, I met an old man leading a tiny donkey. I asked him the way to Monsieur Viale's farm. I found myself following a path over a hillside covered with terraces that reached down into the valley. After walking a mile or two I came to an old farmhouse with a pantile roof mellowed by years of sunshine. At its side the owner had built

443

a taller house which reminded me of suburban Paris. I went to the front door of the tall house, and knocked.

Madame Viale opened the door.

Although I was very young, this woman immediately struck me as being out of place. But it was only when she told me her story later that I realized why. As a girl, she had learned to play golf, ride horses, embroider, play the piano and harpsichord, and she had spent long hours reading the classics over cups of hot chocolate in her sumptuous room. At twenty-two, though she had many suitors, she had shown signs of tuberculosis. There was only one thing for a young person of her social standing to do: go to Menton. Her mother settled her in a villa away from the sanatorium where the lesser mortals went. After a few months, strengthened by the fresh air, she began to take walks through the countryside.

One day she was following a rough path and twisted her ankle.

She spent three hours sitting on a rock, thinking that no one would ever come by, when she heard footsteps. It was Monsieur Viale, the farmer, returning to his farm. He was in his thirties, with a moustache like Clark Gable's. He took the young woman in his arms and carried her to his house. It was a frightful scandal. They were married three months later at the town hall of Gorbio because Viale was a free-thinker, and her family cut her off completely. Fourteen years later, she was still there.

She was to tell me this story about four times during the first week. Even before Viale arrived, I already knew that I could stay on and that my job would not be to clean out the stalls of the few remaining animals, not to hoe out the weeds that sprouted between the vinestocks after rain, but to listen to the mistress of the house as she sat on a sofa with a cup of tea and talked!

Viale agreed to hire me immediately. That night I slept in a tiny room he gave me, as happy as a lark. Next morning, I went off with my boss, to raise some dry-stone walls, with me holding the plumb-line. I also remember mixing mortar and carrying it to Monsieur Viale, who was on a ladder, patching the holes in the farmhouse walls.

I ate with them, and Madame Viale began telling me about her past—her visit to the Bagatelle exhibition in July 1924, her début

444

in society, her first Viennese waltz with an Italian officer, and so on. Viale got to his feet and I prepared to follow him. He motioned me to stay put. "Have a bit of a rest—you worked hard this morning."

I didn't dare tell him that I would have preferred to be with him in the fields than listening to an account of high society; but I sensed that this too was part of my work—he and I were in collusion.

I spent ten days there, mostly listening to the never-ending stories of my high-born *patronne*. I ate very well and forgot the war, which Madame considered rather indecorous, fought by dull-witted, trivial people.

On the tenth day, after the evening soup, I asked Monsieur Viale if I could go down to town the next day. It was a Monday and my brothers would be off. I would come back about five in the evening.

The following morning, I went down the mountainside as planned. Besides my wages, I carried a box of eggs and a slab of bacon, both of them priceless. I could already smell the enormous omelette Maurice and I would make for lunch. I remember turning back to look at the farmhouse, and thinking that it was a good place to live until peacetime. I would have felt deeply grieved if I had known that I would never see them again.

On Mondays my brothers slept late, and I was surprised to find them all up. Albert and Maurice were in their pyjamas and having breakfast. Henri was finishing his coffee near the window. He was wearing a dark suit, there was a closed suitcase on the table. Even before I had shut the door, I knew something was wrong. I asked, "What's the matter?"

"Things aren't too good," Albert said.

On the dresser lay a letter covered with rubber stamps, most of them showing an eagle. I swallowed, "Mother and Father?"

Albert nodded. "You might as well know—they've been arrested."

Henri explained what had happened. There had been a huge round-up in our neighbourhood and Mother and Father had only just escaped. They had left everything, taking one bus after another. Finally, they had arrived near Pau, completely exhausted. They had managed to cross the line but had been caught by the

445

Vichy authorities and put into a camp. They had managed to get a letter out—the letter my brother had just received.

What Henri didn't tell me was that the camp was a transit camp from which trains left every day, taking the prisoners to resettlement camps.

I read the letter Father had written. At the end, he said, "If you meet up with the hooligans send them to school. It's very important." Mother had added a line after Father's signature. "Kisses to you all. Be brave."

I looked at my brothers. "What should we do?"

Henri pointed to his suitcase. "As you see, I'm going to Pau."

"But they know Father and Mother are Jewish, so they'll know you are too. And they'll keep you there."

Albert smiled weakly. "We talked it over half the night and finally agreed it's worth a try." He fiddled with his spoon, trying to balance it on the rim of his bowl.

"I'll be back as soon as possible," said Henri. "Meanwhile, this afternoon Albert will see about school for you two. It was good of you to work, but perhaps we didn't pay you enough attention. So you must do what Father said and study hard. What do you say? All right?"

Ten minutes later, Henri left. At noon, we made a superb omelette with my bacon. Albert put up a show of enthusiasm about the money and food I had brought home, but his heart wasn't in it.

At one thirty, we entered the school. The headmaster asked to see our school records and I thought with relief that they must be slumbering peacefully in the cupboard in the primary school in Paris. Secretly, we hoped that it would be impossible for us to register for school. But after much humming and hawing, the headmaster sighed and looked us over from head to foot, scenting potential troublemakers. "All right," he said "they can go to their new classes."

"Now?" Maurice stuttered.

The headmaster frowned; for him, that question must have represented the first act of insubordination. "Yes, of course now," he said severely.

447

Albert took pity on us. "I'll bring them tomorrow—I've got to buy them satchels and exercise books."

Through acquaintances he had made at the shop, Albert was able to get clothing coupons, and our last hope faded; we found ourselves in front of a shabby mirror in a tailor's fitting room in the garb of infamy—a black school pinafore with fine red piping. Next came the satchel, pencil box and exercise books. There was no escaping any of it.

Later we went down to the beach and kicked the football about. But we were haunted by the thought of our parents. Father wouldn't be coming to tell us stories of pogroms any more. Now he was actually living through one, the worst that history had ever known.

My schoolmaster turned out to be a mistress. Almost all the men had gone to war and the only teachers left were women or old people. Maurice got a very old gentleman with a goatee who tried three hundred times a day to impose silence on a wild mob of thirty-five pupils in a classroom thick with flying pellets. Maurice made paper planes, built up a new store of marbles, and learned absolutely nothing.

I wasn't so lucky. Our schoolmistress was young, pretty and pleasant and, without realizing it, I worked fairly hard.

The Vichy government distributed a four-o'clock snack of biscuits which gave rise to an infinite number of complex dealings. My particular deprivation was sweets. I used to swap four marbles for my neighbour's biscuit. Later at break, I would win back my marbles; my aim was improving, and the Joffo brothers began to earn themselves a reputation as skilled marksmen.

I had met Virgilio again, and we became proper friends. We used to stop in front of his house after school and play endless games of five-stones, a game which he much preferred to marbles. Every evening I would look into the letter-box on the door, but never was there a letter, although Henri had been away for a week. Albert smoked ten days' ration of cigarettes in two days, and I sensed that he was worrying himself sick.

One evening he announced that, if we hadn't received any news by Monday (it was Thursday), he would leave on Monday night. If he too failed to return after nine or ten days, we would have to leave Menton and go to a village in the Massif Central where one of our older married sisters had been in hiding for some time. "Do you understand?"

All I understood was that we had split up, come together and were now splitting up all over again. There was no end to it. Maurice got to his feet without a word and stacked the plates in the sink. Just as he turned on the tap, a key rattled in the lock and there was Henri, beaming. "They're free."

Henri put down his suitcase and took off his tie like the hero of a detective novel. We still had one egg left and Albert cooked it while Henri began his story.

As soon as he reached Pau, Henri had found out that the Jewish families were being kept in the municipal stadium. They were arriving in their hundreds. Tents were put up, guarded by policemen. No visitors were admitted without permission from the camp commandant, and this was hardly ever granted.

At a loss, Henri had a drink at a nearby bar and managed to strike up a conversation with a gendarme. Henri said that his parents had been arrested by mistake, that they had never engaged in politics and weren't Jewish, and that his father was just coming to Menton to help him in the barber's shop. The gendarme expressed sympathy, and left; Henri too was about to leave when the gendarme came back with a sergeant.

"François told me that you were a barber . . . . Do you think that you could give me a little trim? I'm on duty and don't have time to go into Pau. The captain doesn't like long hair and I wouldn't want to lose my leave."

They ended up in the back of the bar. Henri, wielding the scissors and razor borrowed from the proprietor and using hot water from the percolator, gave the sergeant the best hair cut of his life. He wouldn't accept any money but asked him to have a word with the colonel in charge of the camp to try and arrange an interview.

The sergeant said, "I can't promise anything, but be at the gate tomorrow morning at ten and I'll see what I can do."

Henri spent the night in a hotel, and next morning was at the

449

gate. The sergeant took him off towards a stone building set apart from the others. On the way he told him, "He's willing to see you, but watch out. He's a tough one."

Henri entered a first office where he had to wait for ten minutes, then a second one where a man with an iron-grey moustache, hooked nose and bald head didn't give him time to speak. "Henri Joffo," he said, "make it brief and don't forget that, in coming here, you are risking your freedom. We are under orders to hand over all foreign Jews to the occupying authorities."

"But Colonel . . . ."

"I make no exceptions. I have six hundred suspects here and if I released a single one of them without proper evidence, I might as well let them all go."

"Colonel, I am French. I was at Dunkerque in Flanders, in the Belgian campaign. I have not come here to ask you to make an exception. I have come to tell you that there has been a mistake: nobody in our family's Jewish."

The colonel asked for proof.

"First of all, it's easy to see that my mother is Catholic; you have her identity papers. Her maiden name is Markoff. I defy anyone to find me a single Russian Jew with the name Markoff. The Markoffs are direct descendants of a branch of the Romanovs, the imperial family."

"What about your father?"

This was the biggest bluff of all.

"As you know sir, all Jewish people have been stripped of their French citizenship by the German authorities. Now, my father is French, as you can see from his papers. If he is French, then he can't be Jewish; but if you want further confirmation, you could ring police headquarters in Paris."

We were hanging on to Henri's every word. "That was a gamble," Henri continued, "but I had a hunch that he would give in. I sensed that this warder role disgusted him and that he might release two people if he felt he had sufficient grounds for doing so. Anyhow, he picked up the telephone before I'd even finished the sentence."

Henri mimed the scene, glueing an imaginary receiver to his

450

ear. "'Get me Paris police headquarters. Identity verification department.'"

He resumed his normal voice. "It was hard to put on the complacent look of someone whose story is about to be backed up. Because, the whole time he was waiting to get through, he never took his eyes off me. If he'd caught the slightest sign of uneasiness, that would have been it; I might as well have set off for the reception centre for new prisoners."

I saw the scene perfectly in my mind, I could hear the voices, Henri's voice, the hard, dry voice of the colonel, and then a far-off nasal twang at the end of the line, a voice that would spell out life or death.

"'Hallo! This is Colonel T. from the transit camp at Pau. I'd like information on a person named Joffo, J.O.F.F.O. Residing at 12 rue Clignancourt. Occupation, barber. Has he lost his French citizenship? . . . . I have his son here with me now . . . . No, the mother isn't Jewish; he claims that the father isn't either. All right I'll hold on.'"

"While we were waiting," Henri went on, "I still had one hope— that it would be impossible to supply information like that. I imagined filing cabinets with dusty documents by the ton . . . so that nobody could ever find anything. We went on waiting and I felt more hopeful every second. The moment would come when he'd get tired of wasting his time and slam the receiver down. But that wasn't what happened. 'Yes, I'm still here . . . . Good. Thank you very much.' The colonel rang off and got to his feet. 'Quite so. Your father has not been stripped of French citizenship. I shall order his release, and your mother's as well.'"

"Thank you sir." Henri bowed. Half an hour later, the three of them were together again in Henri's hotel room.

It was Albert's turn to snatch a cigarette. "How were they?"

"All right. A little thinner, of course, and they certainly needed sleep. They send you boys their love."

"But where are they now?" asked Maurice.

"They're in Nice. They need a little time to get settled there, and as soon as they're ready, they'll let us know and we'll go and see them."

I broke in, "How come the man at police headquarters said Father wasn't Jewish?"

"I thought about that a lot," Henri said. "There are two possible explanations. First the loss of citizenship might not have been registered yet . . . some delay in the paperwork. Or else . . ." I saw him hesitate, "or else the bloke said the first thing that came into his head because he couldn't find the file."

Another possibility was running through my mind. Timidly, I hazarded, "There might be another reason. Perhaps it was the colonel. Perhaps they did tell him over the phone that Father was Jewish and perhaps he said what he did so that he could let them go."

Henri leaned his elbows on his knees. "Frankly, I don't know," he finally said. To me he said, after a moment, "Jo, if you're ever at a loose end, you could always earn a living by writing detective stories."

I went to bed feeling absolutely certain that I had found the solution: a hero who hid his generosity under a grumpy exterior. Yes, that must be how my parents' lives were saved.

FOUR DAYS after Henri's return, we received the first letter from Nice. Father was doing well; he had found a flat near the church of La Buffa. It would be easy for Albert and Henri to find work in the town. He would work too. The summer season was approaching and the place would be busy. He ended his letter by saying that within a month or two we would all be together again, like in Paris.

I thought that a "month or two" was terribly far off. I was eager to see them again and I also wanted to see Nice. The very name set me dreaming; I imagined it full of palatial hotels frequented by women bedecked with jewels and furs, smoking long cigarettes in long cigarette holders.

Two more weeks went by. The weather was now warm and the trees in the gardens of the villas were covered with buds and leaves. Soon we would be swimming. One day after school we went to buy bathing suits. Maurice bought a blue one with white stripes; mine was white with blue stripes. I tried mine on that

vening and did some spectacular somersaults on the bed.
Maurice was drying dishes.

It was then that somebody knocked at the door. It was two
gendarmes.

The smaller one produced a piece of paper which he unfolded
slowly. "Albert and Henri Joffo."

"I'm Albert, but my brother isn't in."

He was a dazzlingly quick thinker; if they were planning to
arrest him, Henri would have a faint chance of getting away.
Henri understood. I saw him back silently into the bedroom where
he waited, ready to slip under the bed.

I was sure that the worst had come: they must have sorted out
the mistake in Paris; the camp commandant must have given the
alarm. We should have moved as soon as Henri came back.

"What can I do for you?"

"Have you got your identity card?"

Albert took it from his wallet. He cast a brief glance in our
direction which said, "Keep calm, the worst hasn't happened."

Maurice kept on polishing the same plate. I was still in my
bathing suit, standing on my bed.

"Here are two summonses, for you and your brother," the
gendarme said. "You have to report to police headquarters within
two days. It's for the S.T.O."

There was a short silence and the one who still hadn't spoken
said, "Everyone does it, you know . . . ."

"Of course," said Albert.

The same policeman replied, "We just bring the orders—we
don't make them."

"Naturally."

"Well, that's about it," concluded the other. "Good evening,
sorry to have bothered you."

The door closed. Henri emerged from the bedroom.

"What is S.T.O.?" asked Maurice.

"*Service de Travail Obligatoire*; it means we're going to
Germany to cut the Krauts' hair. At least, that's what they think."

We held a brief council of war. Their course of action was clear:
they weren't going to Germany. By the same token, they clearly

453

couldn't stay in Menton where the police would certainly come back.

"O.K." Henri said, "We'll start packing straight away, and we'll leave at dawn."

"Where are we going?"

Albert turned to me with the look of somebody about to announce a pleasant surprise. "You'll like this Jo: we're going to Nice."

I had trouble getting to sleep. I would miss Menton, the old streets, my friend Virgilio, even the schoolmistress, but I didn't feel sad. I would see my parents again. Tomorrow. I would put on my haversack once more, and soon I'd be in the city of a thousand grand hotels, the golden city at the edge of the blue sea.

Chapter 6

"Marcello! Marcello!"

I rushed after Maurice, who was running across the Place Masséna. It was hard running with a wicker basket on each arm, particularly since they were full of tomatoes. The one on my left arm was full of the long ones called *olivettes*; on my right were little round tomatoes, which the people of Nice called "love apples".

The soldier in front of us stopped. The sun lit up his face; he was laughing at the sight of me so weighted down. If he had not had a splendid broken nose and curly hair gleaming with brilliantine, he would have resembled Amedeo Nazzari, the film star; but Marcello had spent too many evenings in the boxing ring of a Turin suburb to keep a Grecian profile.

"Here, hand over the tomatoes!" He spoke French fairly correctly, but his accent was catastrophic. "Follow me; we're going to Tite's."

Tite's was a tiny bistro near the harbour frequented by local pensioners and, above all, by Italian soldiers, who would sing and play the guitar before going on a picturesque kind of guard duty at the strategic points of the town. We often traded there. Old

454

Madame Rossi always left the kitchen door open, so the place smelt of onions twenty-four hours a day.

Marcello's friends were there, three soldiers who threw open their arms to welcome us. There was a tall student from Rome with glasses, who looked more like an Englishman; a Parmesan carpenter (before meeting him I thought all Parmesans were cheeses), and a Venetian corporal older than the others.

Triumphantly, Marcello moved aside the glasses of wine on the table and put down the two baskets of tomatoes.

"Here's your bargain."

They jabbered away good-humouredly and Carlo (the student) offered us the litre of olive oil from behind the bar.

Through the vagaries of the Italian commissariat, the occupying troops were inundated with olive oil in every form—tunny in oil, sardines in oil, drums of oil itself. The pleas of the mess officers went unheeded, the oil poured in. The Italians finally tumbled to the fact that the oil was a valuable commodity for trading for vegetables, tomatoes and lettuce—something other than their eternal tinned fish. We had got in touch with a gardener who sold us tomatoes, we supplied him with Italian oil, and he paid us the surplus in cash. With that money and the cigarettes that my corporal pilfered for us from the commissariat, we would buy black-market flour which we delivered to Tite's café, where the Parmesan, using old Madame Rossi's kitchen, would manufacture macaroni. We would get a refund on that, with which we bought more tomatoes. In two months Maurice and I amassed a small fortune.

When walking past the Négresco and the Ruhl, Maurice would nod towards the sumptuous façades and say, rubbing his hands, "If things go on like this, we'll be able to buy those places."

Marcello was already slicing the plum tomatoes into a huge salad bowl. "What we need is some herbs to put in . . . I don't know how you say it in French."

"Parsley."

"Yes, that's it. Parsley."

Maurice and I exchanged glances. The butcher near the docks might have some. I knew him vaguely; he was a smoker.

455

I turned to the corporal. "Could you get me two packets for this afternoon?"

"Yes, but you'll have to come for them. Four o'clock."

Two packets should get me a haversack full of parsley, a largish steak and a tip, if my approach was right. I gulped down a glass of *grenadine* paid for by a soldier of the occupying forces and went out again with Maurice.

"I've got to go up to the barracks," said Maurice. "One of Marcello's friends has got some real coffee, and what he wants is lentils."

"Do you know where to get some?"

Maurice had turned into a living directory. He knew where to find everything from butter to ties. "I think that the man in the shop on the rue Garibaldi has some. I'll go there now. Will you concentrate on the parsley?"

"All right, and we'll meet back at the house."

"You know, what we really need is a bike."

That was an old dream. But finding a bicycle wasn't as easy as finding eight kilos of tomatoes. And it wasn't just a matter of the bike—we would need tyres, and they were virtually priceless.

Anyhow, I didn't have anything to do for a while, so I took a stroll along the promenade. The beach was packed, particularly in front of the hotels. Italian officers were sitting on the terraces, their uniforms gleaming in the sunlight. Theirs was a pleasant war! There were elegant women sitting with them, and their dresses were not the kind you got with clothing coupons. They had their hair done by Albert and Henri in the hairdresser's opposite the Hotel Adriatique.

My brothers had been forging ahead: they no longer worked in some small barber's but in a really smart place and they were often summoned to some luxurious flat or to a suite in one of the grand hotels.

Father and Mother had settled comfortably into their flat and, if it hadn't been for the BBC broadcast each night, I would have felt we were spending a holiday on the Côte d'Azur. My dreams had almost come true: I was running wild in that glittering gilded city where money seemed to flow like water.

456

The Nice newspaper proclaimed German victories persistently. On the Russian front, the Panzers had reached Stalingrad and would presumably soon take it. But on the evening radio, despite the jamming, I heard a different story about Stalingrad, lots of Germans had died and all armoured vehicles were totally, helplessly immobilized in the mud.

Whom should I believe? I often talked about it with Maurice on the beach, but it was so difficult, while we were swimming in a warm sea, to imagine fields of snow or the night sky torn by gunfire and planes—I could barely believe in the reality of the war any more. One dark spot loomed on the horizon: September. Going back to school. There was one just near our house and I would hurry past it every morning so as not to see the row of classrooms, shaded by six enormous plane trees.

I left the beach and went home.

"Is that you, Joseph?" called my mother over the sizzling sound of frying fish. "Go and wash before lunch. Is Maurice with you?"

"No, but he's coming. He went to the shop on the rue Garibaldi to get some lentils."

Father came in, tousled my hair. "You two and your business deals . . . ."

But I knew that he really was pleased that we could fend for ourselves. One day, I overheard him saying to my mother, "You know they joke about buying the Hotel Négresco? Well, sometimes I wonder if they won't actually manage it!"

Maurice came in, gulped down his meal and we jumped up.

"*Now* where are you going?"

Maurice launched into a complicated explanation: the shopkeeper he had been to had sold out of lentils, but he could get some in exchange for resoling leather shoes. For that, we had to persuade the cobbler on the rue Saint Pierre to exchange his services for one or two litres of oil.

Father raised his head over the top of his newspaper. "Speaking of cobblers, I will tell you a story. It goes like this: one man says to another, 'There's a simple way to get all men to live in peace—just kill all the Jews and all the cobblers.' The other man reflects a moment, then asks 'But why the cobblers?'"

There was a surprised silence; then Mother began laughing. I asked, "Why the Jews, too?"

Father smiled bitterly. "That's just what the second man didn't ask, and that's why the story is funny."

We left the house, deep in thought. On the square we saw the guard changing. The soldiers were sweating in their uniforms; they had their rifles over their shoulders, but one of them was holding a mandolin in his free hand.

The war might have been on another planet.

THE COURTYARD was gleaming in the rain. It was already cold, and the teacher lit the stove in the classroom every morning. From time to time, as I struggled with a geometry problem, the teacher would get up and poke the stove so that a more intense wave of heat would envelop us.

With a trampling of feet and creaking of benches we stood up. The headmaster had come in. He was a thin man whose trousers came up almost to his armpits. He came in once a week to give us singing lessons. Behind him, two pupils were installing a harmonium on the platform; this instrument emitted a particularly unpleasant squealing sound. The headmaster motioned us to be seated, "Let's see if you've made any progress. Camerini, go to the board and draw me a nice treble clef."

The lesson began; I was not very talented and as soon as the notes went above "A" I was lost.

. "Now, we'll sing through our song, and I hope you'll put some feeling into it. I'm going to ask François to sing it through once alone."

François was a walking disaster. He rarely left school with the rest of us because he was almost always kept in. None the less, François was the headmaster's favourite because he had a wonderful voice. This lord of the rowdies, this shooter of rubber bands, had the most beautiful soprano voice I have ever heard.

"*Allons, enfants de la patrie . . . .*"

We listened to him in total silence.

The headmaster raised his hands like a conductor. "All right now, all together this time."

458

We sang the *Marseillaise* with great feeling.

Father was pleased that we sang such songs. Someone could have complained to the authorities and the headmaster could have been in trouble . . . . At the time, we didn't know the skinny man with the belted up trousers was one of the local Resistance leaders.

NOVEMBER 8 was Mother's birthday and Maurice had agreed to loosen our purse strings to buy her a gold brooch, shaped like a sea horse with red stones for eyes.

Since starting school business had slackened off—first of all, because we had less free time, then because it wasn't the tomato season any more. Also, the Italian commissariat had finally realized its mistake and had stopped flooding the garrisons on the Côte d'Azur with oil, so that the main currency had been eliminated.

Mother was pleased with her presents; she immediately pinned the sea horse on her dress, and hugged us. Then she kissed Father and my brothers, who had given her a sewing machine. A priceless treasure at the time.

"A present worthy of a Romanov," Henri commented. It was a well-worn joke but we still thought it funny. A good many years before, a Jewish girl had left her country with the help of forged papers; those same papers had saved her life only a short time ago in Pau.

She slipped out of the room and came back with a cake, a kind of *Gugelhupf* which even had the traditional almonds on top. Father swallowed the first mouthful and got up. It was time for the English broadcast. Albert was telling us about an irritating customer who claimed that Hitler was an intelligent man, since he was rising to power not only in his own country, but in most of Europe as well. Just then, Father came back looking rather pale.

"They've landed," he announced. We stared at him, our mouths stuffed with cake. He leaned over my mother and took her hands. "Happy birthday," he said. "The Allies have landed in North Africa, in Algeria and Morocco. It's the beginning of the end. With a new front on their hands, the Germans are finished."

We bent over the map. It was just a few centimetres of blue paper from Algiers to Nice; just the sea to cross and they'd be here; we had nothing to fear now. From that evening on we went through a ritual that I suppose most French families observed at the time: we stuck little flags linked together with darning wool into a map hanging on the wall. We painted the flags red for the Russians and added white stripes for the Americans. As the BBC reeled off names of the newly-won towns we planted the flags of victory.

Once Stalingrad had been retaken, there was Kharkov, then Rostov, then Kiev. There was also a great battle at El Alamein, but I was most thrilled when, on July 10th, 1943 the Allies landed in Sicily.

I remember it all clearly. There were only three more days of school, the weather was fabulous. Everything was happening all at once; the summer, the holidays, and the Allies. In the streets the Italians strolled imperturbably, as though events had nothing to do with them, accompanied by girls even prettier and browner than those of the year before.

With the good weather, tomatoes were back and we resumed business operations. I managed to get hold of a bicycle through a friend at school. It was a bit small for me but by sitting well back on the saddle I could just about ride it.

On the last day of school, there was a prize giving. Maurice, who had grown a head taller and was fast becoming a muscle man, won a prize for gymnastics. I won one for reading, and came home proud as a peacock. I had a sunny future: two and a half months of freedom, a bicycle, and the conviction that, by the end of summer holidays, we would be free.

I RODE UP the hill standing, leapt off, a quick turn of the pedal to prop the bike against the kerb, and I grabbed the sack of semolina. There were two cupfuls, but that was enough for one of Mother's cakes. I got the semolina in exchange for tins of corned beef obtained in an earlier deal.

I met Maurice on the stairs; he gestured excitedly.

"Come with me."

"Hang on. I've just got to drop off the semolina . . ."

"Hurry up. I'll wait for you downstairs!"

I went up the stairs two at a time, left the semolina and came back down four at a time.

We ran all the way to the town limits. After crossing a field we finally reached the rubbish dump. What with the heat, the smell wasn't pleasant and the place was thick with flies. We climbed a path strewn with dirty papers and rusty springs and arrived at the top of a plateau of refuse.

Maurice stopped, panting. Ahead of us, two of his mates were squatting.

"Look!"

I bent forward over their shoulders.

Resting on a cushion of detective novels were four rifles, their butt-plates gleaming.

"Where did you find them?"

Maurice's friend Paul turned to me.

"Under a mattress, and I can tell you one thing—they weren't here yesterday. Somebody shoved them in there during the night."

"What shall we do with them?" the other boy asked.

I thought about the men in the Resistance who needed them so much. But how could we contact them?

Maurice took the initiative. "The best thing to do is hide them again, but properly this time. They're Italian guns left behind by soldiers. I heard that Italian soldiers are starting to desert. People are saying Mussolini was arrested."

I was stupefied. "Arrested . . . but by whom?"

"I don't know. We should go to Tite's and find out what's going on. But watch it—not a word about the rifles."

THE CURTAIN was drawn in the doorway of the bar to keep out the heat. Inside it was cool and dark.

Most of the soldiers we knew were gone. Carlo and the Parmesan had been sent to Sicily to stem the Allied tide. Their presence, it seemed, was inadequate, Sicily was taken in less than six weeks.

461

My friend, the corporal, had disappeared, too. Marcello had received a month-old letter from him telling him that his new regiment was awaiting an Allied landing on the Italian mainland. As for Marcello, he had become barman at the officers' mess and seemed determined to conclude the war shaking up cocktails on the Côte d'Azur.

The new customers were younger but less gay. One of them, a very serious, gentle boy who had studied accounting, became my friend. He was sitting there that afternoon, working at his French with the aid of a grammar book and a dictionary which a certain schoolboy had supplied in exchange for cigarettes. He was hoping to be able to speak French before the end of the war, so that he could get a better job. He closed the book with a sigh when I sat down.

"I'll stop now, Jo. I just don't have the time."

I looked at him in surprise. "Why?"

"Because we're going away soon."

Patiently, he explained. "Mussolini isn't in charge any more—it's Badoglio, and everybody expects him to make peace with the Americans."

I felt a flash of hope. "If you're going, then we're free."

He looked at me sadly. "No, if we go, the Germans will come."

The bar, already in shadow, grew darker.

Maurice asked, "Is that really so?"

"Nobody can be sure. But if we make a separate peace with America, we'll be at war with the Germans. Nobody wants to fight. Some of us have already left."

I thought about the four rifles we had found at the rubbish dump.

"Are there any deserters?" He nodded. "What about you? What are you going to do?" I asked.

His gaze slid over the few bottles that still stood on the shelves behind the bar. "I don't know. I don't like the war. But it's dangerous to run away from the army. You can be shot."

In the days that followed, soldiers deserted in droves. On September 8th, the news became official: Marshal Badoglio had signed the armistice near Syracuse. Units were crossing the

462

border to carry on the war, against the Germans this time. One morning, Nice woke up to find that the Italian occupying forces were gone. London announced that Hitler was sending thirty crack regiments across the Alps and that he would occupy all of Italy.

On September 10th a train pulled into the station and a thousand Germans got off. Among them were SS troops and men of the Gestapo. The second Occupation had begun.

Chapter 7

It was six o'clock.

Time dragged now that we were cooped up in the house. I had spent the afternoon reading and helping Mother kill the weevils that had got into the few beans we had left. We simply watched the clock until Albert and Henri got home, and every passing minute was a minute of anguish.

Three days ago, the Gestapo had moved into the Hotel Excelsior. The *Kommandantur* was at Place Masséna and round-ups had begun. Many Jewish people had already been arrested as a result of casual denunciations. Our shutters were closed, even though it was still broad daylight. Father was pacing back and forth. "What can they be doing?"

Footsteps in the corridor—it was them.

Henri collapsed into a chair. "Well, it's very simple," said Henri. "We've got to leave, and fast. We heard some German customers talking amongst themselves today. The drift was that they're arresting all Jews, holding them at the Hotel Excelsior and, every Friday, taking them off in special trains to the German camps."

Father sat back and laid his hands flat on the tablecloth.

"Henri is right," he said. "We'll have to split up again. And we'll stick to the method that's worked for us so far—set off two by two.

"First you two, Henri and Albert. You'll leave tomorrow for Aix-les-Bains. I know someone there who will hide you. Joseph and Maurice, you're leaving tomorrow morning for Golfe-Juan, for a camp called 'New Harvest'. It's supposedly a paramilitary organization run by the Vichy government, a part of the *Compagnons de France*. But you'll soon see that it's not quite like that."

"What about you two? What are you going to do?"

"Don't worry about us. We're old hands at this game. And now let's have supper. You must go to bed early, so as to be ready for tomorrow morning."

When I went to the bedroom that night, I found my haversack on the bed. It seemed to me, as I looked at it, that I had already left Nice and was out on the road, walking endlessly towards a goal—a goal that wasn't in sight.

New Harvest.

There was a big sign over the iron gate, and behind the gate we saw teenage boys in blue shorts, shirts and berets carrying canvas bags containing water, or chopping wood. It was like a scout camp, and that was something that had never appealed to me. It didn't seem to be working its magic on Maurice either.

"Well, shall we go in or not?"

We had brought along part of our savings and I felt like suggesting that we carry on northwards. We could hide on a farm, work a little . . . On the other hand, this Pétainist camp was certainly the last place that the Krauts would think of looking for two Jewish children. So it was safety first.

"Let's go in."

Together we pushed the gate open.

We were greeted by a tall, gawky boy in flapping shorts. He clicked his heels and gave an elaborate salute.

"Are you new here? Who sent you?"

I took an instant dislike to this character, and Maurice didn't seem particularly enamoured of him, either.

"We'd like to see the head of the camp, Monsieur Subinagui."

"Follow me."

He wheeled round and marched us off towards a large hut that rose above the tents. He knocked, opened the door, clicked his heels and announced, "Two new boys who want to speak to you, sir."

"Thank you, Gérard. You may go."

Gérard did an about-turn, and marched out at the double.

We must have looked astonished, for the director said, "Gérard is a good boy, but his father was a sergeant-major in the regular army and he was brought up accordingly."

He was very dark with a high forehead, and something enigmatic about the eyes. I had the feeling that this man already knew all about me. Something about him fascinated me: even in that gloomy hut, surrounded by filing cabinets, old chairs, and all manner of jumble.

"Your father spoke to me about you. I agreed to take you even though you're under age, but you both look big enough. I think you'll like it here and . . . you'll be safe."

He didn't say another word about that, but it was unnecessary.

"You have two choices: you can stay inside the camp and help by cooking and cleaning, or you can go out to work and come back to eat and sleep. Your bed and board would amount to roughly three quarters of your wages."

"What kind of work would there be?" said Maurice.

"You can help the local market gardeners or else go to Vallauris where we have set up a pottery workshop. We sell our products to keep the community going."

"I wouldn't mind trying the pottery," I said.

"Me too," said Maurice reluctantly.

Subinagui laughed. "It's noble of you to make that sacrifice. I get the impression that you two stick together? All right, then. Vallauris it shall be. You'll start tomorrow morning. Best of luck!"

Gérard was waiting for us outside. He led us to a tent, and showed us our beds. At the foot of each bed lay two folded blankets and two sheets sewn together to make a sleeping-bag.

"Supper's at six o'clock," said Gérard. "Lowering of the colours at seven, showers at eight thirty, bed at nine, lights out at nine fifteen." He clicked his heels yet again, saluted and marched off.

A voice came from under a bed. "Don't worry about him. He's a bit cracked but he's good-hearted."

465

A head appeared, a mop of wiry hair, two eyes like coffee-beans and a bulbous nose: I had just met Ange Testi.

While I was making my bed he told me that he should have been peeling potatoes. He had bowed out, claiming a stomach-ache. He was going to use the same excuse next morning at sick bay, hoping to be excused a few days' work.

I pulled on the blankets and asked him, "Do you like this place?"

"Yes," said Ange. "It's great. There are lots of Jews."

I gave a start, but he had said it quite innocently; he was lying sprawled out on his mattress, and in fact, I cannot remember having seen much of Ange in the vertical position. He had a distinct preference for lying down.

"You're not Jewish?"

"No, and you?"

He gave a little laugh.

"Don't worry. Baptism, catechism, communion, confirmation, and choirboy into the bargain."

"How did you get here?"

He clasped his hands behind his head and glanced around him like a blissful Buddha. "Well, you see, I'm on holiday. Honestly. If you don't mind, I'll go back under the bed, because if the bloke in charge of the kitchen catches me he'll give me hell."

Ange was an Algerian. He had wanted to spend his holidays in France after hearing its wonders vaunted by his father and grandfather. He had been staying at a cousin's house in Paris when the Americans landed in North Africa. After a day or two he grasped that, for as long as the war continued, he couldn't get home. "Just think of it—if the war goes on another ten years, that'll mean a ten-year holiday for me."

His Parisian cousin having conceived of the preposterous idea of getting married, Ange found himself out on the streets without much money. Lured by the sun, he had come south. He begged for a few days and then, by chance, passed by the main gate of the camp. Subinagui had kept him and he'd been here ever since.

A bell announced six-o'clock supper. As Ange knew all the tricks, we found ourselves seats at a trestle table near the canteen.

466

The noise was deafening. There were two Belgians next to me; they too were waiting for the war to end so they could go home. Opposite me sat a tow-haired boy named Jean Masso, whose parents lived in Grasse; I thought he and I might become friends.

After the meal everybody assembled near the flagpole while the flag was lowered. After that, the boys went back to the tents, they played draughts, cards, a gambling game called *petits chevaux*. I played a game of dominoes with Ange, Jean and Maurice, and at nine o'clock I was in bed.

In the dark above me, I heard the buzzing of insects, but that wasn't what bothered me. It was the thousand and one noises of communal life; the creaking of the beds, sniffling, coughing, the breathing of sleepers. It wasn't until the small hours of the morning that I finally fell asleep.

A whistle-blast pierced my eardrums and I sprang out of my bed in terror. The boys were already folding up their blankets, exchanging the first insults of the day, milling about at the wash basins. Only Ange Testi seemed in no hurry to get out of bed.

"Joffo, Maurice and Joseph, wanted in the supply room, fast!"

I acquired three shirts with patch pockets and shoulder tabs, a pair of shorts and three pairs of socks, all in the same shade of blue. Dressed like that, I felt my morale plummeting. I couldn't stand regimentation.

The village of Vallauris was quite near Golfe-Juan. On the outskirts was a tall building whose roof had collapsed. This housed the pottery workshop of the *Compagnons de France*. Pots of all shapes and sizes were lined up along one of the walls. All of a sudden I found myself in front of a potter's wheel and a lump of clay, and was told to get on with it.

From the first moment, one thing struck me with blinding clarity; you can love a craft and yet come to loathe it very quickly if the conditions are wrong. I wanted to make pots; I liked the sight and feeling of the clay, what I wanted more than anything else was to create a pot that was my own—different from any of those I saw lined up against the wall.

The potter who had taken me into his charge did not share this view. Perhaps he was right; perhaps one has to be an imitator before becoming a creator. Be that as it may, every time I tried to give my work a personal touch, I was shoved off my stool and, with economical expertise my mentor would re-establish the favoured proportions.

After two hours of this, he stopped the wheel and looked at me perplexed. "No sense of proportion," he muttered. "We're going to have trouble."

I took a chance.

"Could I make one without a model—just for fun?"

I had made a most serious blunder and it earned me an angry lecture: the pottery workshop wasn't intended for fun; practice makes perfect; potters don't improvise; and so forth.

When he seemed recovered, the potter flattened my mound of clay and said, "Start again. I'll be back in ten minutes."

I pedalled glumly; he came back, frowned, growled and stuck me behind one of his disciples who seemed to have been glued to his wheel for a thousand years. Rigid with boredom, I watched him create yet another identical pot. I went back to my own wheel after an hour, but by then it was lunchtime.

Maurice hadn't made much of a success of it either.

By the end of the day, my head resounding with barked commands, clay up to my armpits and sweat running down my back, I concluded that, if I didn't wish to yield to the temptation of slapping a couple of pounds of clay in the master's face, I had better give up pottery for good.

That was my only experience of the art which was to become so famous on the very site. Let it be known: for a day, I too was a potter at Picasso's Vallauris.

The first thing we did that evening was to report to Subinagui. He didn't share the master's pedagogic notions either. After consulting a file, he said, "Give the kitchens a try. The work is less artistic, but you will enjoy more freedom."

THAT WAS THE start of three wonderful weeks. Maurice helped the butcher and spent his days cutting out steaks and playing a card game called *manille*, I stirred cauldrons of mashed potatoes, tossed great bowls of salad, sliced cartloads of tomatoes, always in

468

the company of Masso and Ange, who gladly gave up his siestas to work with me. We were an inseparable trio.

The black market inside the camp was mostly in sugar and flour. I sometimes slipped a few chocolate bars under my shirt but I didn't take part on a large scale. Not that I was particularly honest, but I couldn't have borne it had Subinagui found out. I knew the difficulties he was having supplying the camp with food.

There were happy evenings when we would sit around and listen to guitar music. I loved the smell of the pine trees and the sea when the darkness fell and the breeze sprang up, blowing away the heat of the day; then, we would relax and sing. That did us good; it reminded us of peacetime.

Still, we knew that the war was still on; fighting was raging in Italy; the Germans had captured whole regiments of their erstwhile allies and I wondered what had become of my friends from Tite's. Despite all their efforts, the British and Americans had stopped south of Naples and the Germans were retreating less in Russia, and seemed to be getting ready for a great offensive.

We didn't talk much about such things in camp. Some of the boys were staunch supporters of Pétain: others were frankly pro-German. Maurice told me not even to confide in my friends. The hunt for Jews had intensified. Apparently pretence had ended: any Jew—anyone suspected of being a Jew—was being shipped to German camps.

One morning while I was cleaning the top of the kitchen stove, Maurice came towards me in his big navy-blue apron. "Jo, I've been thinking about what we ought to say if the Germans make a raid and start questioning us. Subinagui talked to me about it. We'll have to make something up, a whole life history. And I think I've got an idea. You know Ange's story?"

"Of course. He tells it often enough!"

"Well, that's our story too."

"You mean we came over from North Africa on holiday and we stayed here because of the Allied landings?"

"That's it. The great advantage is that it's impossible for them to check our story—they'd have to believe us."

469

I looked at Maurice. No doubt he had everything planned, but I had to be sure. To do that, I had to ask the questions that we might be asked.

"What kind of work do our parents do?"

"Father is a barber; Mother doesn't work."

"And where do we live?"

"Number ten, rue Jean-Jaurès."

That called for an explanation. "Why rue Jean-Jaurès?"

"Because there's always a rue Jean-Jaurès, and ten because it's easy to remember."

"And if they ask us to describe the shop, the house, the floor we live on, anything like that—what are we going to say?"

"Just describe the house on the rue Clignancourt."

I nodded. Suddenly he grabbed me by the shoulder; shaking me he shouted, "Und vare is your school, leedle boy?"

"Rue Jean-Jaurès, same street, a little farther down."

He gave an approving uppercut. "That's good," he said. "Very good. You're a bit backward in some ways, but you've got good reflexes. Here, block this one . . . ." He circled round me, dancing.

That same evening, when we were already in bed, I got up on one elbow and leaned across the gap between our beds. "Your plan won't work."

He raised his head. "Why not?"

"Because Subinagui has our identity cards. He knows where we come from and if the Krauts ask questions, he'll have to tell them."

"Don't worry," came the cool reply. "I'll talk to him about it. He'll help us."

Silence fell. Some boys were already asleep or reading by torchlight under their sheets. Before finally going to sleep, Maurice added, "You know, I think some of the others here are in the same boat as us."

"HEY, YOU TWO JOFFOS, do you want to come down to Nice with me?"

The engine of the van was running and Ferdinand already had his foot on the running board.

470

Ferdinand was twenty-four, and very skinny. He was the bursar of the centre, and Subinagui's right-hand man.

It was Friday, and three o'clock, and Ferdinand was going down to the town to settle some bills.

Maurice and I just happened to be there when the proposition fell into our laps. An afternoon in Nice! A windfall.

"What about getting back?"

"We could take the evening bus. Yes or no?"

It was too tempting. With our camp uniforms, we were in no danger. And I so wanted to know what had become of our parents. I had the feeling that just by seeing the outside of the house, I would know if they were still there. And then . . . well, if everything was quiet, we could nip up for a moment.

The van turned, its wheels spinning on the gravel near the entrance, and drove through the gates. Ferdinand turned to us.

"Do you know anybody in Nice?"

"No. We're just going to walk around."

When I suddenly saw the bay broadening out at the bend in the road, I felt a rush of emotion. There, in the jumble of tiny houses behind the church of La Buffa, was our house.

"I want to see a friend on the rue de Russie," Ferdinand said. "I won't be long. Then I'll show you where the bus station is, and you can go off."

"Fine."

The van stopped and once more we were upon the pavements of Nice.

"Here we are. I won't be a couple of minutes." Ferdinand disappeared through an old porchway.

I had forgotten how hot these streets were. There were buildings between us and the sea, preventing any cool air from reaching us. The streets were deserted; down the road was a signpost in German.

"What's he up to?" murmured Maurice.

I found it hard to judge how much time had gone by without a watch.

"He's only been gone two minutes, if that much."

"You're out of your mind. He's been gone at least ten."

471

"How can you know how long he's been gone?"

Maurice put on the lordly air that always exasperated me. "I can just feel it. If you can't feel the difference between two minutes or three-quarters of an hour, you might just as well jump into the sea."

I let the insult pass; it was too hot to fight. Instead, I just sat down on the ground in the shade of the wall.

Maurice was pacing up and down. Suddenly he said, "I'm going to see. I don't want to spend the whole afternoon hanging around here." He pushed the door open and went inside.

It was true; he was right; time was passing and we were just wasting it stupidly, sitting on a stifling street. If only I had something to play with—but there was nothing. My pockets were empty and there weren't even any pebbles to go some way towards making up a set of fivestones.

And now it was Maurice who wasn't coming back.

What were those two idiots doing? I was dying of boredom, in front of a door, while . . . . Well, I was going inside too. They were not going to push me around just because I was the youngest.

It was pleasant in the courtyard; there was ivy on one of the walls, an archway at the end, and a pile of children's toys near a sandpit. No *concierge*. A staircase, and that was that.

I crossed the courtyard and put my foot on the first step. The wall hit me; my palms smacked against the bricks as I threw out my hands so as not to split my skull. Pain streaked down my back; I turned round. There was a soldier; he had sent me flying with the barrel of his submachine gun. The grey-green of his uniform captured all the light in the hallway. The black circle of the muzzle was a few inches from my nose.

He bent over me, reeking of cigarettes. His hand squeezed my arm hard and the tears welled in my eyes.

"Jew," he said. "Jew."

He catapulted me headlong into another room. The door closed behind me.

Maurice was there; so were Ferdinand and two women, one of whom was crying. She had blood trickling down her forehead.

I sat down in a daze. I didn't understand. It was all a dream. A few minutes ago I was out on a street; it was summer, and I was free. Then there was a courtyard, a brutal shove, and now . . . .

"What's happening?"

"It's my fault," whispered Ferdinand. "They had a Resistance centre here which provided people with forged documents."

Maurice looked at him. "But why did you come here?"

"With all the rumours running round the camp lately, I got worried. I had this address and I wanted to get away before the Krauts arrived in Golfe-Juan."

I stared at him stupidly. "But why?"

Ferdinand glanced at the door. "Because I'm Jewish." He looked at us. "Don't worry; when they find out you're not Jews they'll let you go."

He looked at me. He needn't have worried. I knew the lesson by heart. There weren't going to be any mistakes.

"What are you going to tell them, Ferdinand?"

A sob shook him. "I don't know . . . I just can't believe it. I'd had it all worked out to get a new identity card, and just when it looked as though everything was all right . . . ."

The women just sat on their chairs, motionless. It was terribly hot. The room had been painted with gloss and furnished with chairs and a wardrobe, nothing else. No window. The light was on; without it we could have seen nothing. We sat there for three hours. My backside ached from sitting for so long. Perhaps they had forgotten about us. They probably weren't concerned with us anyway. They must be after the bigwigs, men they had been looking for for a long time. What were we to them? Precisely nothing. Two frightened women, two kids and a bag of bones—what a haul!

What I least understood was the soldier's brutality, his pointless violence. I had the feeling that his lifetime's ambition was to smash me against that wall. Why? Was I his enemy? We had never seen each other before; I had never done anything to him, and he wanted to kill me. It was only then that I began to understand Mother and the people who used to come to the shop

473

in Paris, who used to say that war was absurd. In my history book, war was picturesque and exciting, presented in an aura of agreements, treaties, reflections, decisions . . . . How could anybody think that Philippe Auguste, Napoleon, Clemenceau and all the wise and highly placed ministers and councillors had been madmen? No, surely war wasn't absurd.

Then suddenly the leaders of *this* war, grown-ups with neat ties and flashing medals, had deemed it necessary to throw me, a child, into a locked room—I who had done nothing, who didn't know a single German.

The door opened. Now there were two of them, rifles slung across their fronts. "Outside! Get a move on!"

We stampeded for the door. I grabbed Maurice's hand. Whatever happened, we mustn't get separated. The two women were in front, Ferdinand puffing behind me.

Outside, a truck was waiting. We bounded into the back and one of the two soldiers climbed in after us; the other one lifted the heavy iron tail-board. There were no seats, so we had to stand. We clung together and the truck lurched forward. I saw the street turn sharply and disappear.

At last, the truck stopped abruptly. Once out in the bright sunlight, I had no difficulty working out where I was. In front of us was the Hotel Excelsior, headquarters of the Gestapo in Nice.

Chapter 8

The foyer was packed with people, children and suitcases. The noise was infernal. Near me was a couple in their mid-sixties. The man was bald and wearing his Sunday best; the woman was short and must have just had a perm. From time to time they looked at one another, and I was afraid.

I was young, very young, but I understood that those two old people were looking at one another like people who have lived together all their lives and who know that they are about to be separated; they would travel the rest of the way alone.

Suddenly, there was a great stir. At the head of the stairs, two

474

SS men had appeared with a civilian holding a list of names. At each name he read out, he looked round to see if someone had stood up; then he crossed the name off the sheet. As soon as their names were called, the people went out through a side door. Presumably a lorry was taking them to the station. Soon we would be all alone, just the five of us, leaning against the end wall.

"Meyer, Richard, seven, two, nine."

The old man standing with his wife didn't flinch. Slowly he bent down, picked up his little suitcase and walked forward unhurriedly.

I admired him for that calm, for his confidence; I knew that, at the moment, he wasn't afraid.

"Meyer, Marthe, seven, three, oh."

The little lady picked up a smaller suitcase, and I felt tears in my eyes. They were together again at the door. I was glad that they hadn't been separated.

The foyer was now empty. The man in civilian clothes—an interpreter, apparently—gestured to us to go upstairs. Once there we stopped in a corridor with rows of doors. "Go in you two," he said, motioning to the women.

The three of us continued standing in the corridor, unguarded. I wanted to pee—it had been a long time and I was afraid.

"Will you be all right, Joseph?" Maurice whispered.

"I'll be all right."

The door opened and the two women came out. Both of them were crying. They went downstairs and we went on waiting. It reminded me of the dentist's on the rue Ramey, when Mother used to take me after school.

The interpreter appeared. This time all three of us went in.

It used to be a hotel bedroom but the bed had gone; instead there was a table with an SS man behind it. He was in his forties, with glasses, and seemed tired. He was holding Ferdinand's identity card. He beckoned to the interpreter to translate.

"Are you Jewish?"

"No."

"If you aren't a Jew, why do you have a forged identity card?"

I didn't look at Ferdinand; I knew that if I looked at him, I wouldn't have courage left for myself.

475

"But . . . those are my papers."

"We can easily find out if you're a Jew or not, so don't give us any trouble. Come clean right away and we won't say any more about it."

He gave the impression that we need only talk and everything would be all right.

"No," said Ferdinand. "I'm not Jewish."

The SS man got to his feet, removed his glasses, came round to the front of his desk and planted himself squarely in front of Ferdinand.

A ringing slap on Ferdinand's cheek set his head wobbling; a second crack sent him reeling back a couple of steps. Tears streamed down his face.

"Stop," said Ferdinand.

"Go ahead, talk. Where are you from?"

In a voice that was scarcely audible, Ferdinand spoke. "I left Poland in 1940. My parents were arrested. I went through Switzerland and . . . ."

The SS man gave him a friendly pat on the shoulder. "There, you see? Don't you think you should have talked sooner? All right, you can go down. Show that to the man at the foot of the stairs."

He held out a green ticket; I was soon to learn what that meant.

"Now, you two. Are you brothers?"

"Yes, he's Joseph and I'm Maurice Joffo."

"And you're Jews."

"No, we aren't Jewish. We're from Algiers."

The SS man now had his glasses on and was scrutinizing us. "What were you doing on the rue de Russie?"

"We had just come from the New Harvest camp, for the *Compagnons de France.* We went along with Ferdinand and were waiting for him, that's all. He told us he was going to see a friend."

The SS man rolled a pencil between his fingers.

Maurice was gaining confidence. He launched out into our pre-arranged story: Father, a barber in Algiers; the school; the holiday and then the landings in North Africa that had prevented

476

ur return. It all went like clockwork until—"And you're
Catholics?"

"Of course."

"Then you've been baptized?"

"Yes, and had our first Communion."

"What church?"

Oh, no! But Maurice's voice is firm.

"La Buffa. In Nice."

"Why not in Algiers?"

"Mother wanted us to take our Communion in France. She had
a cousin in this part of the country."

"Well, we'll check. First, a physical examination. We'll see if
you've been circumcised."

A soldier pushed us up the stairs. They would find out
everything. I didn't care—I would jump out of the train while it
was moving; they wouldn't get me to Germany.

Then we found ourselves in another room. There wasn't any
desk—just an old man in a white overall. He had very black
eyebrows that contrasted with his grizzled hair.

"Take off your shorts and pants."

The doctor motioned us to come closer. The German who had
brought us in was behind us, near the door. We had our backs to
him.

The doctor examined Maurice. He said nothing.

Then it was my turn.

"So you aren't Jewish, eh?"

I pulled up my pants. "No, we aren't Jewish."

He sighed and without looking at the soldier, he said, "Don't
pay any attention to him. He doesn't understand French. We're
alone here—you can tell me the truth and it won't go outside this
office. You're Jewish."

"No," said Maurice. "Our parents had us operated on when we
were little, because we had adhesions, that's all."

He nodded.

"A phimosis, that's called. Do you know that everyone who
comes in here says he had a phimosis in childhood?" He leant
back in his chair and studied us in turn. I don't know what he saw

477

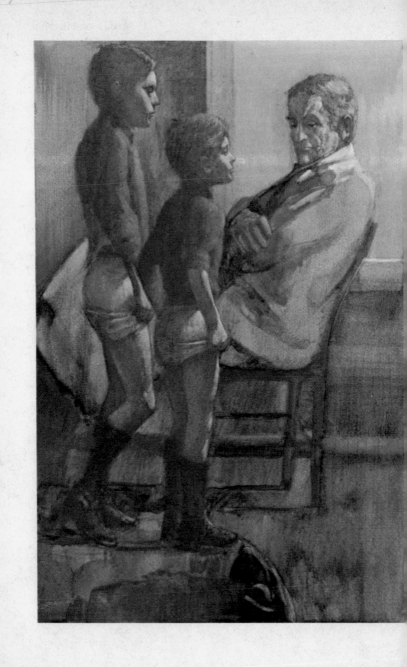

in our eyes, but it was something that made him try a new tack. "My name is Rosen," he said. "Do you know what it means when your name is Rosen?"

We looked at each other. "No."

I added politely, "No, doctor."

He came up to us and placed his hands on my shoulders. "Well, it simply means that I'm Jewish. It also means that you can be honest with me."

"All right," Maurice said, "You're Jewish; *we aren't.*"

The doctor said nothing. He walked over to the coatrack, delved into his pocket and took out a cigarette. He continued studying us through the smoke. All of a sudden, as if he were talking to himself, he murmured, "Well done!"

The door opened and there stood the SS man who had interrogated us.

He asked one brief question. I caught only one phrase of the doctor's reply, but it was one worth catching: it had saved our lives. "*Das ist chirurgisch gemacht worden.*" (This has been performed for surgical reasons.)

WE SPENT the night in one of the rooms which used to accommodate the hotel staff; at six o'clock there was another interrogation. This time we were separated.

The SS man who interrogated me was different from the first. He stopped the questioning now and then to put drops in his nose. There was also a new interpreter. The moment I went into the office I could feel he was going to back me up. The interpreter is everything during an interrogation—just one word, a tone of voice, and everything changes.

"Describe the room that you lived in on the rue Jean-Jaurès."

I knew they were going to compare my statement with Maurice's, but they weren't likely to catch us out on this.

"I slept with my brother; he had the bed near the door. There was a parquet floor with a little red rug, next to each bed, we each had a night table with a lamp on it but the lamps were different. Mine had a green shade and . . ."

"Not so fast—I have to translate."

The interpreter launched into a long sentence. The SS man sniffed and added something. The interpreter looked worried. "Your brother said that the lampshade was pink."

"No, he's wrong. It was green."

"Are you sure?"

"Yes, I'm sure."

An exchange in German. The interpreter quickly came to my aid. "You're right—he said green. Did your father read the newspaper?"

"Yes, every evening after supper."

"The *Alger Républicain* or some other paper?"

Careful. That might be a hint, but could prove a trap. The interpreter seemed to be helping me, but I mustn't trust anybody. "I don't know the name of the paper."

"All right, you can go."

I went back to the chambermaid's room where Maurice was waiting for me.

The door closed. There was a window but we were high up, on the top storey. We leant our elbows on the window sill. If anyone were to look through the keyhole, they wouldn't know we were talking.

"Another thing," said Maurice. "On Sundays we used to swim at a beach, but we don't remember the name."

I thought to myself that there were an awful lot of things whose names we couldn't remember.

SOON IT WOULD be midday and I was hungry; we hadn't eaten anything for twenty-four hours. Footsteps in the corridor: it was the interpreter.

"Joseph Joffo, interrogation."

It was the third since last night.

It was the same SS man with a cold; this time, he was sucking a throat lozenge.

"What games did you play at school?"

That was easy. "We played tag, sardines, football, marbles. Oh, we had loads of games with marbles: ringer, potsies, knucks, chasies . . . oh yes, and we played fivestones too."

480

The interpreter broke the flood and translated. I saw that he couldn't find the word for fivestones; perhaps German children didn't play it.

"I can show you with coins."

He felt in his pocket and handed me some coins. I took five small ones, put them in the hollow of my palm, threw them in the air and caught three of them on the back of my hand.

The officer watched the performance carefully. The interpreter laughed and I felt that the atmosphere was warming up a little, but the German recovered himself. "Tell me about your friends and your brother's friends."

"We had the same friends because we were both in the same school. My best friend was Zérati. One day . . ."

Two hours later, I learned that Maurice had mentioned Zérati. The name struck them as sufficiently Algerian for us to be left in peace for the rest of the day.

About seven o'clock, a soldier led us to the kitchen where we ate a bowl of soup. I wondered if they had arrested Father and Mother. If they had, and if my parents were carrying forged identity cards, we would have to pretend not to know them. No, that would be awful; out of the question. Oh God of Jews, Arabs and Catholics, please don't let me weaken.

THEY HUNG on to us for six days.

There was another interrogation on the morning of the third day and again on the afternoon of the fourth. Then for two days there was nothing. Maurice questioned the interpreter when he met him in a corridor: apparently the Germans were waiting for a more telling piece of evidence before either releasing us or sending us off for deportation. In the meantime, the duty sergeant at the Excelsior was using us in the kitchens. The first morning, I was glad to be out of our room, but that soon wore off; after peeling the potatoes, there was the salad, and then the endless dishwashing. More than sixty SS men and other officials ate in the hotel dining room. That night, I was so tired I couldn't fall asleep. I had the feeling that when they had got enough work out of us, they would kill us. I could also sense my

481

morale failing and I had had a headache almost constantly since the last interrogation.

As I was going upstairs the day before, I had passed the doctor. He looked surprised and went by very quickly. Why had he saved our lives when he must condemn hundreds of others every day? Because he felt sorry for two children? Most unlikely; even yesterday there was a whole contingent of Jewish children in the foyer with green tickets, children a lot smaller, a lot more endearing than us. Perhaps it was because we wouldn't talk; perhaps he had said to himself, "These two are hanging on, they deserve to stay alive. I'll give them a break."

"Look!"

We were going down to the foyer when Maurice squeezed my arm. The foyer was packed and I remembered that it was Friday, the day the trains left.

"To the right," whispered Maurice, "near the column."

Then I saw them, Jean Masso and two others from the camp. The tallest had been next to me that day in the pottery factory.

Jean saw me. His face lit up. I suddenly felt like crying and ran over to him with Maurice at my heels.

We shook hands heartily. Jean hugged me, laughing.

"What are you doing here?" I asked.

"Last night the SS surrounded the camp. We had to get out of bed and take off our pyjamas. They were looking for kids who'd been circumcised. They took me because I'd had an operation when I was six. I haven't been able to explain it . . . ."

Maurice peered around. "Is it just you three? No one else?"

The bloke from the pottery workshop winked. "When he heard that you had been arrested, Subinagui started to watch out."

Maurice gestured eloquently: we must not speak too loud; Gestapo agents in civilian clothes mingled with the suspects. If they heard anything, they took the offenders down to the cellars and nobody knew what happened there.

The boy lowered his voice to a whisper. "You know, there were quite a few Jews hiding in the camp. Subinagui gave them addresses and made them leave in the middle of the night. We got picked up near Grasse. We didn't have papers."

482

Jean was smiling broadly and smacked me on the back. "I'll tell you one thing, Joffo. They're not going to ship us anywhere, because we aren't Jewish."

Maurice pulled me by the arm. "Come on, we'll be in trouble if we don't get back to the kitchen."

We shook hands quickly. I didn't know that I would never see Jean Masso again. The Gestapo didn't have time to investigate his case. They had to supply a contingent of one thousand two hundred for each train. At ten o'clock he listened with stupefaction as his name was called out and he boarded the death train.

In the days that followed, my headache grew worse. I used to wake up with a start, bathed in sweat. I was sure that they were beating people in the cellar.

They had stopped interrogating us now and I didn't know what to make of the oblivion into which we were gradually sinking. Had they forgotten us? Had the file been mislaid? Or were they really carrying out one of their grotesquely thorough investigations?

Every mealtime Maurice had to force me to eat. One evening when I swallowed some mashed potatoes and sausage, I vomited on the staircase as we were going back to our room. I was terrified because, if a German had seen me, he would have hit me. I collapsed on my bed, my heart pounding, my stomach still gripped by spasms. I felt Maurice removing my shoes and mopping my forehead; then I fell asleep.

During the night, I had the curious impression that someone was scratching at our door; I woke up not feeling at all frightened. My fingers groped under the bed and encountered the cold steel of a submachine gun. I went to open the door. There I found myself face to face with the SS man who had interrogated me the second time. His face looked enormous; his eyes grew wide, like two monstrous pools in which I was going to drown; I pressed the trigger. He crumpled up against the wall in a bloody heap.

I felt gloriously well and went out into the corridor. German soldiers and men from the Gestapo rushed at me, screaming, and I let them have a burst. Panic-stricken, they were running in all directions. Now I was sending out a ceaseless rain of bullets, marvelling that my gun was perfectly silent. Jean Masso was applauding, shouting, "Bravo, Joseph, kill the lot!" The blood was lapping round my shoes. I splashed through it, quaking with horror and began to vomit again, collapsing onto a heap of corpses. Then I saw my father coming towards me and I wanted to run to him, but I couldn't shake off the corpses. I made a tremendous effort and opened my eyes.

I was in a room I had never seen before, and a young woman was smiling at me. She understood that I didn't have the strength to open my mouth and she answered all my questions as if she had read them in my eyes.

I had been found early in the morning, lying unconscious in the corridor. I had been moved into another room in the hotel and the doctor who came said that it was incipient meningitis.

She brought me some stewed fruit that she fed to me like a baby. I was afraid of vomiting, but I didn't, much to my relief, because I didn't want to make trouble for this kind young woman.

After she left I closed my eyes again, only to find the darkness troubled by an image that wouldn't go away, an image of a door. I knew that it was the door to the cellar of the Hotel Excelsior. I was in mortal terror that it would open, that horrifying beings would emerge. The moment I saw it open I let out a shriek that brought my nurse running back. I was bathed in sweat, and she sponged my face and neck. I managed to say a few words to her and that seemed to please her; she said that that was a good sign, that I was on the road to recovery. She stayed with me for a good part of the night; every time I woke, I could just see her seated in the armchair and that reassured me.

Dawn came and I realized that I was alone in the room. Then a strange thing happened: I got up and went to the window. I could see a form lying on the pavement below. It was a boy lying in a pool of his own blood. I looked at the face more carefully; it was the face of Joseph Joffo.

That was odd. I was both dead on the pavement and alive in a hotel room. The important thing was to find out which of us was real. My brain must have been working properly because I arrived

484

at this conclusion: I would go out into the corridor and if someone spoke to me, it would mean that I was the real Joseph; if nobody spoke to me, then the real Joseph would be the dead boy on the pavement.

I went out into the corridor. It didn't take long. A voice said sharply, "And where do you think you're going?"

I turned and smiled, the real Jo was alive. I returned to my room. And from that moment on I never saw the cellar door again.

One morning, after I had been there for almost a week, I asked my nurse—whose name was Mademoiselle Hauser—why she didn't wear a white overall like the nurses and doctors. She smiled and said, "I am not a nurse."

I was speechless, then I asked, "Well then, why are you looking after me?"

She said simply, "I am Jewish."

Never did I find it harder to resist uttering the words, "Me too," but it was out of the question. At that very moment there might be men listening behind the door. I didn't answer but I caught her as she passed by, and kissed her. With all my might, I prayed that the Germans would go on needing her for a long time, right till the end of the war; that they wouldn't put her on one of those Friday trains . . . .

One morning, the doctor came in. He read the chart at the foot of the bed, told me to stick out my tongue, and said simply, "Get dressed. In five minutes you've got to be downstairs. Hurry up."

I got dressed. My clothes had been washed and ironed. I was sure my nurse had done that. As I left, I noticed that the little glassed-in office next to my room was empty. I was about to write, "I never saw her again," but though many years have gone by I can still see the lovely face bent over me. Where did you go, Mademoiselle Hauser? For which camp were you destined, on one of those cold and foggy mornings in Poland or Eastern Germany . . . ?

ALL OF A SUDDEN there was Maurice again. He had lost weight and grown paler.

"Things aren't too good at the moment," he told me as we waited to be called into the interrogation room. "There's a new officer in command. He's a bastard. We're going to have to watch our step."

Our file lay open on the desk; there were more papers now and letters, too. So they hadn't let our case drop after all. I was flabbergasted. They had a world war on their hands; they were retreating before the Russians and the Americans; they were fighting in every corner of the globe and yet they still had time to try to find out whether two children were Jewish—and to spend more than three weeks in the process!

The short German in civilian clothes must have been the brute Maurice had mentioned. The interpreter was different too.

The German looked at us, shuffled some papers and murmured a sentence. The interpreter reeled off the gist of it. His voice was without intonation, warmth or stress; "The director of the New Harvest camp confirmed every point of your story."

A warm feeling crept over me: soon we would be free.

"Your case has been going on for too long; we can't keep you here any more. You are the oldest, you can go. You have forty-eight hours to bring back proof that you aren't Jewish. You will need your Communion certificates and you'll have to find a priest in Nice. You work it out. If you're not back in forty-eight hours, we'll make mincemeat of your brother."

Maurice clicked his heels; he must have noticed that they liked that. "Thank you, messieurs," he said. "I'll be back."

THERE WAS NO time to lose. Maurice polished his shoes with a corner of the blanket. I sat down on my bed.

"Maurice, if you've got any hope of getting me released, come back. If not, stay away and lie low. It's better that one of us should stay alive than neither."

He was combing his hair rapidly. "Don't worry. I'll be back in two days." He hadn't kissed me or shaken my hand. But of course, it was only for two days . . . .

The strange thing was that those two days didn't seem any longer than any others. I knew—perhaps I should say I hoped—that they weren't going to make mincemeat out of me. Mostly one's life hangs by a thread . . . .

Next day, after peeling the potatoes, shelling the beans and cleaning the lentils, I was sent off with a tin of furniture polish to work on the doors of the landings.

I was just starting on the first door when I received a kick in the behind. It was Maurice, wreathed in smiles.

I gave him a right to the body; he countered with a pair of hooks, prancing round me and chanting, "I've got the lot."

In a little room at the end of the corridor where they kept all the cleaning things he told me what had happened.

He had taken a chance and gone home; our parents were still there. They no longer went outside and hardly ever opened the shutters. A neighbour did all their shopping. Maurice had explained the situation to them and Mother had cried. Then Maurice had gone to the church nearby.

"I remembered the priest in Dax," he said. "If a priest had saved our lives once, maybe another would do the same thing again."

There was nobody in the church, just an old man putting the chairs in rows. Maurice asked him where he could find the priest. The old man answered that he was the priest. The verger was working in a factory in Germany and he had to do everything himself. Maurice told him everything. The priest didn't even allow him to finish the story.

"Don't worry. I'll make out the Communion certificates and give them to you straight away. I'm also going to explain your case to Archbishop Rémond and he will almost certainly come to your assistance. Go back and tell Joseph not to worry. I'll come and see you in the Excelsior."

When Maurice left he had the certificates in his pocket.

We were hardly out of the cupboard than the interpreter pounced on us.

We went with him to the office. Maurice handed over our papers and the German looked at them.

"*Das ist falsch!*"

One needed no linguistic training to know what that meant.

The interpreter let the words filter through his lips. "These papers are forged."

Maurice had had the time to prepare himself. "Tell him he's wrong. Anyway, the priest is coming to see us and take us away. He said so."

"We'll make our inquiries. You may go."

Our two certificates were safely tucked away in the file; but they hadn't worked their magic.

THREE DAYS later the priest from the church of La Buffa came. He sat on a chair that an SS man brought him. It was a sign of respect rarely accorded at the Excelsior, but it was the only one. He remained seated for three hours. At the end of the three hours, somebody came to inform him that he would not be received.

Gently, he explained that he realized that the Gestapo officers were very busy, but that he would keep coming until the victory of the Third Reich if need be, to prevent the Nazis from committing a grave error from which two children would suffer. He took the liberty of adding that the Archbishop had been informed and was ready to intervene at the highest level, in Berlin if necessary.

We had stumbled upon the most stubborn, the wittiest priest in the whole of the Alpes-Maritimes; and, more to the point, the most bent on foiling German plans for Jews.

The next morning, the priest trotted past the guards, seized a chair, murmured, "Please don't worry about me," to the SS men playing cards nearby, and settled himself outside the office.

At noon, he plunged his hand into a deep pocket of his cassock and came up with a sandwich. He ate with gusto, then seeing an SS guard watching him with loathing a few yards away, rose and asked him in German, "I'm sorry to trouble you, soldier, but would you be good enough to bring me a glass of water?"

After this performance, he quickly became the hotel's main attraction, and the senior officers soon realized that this could present a certain danger; accordingly, at two o'clock, he was the first person to be admitted.

He returned the next morning, but this time he was shown into the office straight away. He brought out our two baptismal certificates and a handwritten letter from the Archbishop

488

explaining that the certificates had been issued in the cathedral of Algiers and that they were in his possession because they were required for our Communion ceremony which had been held at the church of La Buffa, on the date mentioned. He said that if this evidence was not deemed sufficient, he was ready to come to Gestapo headquarters in person.

Apparently it would have been disagreeable for the Germans to have the bishopric take an official stand against them. Even in those years when France was being drained of her manpower, food, equipment, they could not afford to fall out with the Church of France—with its millions of followers—over whether or not two children should go to the gas chamber. So the Gestapo decided to release us after more than a month's detention.

It was the priest who took us off, holding each of us by a hand. Before leaving the office, he nodded to the German and told us, "Maurice, Joseph, say goodbye to the gentleman."

"Goodbye, m'sieur."

Outside I was dazzled by the sunlight and the wind from the sea. I gave a start: standing in front of the hotel was the van that had brought us there in the first place. Subinagui was at the wheel. He hugged us happily.

"Right, let's go back to camp. You've been hanging around this town long enough."

GÉRARD appeared at the kitchen door. He was still as correct as ever; each night, he put his shorts under the mattress so that they wouldn't lose their crease.

"Jo, telephone."

I dropped the beans I was stringing and ran to the office. Subinagui handed me the receiver.

"It's your father."

My voice must have sounded quavery, because he didn't know that it was me. "Is that you Joseph?"

"Yes, how are you?"

"Fine. So is Mother."

I sensed that he was moved, a little tremulous. He added, "We were very pleased with the way you managed. We got quite a scare when we saw Maurice, but I knew that everything would be all right in the end." Judging by the relief in his voice, he couldn't have been all that convinced. "Were you scared?"

"No . . . well, not really. I was ill for a bit but I'm better now. What about Albert and Henri?"

"They're all right too. They write regularly. We're all doing all right. Listen, I can't talk for long. Give my love to Maurice and a big kiss for you, too. We'll see each other very soon."

"Yes, Father."

"Goodbye, Jo and . . . be good . . ."

When he said "Be good" to me, it was because he didn't know what else to say and I was afraid I would burst into tears over the phone. "Goodbye Father. See you soon."

It was too bad Maurice wasn't there, he was working on a farm a mile or so away.

I went back to my beans. Life at the camp had changed. Testi was gone; his aunt had come for him and I never saw him again. Also, since the Gestapo raid there were fewer of us, and the atmosphere was not so relaxed as it had been. Even so, the camp was paradise for me.

The days were growing shorter; winter was approaching. Another winter of war.

"Is the war going to end soon, Monsieur Subinagui?"

He laughed. "Three months. I bet it won't last three months."

I thought he was a little optimistic. To me it seemed as though it had always been wartime.

I WOKE UP. The torch dazzled me. It was pitch dark. "Quick, get dressed. Don't make any noise!"

What was going on? The others were asleep in the tent. I pulled on my shirt in the darkness. Blast, inside out, of course. I felt Maurice close beside me, scraping his soles on the floor.

This couldn't be a Gestapo raid; there would be shouts, everyone would be up. Subinagui was holding the torch.

"Come on. I'll meet you in the office."

Outside, the night was cool and starry. The tent was wet with dew. Everyone in the camp was asleep.

490

The office was open; Subinagui lit a small lamp and I saw that he was carrying our two haversacks. "You're leaving immediately. I've put everything you'll need in your haversacks—two shirts, underwear, socks and a bite to eat. You'll cut across the fields to Cannes and then take a train for Montluçon; from there you will go to the village where your sister is expecting you . . . It's called Ainay-le-Vieil . . . ."

Maurice interrupted him. "What's happening?"

Subinagui looked down. "Your father was arrested in an SS round-up yesterday and taken to the Hotel Excelsior."

Everything started to spin. The Gestapo was stronger than the czar's army. It had got my father.

"That's not all—your father was carrying his identity papers, made out in his own name. It won't be long before the Germans link him with you and they'll be here looking for you."

Maurice had picked up his haversack. "What about my mother?"

"They warned her in time. She has already left. I can't tell you where, but you can rest assured that your parents would have found a safe place. You must be off now; and you mustn't write. They may be watching the post."

We started off. Everything had happened so fast that I still hadn't registered the news. I only knew that my father was in Nazi hands. What a triumph for the Gestapo if they got their hands on us! But what about the priest of La Buffa? Anyone caught helping a Jew had to share his fate. No, we absolutely couldn't be caught.

The earth was hard and dry but the weeds and vine leaves we brushed past soaked our shorts and shirt sleeves. The camp was already far behind us. The night was so light that the crest of the hills cast its shadow on the terraced vineyards. Where was Montluçon? I had no idea. Probably inland. I was sad to leave the Mediterranean. I would come back to it when I was older, I thought. When it was peacetime.

The path wound uphill. We had to stay away from farmhouses so that watchdogs wouldn't bark, and that meant that we had to make wide detours. Finally, Maurice stopped; there was a road just ahead of us.

"We'll cross it," he whispered.

There was no one coming, so we dashed across the road and, after scrambling up a slope, found the sea at our feet, wide and glittering. We still couldn't see Cannes, but now we had to work our way down through the gardens to the station.

As dawn came we crept past boarded up villas until we reached the centre of town. People rode past us on bicycles; shopkeepers were beginning to raise their shutters.

The station was already crowded, "Two singles for Montluçon."

The clerk consulted books and timetables. "One hundred and fourteen francs, twenty centimes."

Maurice scooped up the change.

"Where do we have to change?"

"It's complicated. First, go to Marseilles; then there's a delay— an hour or two. After that, you go up to Lyons, take the little train for Moulins, and there you have to change for Montluçon. Otherwise, you can go via Roanne, Saint-Germain-des-Fosses and Gannat to Montluçon; or indeed, Saint-Etienne, Clermond-Ferrand and the Bourges line. They'll all get you there in the end. Only—I can't rightly say when because . . ." Spreading his arms to represent an aeroplane, he imitated the sound of an engine and exploding bombs. "You see what I mean?"

We nodded fascinated.

"Thanks," said Maurice.

We walked off trying not to burst out laughing when, a few yards away, we saw the unfriendly interpreter from the Hotel Excelsior.

It was too late for us to hide or run, so we went on moving towards him. I was convinced he could see my heart pounding through my shirt. He stopped. He had recognized us.

"Good morning, m'sieur."

"Good morning."

He still had that expressionless voice but for the first time, I thought I saw the ghost of a smile.

"Going somewhere?"

"Yes, we're going to another *Compagnons de France* camp."

"That's good. Where is it?"

I launched into improvisation. "It's in Roanne, a long way from here. We've got to change in Marseilles, Clermont-Ferrand, Saint-Etienne and Moulins."

"I see. Well, well."

Maurice perked up. If we hadn't been arrested, it was because the interpreter still hadn't heard about my father's arrest. "And you, m'sieur, are you still working in Nice?"

He nodded. "I had a few days off. I'm going back now. Well, goodbye. I wish you a pleasant stay in Roanne."

"Thank you, m'sieur. Goodbye, m'sieur."

The train pulled in. Contrary to what the ticket-man had told us in Cannes, there was a connection from Marseilles for Lyons almost immediately. As far as Avignon, the journey was almost pleasant; but after that an unexpected enemy confronted us: the cold.

The trains were, of course, unheated and we were travelling northwards, farther and farther from the balmy Mediterranean. We sought refuge in the lavatory and put on all our extra clothing, but our arms and knees were still bare. In Lyons, on the station platform, which was swept by an icy wind, we held a contest to see whose teeth could chatter the loudest. But when the train pulled in after an hour and a half's wait, the situation was serious. It was only the beginning of October, but never did winter come so early as in 1943. People were tramping up and down the pavements in their efforts to keep warm. In the compartments passengers were wearing their winter clothing— coats, gloves, scarves—and we were still dressed as for summer.

Shivering and blue, we got off at Montluçon under grey skies; a grey ticket inspector took our tickets, and we emerged into a town swept by a glacial wind, that seemed to blow from all directions. Despite a triple layer of socks, my toes seemed to have turned to stone. A frozen Maurice managed to utter, "We've got to do something soon or we'll die of pneumonia."

The well-known exhortation, "Run a bit, it will warm you up," is undoubtedly the choicest of all the absurdities that adults pronounce for the benefit of children. After my experience that day, I can safely say that, when you're really cold, running tires you out, but doesn't warm you up at all. After half an hour of frantic galloping and violent hand-rubbing, I was puffing like a grampus but shivering harder than ever.

"Listen, Jo, we've got to buy a coat."

"Have you got any clothing coupons?"

"No, but we've got to try."

On a bleak square, I caught sight of a tiny shop with almost illegible lettering over the window: "Clothing for men, women and children".

When the door shut behind me I experienced the pleasantest sensation of my life; the shop was heated. I felt the warmth rushing in through each of my pores. Without so much as a glance at the good lady behind the counter, we flattened ourselves against the roaring stove.

The proprietress looked at us in amazement, and indeed we must have been a sight—two small boys in multi-coloured layers of summer shirts, bare-armed in the bitter weather and clutching haversacks.

"What can I do for you, children?" she asked.

Maurice tore himself away from the delights of the stove.

"We'd like coats or heavy jackets. We haven't got any clothing coupons, but perhaps if we paid a little extra . . ."

She shook her head ruefully. "Even if you paid millions, I couldn't sell you anything. We haven't had any coats or jackets for so long we've almost forgotten what they are," she said. "The only thing I can offer you is this." She took two scarves from under the counter. They were imitation wool, but better than nothing.

Maurice paid, and I took my courage in both hands.

"Excuse me, madame, but would it be all right if we stayed here a few more minutes?" My voice must have had just the right plaintive note, because she said yes. She even seemed pleased to have somebody to talk to.

We were still hugging the stove when we noticed that it was growing dark outside. It was too late to take the bus to the village where our sister lived, we would have to find a hotel.

"Listen," the lady said. "You won't find a hotel in Montluçon; both of them have been requisitioned by the Germans. But I can

494

offer you my son's room; the bed will be a bit narrow for the two of you, but you'll be warm."

I could have jumped for joy. That evening she made us the best *gratin dauphinois* I've ever eaten, and afterwards herb tea. I fell asleep instantly, buried deep under a red eiderdown. There was an air-raid warning during the night but even the sirens didn't wake me.

She kissed us when we left and refused any payment. It wasn't so cold outside now, and we were muffled up in our scarves.

The asthmatic bus jolted its way through a landscape that seemed dismal in comparison with the one we had left. The trees were bare and a fine drizzle was dotting the window panes. Less than an hour later, the bus deposited us in Ainay-le-Vieil.

It was more a hamlet than a village: a few houses clustered together, one narrow street, with a butcher-cum-baker's and a grocer-cum-ironmonger-cum-tobacconist-cum-bar. The fields began right at the edge of the village.

Our sister Rosette lived with her husband in one of the houses adjoining the church. She kissed us, and wept when we told her that Father had been arrested by the Gestapo.

In the enormous tiled kitchen she served us real milk in great earthenware bowls and gave us jerseys made of real wool. They were too big, but with the sleeves rolled up they would do.

From the first moment I sensed that, despite her obvious happiness at seeing us again, Rosette was uneasy.

"Listen," she said. "I don't think you can stay here. It wouldn't be wise."

We looked at her in silence.

"The thing is," she explained, "we've got an informer in the village." She rumpled her apron nervously. "A little less than two months ago, two women came here. They moved in with a farmer who lives at the other end of the village. They hadn't been here a week when the Gestapo came. They were taken and the farmer was arrested along with them. He came back three days later . . . they'd broken his arm. He told us that if anyone else tried to hide Jews, he'd be shot."

"But who was the informer?"

"That's the awful part," said Rosette. "Nobody knows. There are about a hundred and fifty people in this village. It's awful, everyone suspects everyone else."

"What about you—aren't you afraid the informer will . . . ."

Rosette shrugged. "No, I don't think so. I've been here a long time and I hope my identity papers will be all right. Still, I've got us a hiding place ready."

I sighed; I would have liked to live in the village a while. But it was clear we would have to leave, and fast. Rosette looked at us; her thoughtful expression made her look like my father. "I think it would be best if you joined Albert and Henri at Aix-les-Bains."

"Where is Aix-les-Bains?"

"In the Alps, right up in the mountains. I'll give you the money for . . ."

Maurice refused with a lordly gesture. "No need to, we're still getting along on the money we saved in Nice."

So it was decided. Actually, I liked the idea: first the sea, then the mountains. I would be glad to see Albert and Henri again. Quickly, Rosette packed our haversacks with socks and sandwiches. There was no bus, so once again we would set off on foot. Now I could walk for hours without getting blisters; the soles of my feet had hardened. I had grown too. Grown, hardened, changed . . . . The child I had been eighteen months ago—the child lost in the train to Dax—I knew he wasn't the present me. He had been lost forever on some Provençal track, in the corridors of a Nice hotel; they hadn't taken my life; they had done something worse—they had robbed me of my childhood.

Chapter 9

The hardest part was making sure that you didn't tear the paper and, most important of all, that you didn't spoil the colour under the number. It was a precision job. Ideally, one should have had a very bright light and a watchmaker's lens, the kind you screw over your eye.

I stuck out my tongue, bent my head over the table-top, and

scratched gently with the razor blade; little by little the black bar of the 4 disappeared converting it into the number 1. The advantage was inestimable; number 4 coupons entitled you to starches; number 1 coupons were good for a kilo of sugar.

Those in the village who knew about my talents would hand over their precious coupons to me; I would return them "converted". In exchange I received a little money. If things continued well, I'd be making profits equal to those I made in Nice.

I blew on my fingers; this wasn't the kind of work you could do in mittens even though it was freezing in my room. The ice I broke in the earthenware jug this morning had hardened back into a more delicate form trapping slivers of soap like dead fish.

It was dark and I was sleepy; tomorrow morning at four o'clock Monsieur Mancelier would be tapping against my door, and I was already anticipating the difficulty I was going to have tearing myself away from the blankets and plunging into clothes that were cold despite a night under the mattress. I would be pedalling through the snow on my newspaper rounds. Mancelier's bookshop-stationer's was located on the square, with a view over the mountain range which served the town as a backdrop.

New people had come into my life in the two months that I'd been living in the village of R——. The most important of these were the Manceliers, my employers. Here is the family portrait.

That's the father in the middle. He has a moustache and the eyes of a man who isn't easy to live with; he is somewhere in his fifties, with one knee that won't bend and one hip that bends too much; this double misfortune explains the cane he goes around with. You will notice two ribbons in his buttonhole—the Military Medal and the *Croix de Guerre*. He received both in the First World War, fought in the battles of the Marne and Verdun under the command of Pétain, who still ranks as his idol. There are photos of Pétain in the parlour. Ambroise Mancelier thinks that collaboration with Hitler is the only hope for the survival of France.

One important detail: my revered employer can't stand Jews. Personally, I have the feeling that he has begun to warm towards

497

me in the last two months. True, I have nothing to do with the "accursed race", as is well known.

But to continue with the portrait. Beside him stands his wife, Marcelle. She has no distinguishing features. She is simply a grey-haired lady who handles the administrative side of the business. Behind her is Raoul Mancelier, the married son. He rarely comes to the bookshop. He too supports Pétain.

And then, standing beside them, is Françoise.

Françoise Mancelier. Nowadays, when I think back to those years, nothing comes to mind sooner than that little girl's face— even before the face of my father. Françoise Mancelier was a little over fourteen and I still hadn't quite turned twelve. To call ours a love story is hardly correct—because nothing happened, nothing took place—neither kiss nor declaration, nothing . . . . It was just that I felt her blonde, smiling presence constantly, whether I was in the shop, in my room or out on the road. When I think of it, I'm amazed at how little she said to me. "Good morning, Joseph," "Joseph, would you go to the grocer's . . . to the baker's . . . ." I felt that she could never love me, that a difference of two years was too great, that she was a young lady and I was a little boy.

Anyhow, I had started off badly in that family. I came to R—— one Sunday after spending two days in Aix-les-Bains. Albert, Henri and Mother (who had joined them there) had been delighted to see us, but it was too dangerous for all five of us to be together. So Maurice had left for R——, where one of Albert's friends, who ran the Hotel du Commerce, had taken him on. A few days later, Maurice heard that Mancelier's shop was looking for a delivery boy and so I landed there. Ambroise Mancelier had placed a firm hand on my shoulder. "My boy," he said, "you sleep under my roof, eat at my table and work in my shop. You're part of the family, so to speak. You take part in all its activities; and you will understand that the custom we hold most sacred is that of going to Mass every Sunday at a quarter past eleven. So hurry up and get dressed."

You don't contradict a man like Ambroise Mancelier; and it meant I would spend an hour in the intoxicating company of the.

498

beautiful Françoise. My beloved knelt in front of me, which enabled me to admire the nape of her blonde neck. I conscientiously imitated the worshippers as they knelt and made the sign of the cross. The service lasted almost an hour, then everyone shuffled out.

We were among the last, and suddenly, in front of me, a stout lady dressed in black dipped her hand in a kind of scallop shell fixed to a pillar. She turned round, and extended two pudgy fingers towards me. I was surprised, because I didn't know her.

I shook her hand heartily. "Good morning, madame."

Why is Françoise hooting like that? Why is Monsieur Mancelier turning round and raising his eyebrows so alarmingly?

I sensed that I hadn't done the right thing, but the awful part was Françoise: never again would she take me seriously. How could anyone want to marry a man who says good morning to a lady who is proffering holy water? To redeem myself, I would have to win the war single-handed or save her from a fire or a shipwreck . . . But how do you save someone from a shipwreck in the Haute-Savoie?

Another Sunday—the meal after Mass. Madame Mancelier had put on her apron and was bustling about the kitchen stove. Françoise had opened the door of the sideboard, and the china bowls clinked as she took them out.

Mancelier was seated in the armchair. He always read thick books by generals and colonels. From time to time, he whinnied with satisfaction.

The meal began with radishes from the garden; they were all hollow. That was something that never ceased to amaze my employer. He watched over them, watered them, fed them, all to no avail. Once through that pink layer, one's teeth encountered empty air. I was surprised that he hadn't blamed his hollow radishes on the Jews. True, he was too busy with something else now—Europe.

"When it comes to politics—for a man who isn't a Turk or a Negro or a Communist—there is only one ideal—Europe."

I didn't have the slightest desire to argue. I was too busy stealing furtive looks at Françoise.

"Now, who wanted to create a new Europe? A Europe capable of fighting its adversaries from west, east or south? History doesn't record many such men. There are only . . . how many are there, Joseph?"

I gave a start. He was thrusting a sturdy hand towards me with three fingers extended.

"There are three, Monsieur Mancelier."

"Very good, Joseph. There are three. Louis the Fourteenth, Napoleon, Philippe Pétain."

He downed a gulp of red wine. "And the strangest part is that not one of these men was understood during his own lifetime. The masses, that pack of bastards and morons . . . ."

Madame Mancelier sighed. "Please Ambroise, do watch your language."

". . . So the masses opposed these men of genius. They guillotined the first one's grandson; they threw the second into prison, but the third is a tough customer. He's been through Verdun, and when you've been through Verdun, you can get through anything."

I wasn't listening any more. I had finished my beans and was waiting for dessert. Neither Françoise nor her mother concealed the fact that they were bored to tears.

When coffee was served, Raoul and his wife arrived. Then it started up again, worse than ever. Raoul was no longer very sure of a German victory; he foresaw difficulties, in particular "the sledgehammer of American technology". "If they'd done what I'd said," said Raoul, "we would have joined up with Hitler and Mussolini back in '36. Nothing could have stopped the three of us, we'd be the rulers of the world."

"And why didn't we do that?" Raoul's wife asked.

Then Ambroise Mancelier burst out with a laugh that sent his coffee flying.

"Because," he said "the government was rotten with Jews."

Françoise had left to do her homework; so I asked permission to leave, and ran towards the Hotel du Commerce.

Maurice was waiting for me, his pockets bulging with spoils from the kitchen. As we walked, he would tell me the latest news.

500

He was working under the head chef who was in the Resistance and listened to the BBC. The news was good: the Germans were continuing to retreat. He pointed to a distant mountain.

"That's where the *maquis* hide out. There are lots of them. They're attacking lorries and trains."

I jumped with excitement.

"What if we went there?"

"No," said Maurice, "they won't take us; we're too young."

Rather disappointed, I walked out onto the football pitch, and it was thus that the thwarted defendants of freedom amused themselves until six o'clock.

At first, we had had trouble being accepted by the local children. They all went to school and we didn't, which was a cause for envy and hence animosity. Then they saw me on my bike with my canvas bag, doing my paper round and, at last, the Joffo brothers were accepted.

APRIL 1944.

Things were bad for the Germans, the *maquisards* were striking all over the place. Two days ago, they had blown up the engine-shed at the station.

Mancelier was very uneasy. I caught him looking at Pétain's portrait with an expression that wasn't exactly critical but that was no longer totally admiring. That was how I could tell that the Allies were advancing; Ambroise's glance was more revealing to me than the news.

In any case, the weather was good and the spirits of the people had risen. I pedalled happily along. Just four more papers for the Hotel du Commerce and my morning's work was done.

The hotel door slammed behind me and I greeted the customers at the bar. The *patron* was there, chatting.

A squeal of brakes made me turn round. Through the curtains I could see two lorries blocking the street.

"Look!"

There was no need for me to tell them. The drinkers were watching the soldiers jump down; their uniforms were black and they wore berets pulled down over one ear. They were the hated

501

hunters of Resistance fighters, the *miliciens*. Two of them headed straight for the hotel.

"They're coming in," said the proprietor.

"Here, you . . ."

One of the customers, a small man, quite old, all dressed in dark corduroy, smiled and came towards me and took a crumpled envelope from his pocket. He dropped it into my delivery bag; and put his newspaper on top of it.

The *miliciens* pushed the door open.

The little man's lips didn't move, but he was speaking. His eyes weren't on me anymore, but it was me he was talking to.

"Monsieur Jean," he said, "at the Cheval Blanc."

He pushed me towards the door. I went out and bumped into two black torsos crisscrossed with belts. Their faces were sunburnt, the shadow of their berets hid their eyes.

"Hands up. Quickly."

The *patron* opened his mouth and a tanned hand seized him by the shirt front and thrust him up against the bar. The second *milicien* looked at me and jerked his thumb towards the street.

"Out of here, you!"

I walked between the two soldiers, my newspaper bag under my arm. The bag was dynamite, but dynamite doesn't always explode.

Outside, the square was swarming with men in black. I got my bicycle and set off. A newspaper boy was hardly going to attract attention. Who, I wondered was the little man in corduroy?

At the corner of the square, I turned round.

There he was, between two *miliciens*; he had both his hands on his head. Perhaps it was just a face he was making, but I felt he was smiling at me.

Now, to the Cheval Blanc, and fast. I knew it; I delivered their paper every morning.

There were only a few customers at this time of day. When I came in, Maryse, the waitress, looked surprised to see me; she stopped wiping a marble-topped table.

"What are you doing here?"

"I'm looking for Monsieur Jean."

I saw her give a start. "What do you want with him."

502

"I've got a message for him."

She hesitated. "Come with me."

We went through the kitchen and courtyard, and she knocked at the garage door in an odd way, a series of raps and then, after a pause, another knock.

The door opened. There was a man inside, wearing riding-boots. He looked a bit like my brother Henri.

Maryse pointed to me. "It's the paper boy. He'd like to talk to Monsieur Jean."

"What do you have to say to him?"

His voice was stern.

"A customer at the Hotel du Commerce gave me a message for him. A short gentleman, all in corduroy. The *miliciens* have just arrested him."

His hands were resting on my shoulders, strong but gentle. "Give me the message," he said.

"I can't do that; the man told me to give it to Monsieur Jean."

Maryse gave me a dig with her elbow. "Go ahead," she said. "This is Monsieur Jean."

I handed him the envelope. He tore it open, read it, then ruffled my hair. "Well done," he said. "Maryse will be our go-between. When I need you, she'll let you know. Now go home quickly."

And that was how I joined the Resistance.

ACTUALLY I must admit that that was my sole and very modest contribution to the cause of free France. I waited impatiently for Maryse to contact me and I would often go past the Cheval Blanc, but the waitress just dried her wine glasses and glanced at me with disdain. They must have decided that I was too young; perhaps, above all, it was my involvement with Ambroise Mancelier that made them distrustful.

The sixth of June, the day of the Normandy landings, was the most tragic for the old Pétainist. His cane hammered the corridors and his wife wouldn't go downstairs to the shop any more. There had been a few exchanges with the customers which indicated that the climate had changed.

One afternoon, the baker's son came in. It was said that he was helping the guerrillas, supplying them with flour and taking them bread. He pointed to the window where a book glorifying Pétain stood on display.

"How much?"

"Forty francs."

"I'll buy it; but just leave it in the window. You won't mind that, will you?"

The proprietress turned red. She mumbled that she couldn't see why he wanted it since he wasn't planning to read it.

She understood soon enough.

Young Mouron picked up a price tag that was lying on the counter and, with a red pencil, wrote SOLD. Then he took the tag and glued it on to the cover, smack onto the tie of *le père* Pétain, Saviour of France.

She blanched and said, "I'd rather put it aside for you; I can't keep a book in the window if it's been paid for."

Mouron stared at her coolly. "Then I won't buy it; no point paying out forty francs when I'll be getting it for nothing in a few weeks." He opened the door and, before slamming it, said, "See you very soon, Madame Mancelier." From that time on, it was I who did practically everything in the bookshop.

Françoise had gone away to an aunt's house near Roubaix, and I was left sad at heart, with the two old people who no longer dared to go out of their house. One evening, there was a clatter of broken glass. A window had been broken in the kitchen.

Each evening, after adding up the day's meagre takings, I'd meet Maurice and we would go up the church tower. From there we could watch the lorries full of German soldiers coming up from the south. Sometimes there were long convoys of ambulances. We had no news from Aix-les-Bains, as the post no longer came through; trains were being blown up, and nobody travelled.

Maurice saw some *maquisards* one night at the Hotel du Commerce. They had a car and machine pistols and were wearing leather jackets and hobnailed boots. They were optimistic; it was rough at times, they said, but it would soon be over. They told Maurice that the little man in corduroy had been shot against the wall of a farmyard. That made me ill for a whole day.

The baker spent his time up on his roof watching the Germans through field-glasses. One day he said he had seen tanks and panzers arriving. By evening, the village was in a panic, convinced that the Germans were going to use R—— as a stronghold to stop the Allied advance. Soon gossip had it that if we were liberated, the Third Reich would collapse.

They had been making American flags at the Town Hall with the help of the schoolmistress. It wouldn't be long now, the Yanks were no more than fifty kilometres away.

God, it was true; it was going to be over. I scarcely dared think it as I pored over the accounts, alone in the empty shop. The Manceliers had shut themselves up in their rooms overhead.

On the other side of the shop's shutters it was a summer night. A group of young people were talking in the square, despite the curfew. There was a dull roar in the distance; the sound of war, perhaps, coming towards us.

I finished my book-keeping. I rubbed out a smudge below the line separating one day from another, and wrote in tomorrow's date.

July 8th, 1944.

"Jo, Jo!"

I thought it was Maurice's voice calling me, but that was impossible; at this hour, he would be sleeping. It must be a dream.

"Jo! Wake up, will you!"

This time I opened my eyes. I pushed the shutters open. The square was still deserted. It was just before dawn, the moment when creatures are shaking off the last mist of night.

Down below, Maurice was looking up towards me. He was alone, the only living being in the whole square. He smiled at me.

"They've gone."

It was as simple as that. I was leaning out of my window one fine summer morning and it was all over. Nobody was trying to kill me any more. I could go back home, travel by train, walk in the street, laugh, ring doorbells, play marbles.

The two of us walked through the village. There was a crowd

506

in front of the baker's shop, young people on bikes with Resistance armbands and small pistols stuck in their belts. I knew some of them; they weren't the real members of the underground. They had just blossomed out suddenly on the very morning that the Krauts had moved off farther north.

And then the streets filled up; the windows were decorated with flags, French, British and American. There was a lot of joviality in the Cheval Blanc and the Commerce and I was deliriously happy. There weren't any papers to deliver that morning. They didn't come until the next day, and when they did come they were different ones: *Les Allobroges, Le Dauphiné Libéré* and so on . . . . I sold hundreds of copies; people didn't even wait for their change. As I look back now, I find it hard to isolate any images from that whirlwind of a day. In the afternoon, three girls who had been friendly with the Germans had been forced to walk through the streets: their heads had been shaved and swastikas painted on their faces. Perhaps clearest of all, I see the pallid face of Ambroise Mancelier backed up against the flowered wallpaper with everybody crowding round him, headed by the young Mouron. The time to settle old scores had come.

The first slap rang out like a pistol shot. I had just arrived and I saw old Mancelier's head strike the wall. I went up to Mouron.

"Let him go. He's kept me hidden here a long time, and it could have cost him his neck to hide a Jew."

A silence fell over the room. Mancelier was wild-eyed with horror. Mouron looked mulish.

"That doesn't stop him from being a collaborator . . . ."

But they didn't kill him. They took him to prison in Annecy with his wife. When he climbed into the back of the lorry he was trembling all over, but I was the only one who really knew why. To owe his neck to a Jew was hard to stomach.

The strangest twist of all was that I was now the proprietor of the bookshop; I felt like taking a paintbrush and blotting out the name *"Librairie Mancelier"* and putting my own name up there. All the underground papers had come out into the open, and I became the dispenser of world news. Sometimes I put in more than fifteen hours a day. My till was overflowing. The money would go to Mancelier's successors of course, but for the moment I was in charge.

And suddenly one day, on all the papers, in enormous letters that covered the whole front page:

PARIS LIBÉRÉ

It was very early; nobody was awake yet in the village. I gazed at the big bundles of papers, all saying the same thing, and I leapt to my feet and rushed upstairs. My haversack was under the bed, and I knew that this was the last time I would be needing it.

It wasn't far from the bookshop to the station, along a straight, tree-lined avenue.

I whistled as I trotted along. I felt as though the entrance to the Marcadet-Poissonniers *Métro* station in Paris would materialize at the end of it.

But that wasn't what I saw.

There were three of them coming—Resistance armbands on their biceps, ugly German Mausers slung over their shoulders.

"Hey, come here you."

Stupefied, I stopped.

I didn't know them; I'd never seen them in the village; they must come from some other *maquis* unit.

"What on earth do you want?"

One of them pointed to the square I had just come from. This really was the limit. Run in by the Gestapo, pursued throughout the whole war, I had got myself picked up by French Resistance fighters on the day Paris was liberated!

They marched me back to the village square. There was a crowd in front of the shop, mostly blokes in leather jackets, all of them armed, including a very young one whom everybody called "*mon capitaine*".

One of my bodyguards clicked his heels. "We got him, *mon capitaine*."

That took my breath away; I was being hunted just like a German. The young man looked at me, one eyebrow raised.

"Where were you off to?"

"Me? To Paris, of course."

"Why Paris?"

"Because that's where I live."

"And you were going to leave all this lot?"

His hand swept over the pile of newspapers and the bookshop. "I think perhaps you don't understand the situation. You are responsible for the distribution of the newspapers in the village. You must stay at your post. We're still at war and your job is like that of a soldier who . . ."

"Listen. It's three years since I left home, since my family were all split up. Today I can go back, so I'm going, and you can't stop me."

The colonel stared at me.

"What's your name?"

"Joseph Joffo. I'm a Jew."

He took a slight breath, as though he were afraid of injuring his lungs.

"Have you had news of your family?"

"No. I'm going to Paris to get some now."

They looked at one another. I knew that I had won. It was the feeling of relief that caused the tears to run treacherously down my cheeks.

I was on my way again. A dozen or so of them came along to see me off. One of them carried my haversack, and my back hurt from all the backslapping I received.

"How about a sandwich for the train?"

"Do you think you'll get a seat?"

"Give the Eiffel Tower a big kiss for us . . . ."

And Maurice?

I saw him briefly on the way to the station. His boss hadn't let him leave—it seemed the mood of the moment. But I didn't worry on his account. He would sort out that problem fast, if I knew Maurice!

ON THE STATION PLATFORM people were packed solid. They were on their way back to the capital, loaded with sacks of flour, baskets piled with meat, hens with their feet tied—an exodus in reverse. We waited for two and a half hours. Then finally a

509

murmur ran through the crowd, "Here it comes!" There was
surge forward as fingers tightened over the handles of suitcase
and on the straps of rucksacks. The engine was slow
approaching. I felt the surge building up behind me and pushing
me forward, right up against the steps of the moving train. The
doors burst open and a vacuum seemed to suck me aboard. I heard
the door close behind me. My head was on somebody's forearm
the rest of my body was stretched out over a mound of suitcases
and my feet were sticking out of the compartment window!

It was to be a good thirty kilometres before I regained a vertica
position. But I didn't give a hoot. The train was moving—slowly
but it was moving. I knew that I would arrive tonight, tomorrow
in a week—I would be home.

"MARCADET-POISSONNIERS."

One fine day three years ago, I had taken the *Métro* to the
Gare d'Austerlitz; now I was retracing my steps.

The street was unchanged; the same leaden sky between the
gutters of the rooftops, the same smell floating in the air, the smel
of Paris in the morning.

I had the same old haversack. It was easier to carry now.

Madame Epstein wasn't there any more, nor was her cane
bottomed chair. Goldenberg's restaurant was closed. How many o
us had made it?

JOFFO – COIFFEUR.

The same neat lettering. Through the shop window, I could see
Albert, hard at work. Behind him, Henri was wielding the broom.
I saw Mother.

Father wasn't there. I knew that he would never be there again.
The wonderful stories told in the green gleam of the lampshade
were over. In the end, Hitler had done what the czar could
never do.

Henri, Albert and Mother saw me. They were speaking, but
their words were inaudible through the glass.

I saw myself in the shop window with my haversack.

It was true, I had grown.

510

Joseph Joffo

A Bag of Marbles *has sold more than 600,000 copies in France, but its author —bronzed, athletic-looking, with twinkling eyes—takes his success lightly. He was interviewed recently in Paris.*

"No, no, I'm not a real writer. I started off by telling my own kids about my early life, and then just wrote it all down as I'd told it, without a thought for style or grammar.

"I simply wanted my two sons and my daughter to learn, as I did, that a battle is never lost in advance. I wanted them to fear nothing and no one, to fight daily for their place in the sun, their right to happiness.

"As for me, if my brothers hadn't kept an eye on me and boxed my ears occasionally, I might have gone wrong. I was fourteen when the war ended, and fighting for our lives as Maurice and I had been forced to do had left me much too cocky; without my father to head the family, I ran wild. I fancied a life of adventure, saw myself as a boxer or an actor. But my elder brothers insisted that I finish school. I capitulated, but until I was twenty-five I was a rolling stone, gathering only girl friends. Still—and this is important—I cost the family nothing. I would have died of shame if I had had to take money from my mother. Finally I settled down, bought a much-too-large, much-too-expensive beauty salon, and worked like a madman to pay it off.

"Today, business is booming, and my love for my profession doesn't prevent me from taking an interest in many other activities—sports, art, books. But there is one thing I could never live without: liberty. If—by some calamity—a right- or left-wing dictatorship took over and tried to stop me from working, speaking, or thinking as I wish, then I'd pack up my scissors and my combs and seek my fortune elsewhere. The knapsacks are up in the attic. But I hope they'll stay there forever."

Photograph of Robert Lacey on Page 275 by Ian Yeomans.

Photograph of Joseph Joffo on Page 511 by Jerry Bauer.

MAJESTY. Picture credits: Page 165 (top), Page 185 (bottom right), Page 203 (top), Page 203 (bottom), Page 217 (middle): Radio Times Hulton Picture Library. Page 165 (bottom), Page 173, Page 185 (top), Page 185 (bottom left), Page 203 (middle), Page 217 (top), Page 217 (bottom), Page 227, Page 241, Page 242 (bottom), Page 243, Page 259 (bottom): Popperfoto. Page 242 (top), Page 244 (bottom), Page 259 (top left), Page 259 (middle): Keystone Press Agency Ltd. Page 244 (top), Pages 266/267. Patrick Lichfield/Camera Press. Page 259 (top right): Peter Grugeon/Camera Press.